TAMING THE FUTURE

A Revolutionary Breakthrough in Scientific Forecasting

Kenneth E. F. Watt

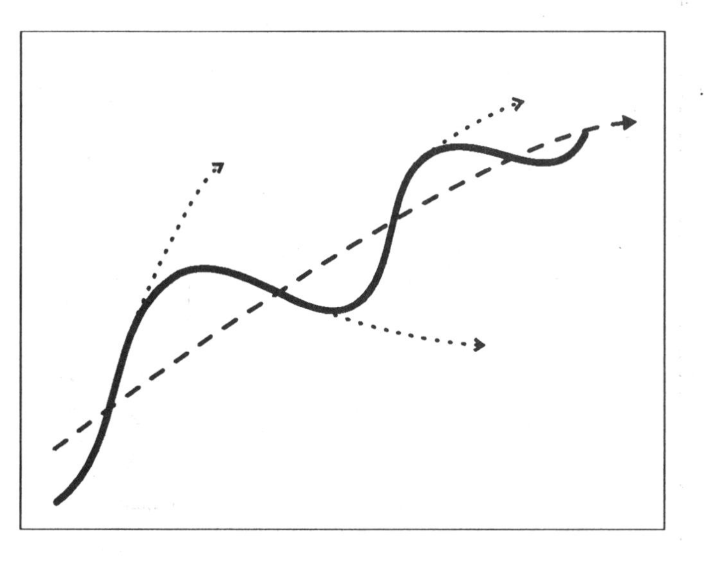

The Contextured Web Press
Davis, California

LEGAL DISCLAIMER

This book presents the results of exploratory research on a completely new approach to scientific forecasting of the future. It is intended to expose a new way of looking at things, that needs a great deal more research, particularly when applied to specific processes, phenomena, or markets.

Readers who invest or make policy decisions on the basis of the research presented here do so at their own risk. They are strongly advised to use the methods described herein to develop their own ongoing research programs focussed on identifying and modelling the behavior of the forces that affect change through time in the investments or policy issues of concern to them.

Models of the type explained herein are useful in forecasting the average trend in variables many years, and even decades into the future. It is important, however, for any reader to note that many market variables, such as commodity prices and stock prices for individual corporations, can undergo very wide-amplitude fluctuations over periods of hours or days for reasons that are not even rational. For example, the price of shares in corporation B drops violently when the earnings per share in corporation A drops violently, because the activities of B appeared similar to those of A to some investors, even when that is a mistaken perception based on lack of detailed knowledge of the activities of both companies. Therefore, to gain the most profit from any forecasting scheme, portfolios must be intensively managed so as to select the appropriate timing for purchase and sale.

Further, no amount of scientific research on the past can produce a model that will forecast even the average trend of a variable in the future with absolute certainty. Science deals with probabilities, not absolute certainty. Science tests the predictive utility of a forecasting model by evaluating the improbability of the hypothesis that the model is not realistic. If a test of the model against historical data series show that it is extremely improbable that the hypothesis is false, then it is judged highly likely that the model is true. It can not be proved that the model is true with absolute certainty, however.

Page layout and design by
F&E KEYBOARD SERVICES
2175 Alameda de las Pulgas
Redwood City, California 94061

Distributed in the United States by
The Contextured Web Press
1116 Dartmouth Place
Davis, California 95616

ISBN 1-880014-04-1

"Constantly regard the universe as one living being, having one substance and one soul; and observe how all things have reference to one perception, the perception of this one living being; and how all things act with one movement; and how all things are the operating causes of all thing which exist; observe too the continuous spinning of the thread and the contexture of the web."

The Roman Emperor Marcus Aurelius
in Meditations, Book VI, verse 40
written about 175 A.D.

Preface

This book is intended to revitalize widespread interest in serious scientific forecasting, and suggest how individuals, corporations, governments or other institutions can generate forecasts to aid in planning. The book is designed to be read as an essay, illustrated by graphs. Readers who wish to learn how to use their own computers to apply my methods will find details on my mathematical models and simulation programs gathered in Appendix A.

Sources of data

In order that readers can check every step of my work and apply my methods to make their own forecasts, all data sources are identified. For U.S. data, the most useful source is *Bicentennial Edition, Historical Statistics of the United States, Colonial Times to 1970*, Parts 1 and 2, U.S. Bureau of the Census, U.S. Department of Commerce: Washington, D.C., published in 1975. (To save space, this will always be referred to as HS.) This document is updated annually as the *Statistical Abstract of the United States*, U.S. Bureau of the Census, U.S. Department of Commerce: Washington, D.C. This yearbook summarizes U.S. government statistics and explains where more detailed statistics can be found. The book is typically published late in one year and has the following year on the cover. In this book this document will be coded as SA (1987), where the year in brackets refers to the year of *publication*—not the year on the cover.

A large number of data series have been routinely maintained by the Bureau of the Census for long periods. These are identified by a letter and number code, such as B1, for number of live births in thousands. These codes allow one to relate data in HS to more recent data for the same statistic in SA. Where a data series used in this book has such a designation, it will be referred to simply as B1 or M217, without reference to HS or SA, in the interest of saving space. (See Glossary for definitions of specific codes.) More detailed explanations of data sources will be used in other cases. For example, "Table 800 SA (1983)" refers to Table 800, in the Statistical Abstract published in 1983.

Rather than using annual yearbooks of all the other countries, which are in their own languages and may be hard to obtain, it is more convenient to use various documents that collate the statistics from all the countries in the world or a region. A very useful collection of data on all the European countries is *European Historical Statistics 1750–1970*, by B.R. Mitchell, Columbia University Press, New York, 1975, and its second edition, published in 1981 by Facts on File, New York. To conserve space, these will be coded as EHS1 and EHS2. Mitchell has published other volumes, which are recommended. Other useful data sources are the volumes of statistical tables published by the various departments of the U.S. government, United Nations agencies, the World Bank, the World Road Federation, and the Economist magazine of London.

Another useful source of long runs of historical data is the journal *Cycles*, published by The Foundation for the Study of Cycles. A very high quality data set for the U.S. producer price index, and the one used for Chapter 5 was from page 17 of *Cycles* for January–February 1985. Detailed citations will be given for all data sources.

Equations and data series

The equations used to describe historical data series were typically nonlinear. Therefore, nonlinear parameter estimation procedures were required. Further, since the historical data series were characterized by wide-amplitude, high-frequency, short-wavelength fluctuations, the n-dimensional hypersurfaces of residual sums of squares were insufficiently smooth for the modern elaborations of Gauss-Newton methods described by Fletcher (1987), Himmelblau (1972) and Lootsma (1972) to converge. Accordingly, the Matyas (e.g. Schrack and Borowski (1972) and Nelder-Mead Simplex ad hoc methods were used for curve fitting (Lootsma, 1972). If convergence stopped, we switched from one method to the other, or expanded the search hypervolume. Also, because many of our equations described change over great ranges of values, some or all of the variables were converted to logarithms prior to fitting. In extreme cases, data were smoothed somewhat by taking moving averages prior to curve-fitting. We strongly recommend Schwefel (1981) for comparative analysis of a wide range of curve-fitting methods.

Acknowledgements

This project has been made possible through the efforts of a great many people over about a decade. It is unlikely that the work would ever have been completed without their help, and to all of them I am deeply indebted.

The single person to whom I am most indebted is my former doctoral student, Jill Shore Auburn. She designed and programmed the software package for nonlinear statistical analysis, graphing, and data handling without which this research would have been impossible. She also read many of the chapters in earlier drafts and offered numerous invaluable suggestions.

Thomas Robertson of Washington, D.C. took my discs of text and encoded graphs, typeset them using Ventura Publisher, and produced the first run of published books. He also advised on numerous other aspects of this project.

Sherman Stein and Paul Craig of the University of California at Davis read early drafts of some of this material. Both of them emphasized to me the role of war in the long wave, and Professor Craig has done independent analyses demonstrating the significance of the "war connection." Both of them brought important books and articles to my attention.

Richard Levins of Harvard and Bernard Patten of the University of Georgia read earlier drafts and offered various helpful suggestions. Barry Hughes in the Graduate School of International Studies at the University of Denver offered many helpful suggestions over the years, and brought the very important work by Joshua Goldstein to my attention. Goldstein, now at the University of Southern California, read an early draft and offered many useful suggestions.

Prvoslav Marjanovic and Brian Vila read an earlier draft, and particularly stressed the need to explore the cultural underpinnings of decision-making.

Cameron Zabel read an earlier draft; his comments resulted in considerable revision, and a new first chapter.

Donella Meadows of Dartmouth offered several useful suggestions at the outset. She pointed out that forecasting, planning and management were all linked through their common concern with formulating "visions of the future"; that is her phrase.

C.S. Holling has been offering me advice, technical analysis, and moral support for 40 years.

Robert May, formerly at Princeton, and now Oxford, George David of San Francisco, and C.S. Holling, formerly at the University of

British Columbia, now at the University of Florida, Gainesville, all emphasized to me the potentially immense significance of AIDS several years ago, when almost no one else shared that view. All of them have read earlier versions of some of this material.

Juan Martinez-Alier of the Universidad Autonoma De Barcelona kindly loaned me the manuscript of Ecological Economics long before the book was available in print.

The late Richard Bellman stimulated my interest in simulation gaming to explore the consequences of various strategic options, beginning in 1960, and was a source of inspiration and advice for many years thereafter.

David Deamer read previous drafts. He first pointed out the significance of volcanic eruptions for global temperature depressions to me, in 1967.

Raul Loyola Berrios of Santiago spent hours convincing me that I should embed my analyses in a historical context, in Caracas in 1973.

The complexity of some of this material requires that utmost care be taken to facilitate the task of comprehension on the part of the reader. We were fortunate, therefore, to obtain the services of Elinor Cruze, who has done a remarkable job not only of editing and clarifying the text, but also of communicating with the reader effectively through her design and layout of the book.

This book is the result of suggestions, and extended discussions with a great many scholars in different disciplines and countries for the last several decades. To all of you, I am very much in your debt.

Kenneth E. F. Watt
Davis, California

Table of Contents

Executive Summary

What We Can Learn

The following summarizes this book's main themes. They are organized into five categories.

1. Forecasting methodology

① There is one central innovation in this book. We have no basis for confidence in any forecasting model unless it demonstrably mimics the past over a very long time, and with very high accuracy. Further, the same model that mimics the past must be able to generate a plausible future for at least several decades, using as input only data for the last few years. I hope this book will popularize application of that standard to all forecasters.

② The forces regulating historical change in any variable must be split into those regulating the long run trend, those regulating wavelike fluctuations about that trend, and those producing high-frequency fluctuations. The separate effects of these different forces may be distinguished by (a) using moving averages to smooth out the effect of forces producing high frequency fluctuations, then (b) fitting a trend equation to a long run of data, and dividing the smoothed data by the values computed from the trend equation to isolate the wavelike oscillations.

③ During any period of history, the critical limiting resource for a society is the fundamental system driver (FSD) regulating the long run trend for all variables. That FSD is always some measure of the status of the nation's energy resources, such as remaining forests for fuelwood, or remaining reserves of oil or coal. For preindustrial countries in which the principal source of energy is sunlight to produce food, the mineral content of the soil determines the efficiency with which the sunlight is used, and therefore measures the nation's energy status. For energy-impoverished post-industrial societies such as Japan, the FSD regulating the long run trend lines is the level of investment in education, research and development, and the capital infrastructure. All of these govern the capacity to generate foreign exchange used to purchase imported energy.

④ Wavelike oscillations about the trend result from FSD which operate with timelags of many years. There may be more than one force producing wavelike fluctuations. If there are, this will be detectable because the waves will not all have the same wavelength.

⑤ There are seven different clusters of variables which could be considered as candidates for influencing any system. However, logic dictates that the three most likely to affect all seven are those where storages take a long time to deplete or supersaturate: fossil fuel reserves, the number of people in a particular age group or year class (the group born in a particular year), and the capital stock, such as refineries or power generating plants. The FSD regulating the long run trend in any variable are most likely to be energy storages. The FSD regulating wavelike oscillations about those trends will be demographic variables, wholesale fuel prices, or measures of capital stock.

⑥ The causes of events are much further back in time than the conventional wisdom has thought. This is true where ever the affected variables have long wavelength, large amplitude waves about their trend lines. The exact length of the time lags in feedback control mechanisms can be determined by study of historical data tables, and by making graphs on the computer screen. For example, graph the value of the dependent variable in year Y against the value of the independent variable in year Y-20 to test the hypothesis that there is a 20 year lag in the hypothesized feedback control mechanism. If the hypothesis is correct, the pattern on the screen will be a decrease from upper left to lower right, with minimal scatter of data points about that declining trend.

⑦ If wavelengths are enlarging or contracting through time, this means that one feedback control mechanism is gradually replacing another. Putting it differently, the system is evolving or developing in response to changes in the "environment" of the system. The model used to mimic that evolution should have a mathematical structure analogous to that used to mimic the WPI.

2. The forces producing change through time in modern societies

⑧ Modern societies are self-stabilizing, or homeostatic systems. This means that without being restimulated, the fluctuations produced by any perturbation would eventually dampen out, resulting in a steady state. The pattern of continuing fluctuation found in the modern world occurs because the gradually dampening oscillations are periodically reenergized by shocks, such as the explosive increases in energy prices resulting from major wars. Other perturbations of equal potential to reenergize oscillations are curtailment of raw material supplies by cartels (e.g. O.P.E.C.), and major volcanic eruptions with force equal to or greater than Tambora in 1815. These shocks may produce outlier data that defeat any effort at precise curve fitting. Years with such data may have to be removed from the data set to facilitate curve-fitting and parameter estimation.

3. The current status of the global system

(9) The two situations changing most rapidly in the world at present are the incidence of AIDS, and the status of global petroleum reserves. The rapid decline in the latter has not had the expected elevating effect on the world crude oil price. Massive overinvestment in the world petroleum industry in the ten years after 1972 intensified competition and depressed price. Indeed, the oil price would be even more depressed at present, but for the remaining fires in Kuwait. The oil price will probably decline for several years, along with the wholesale price index. In both cases the cause was overinvestment in productive capacity. The consequence will be a depression, which will not bottom out until about 1995. However, the global oil market will clear by 1997, resulting in explosive oil price increases. All forecasts should be adjusted carefully for potential effects of AIDS, and a huge increase in energy prices. An intensifying threat due to global deforestation will be climate change. The level of indebtedness of a society will be of great importance in the future. The ratio of loans outstanding to cash on hand in insured commercial banks is a useful measure of the debt situation.

4. The future of the system

(10) The effects of AIDS and energy prices will have become devasting by 2000. There will by then be little controversy about their potential to create real havoc in the following ten years. By 2010 they will both be having effects quite beyond anything visualized by most people now, and their effects will be starting to interact with great force, particularly on demand for transportation. By 2010 talk of either population growth or economic growth will be a distant memory. Everyone will be thinking in terms of population decline, and the need for extremely rapid increase in the efficiency of energy use.

5. The most important indicated responses

(11) Anyone concerned about their personal survival and the survival of friends or family members should operate as if AIDS is an enormously greater threat than revealed by most published statistics. Estimates of the incidence of AIDS are being upgraded annually by agencies such as the World Health Organization.

(12) People should plan every aspect of their lives as if gasoline will cost $100 a gallon or more within ten years. Thus daily round trip commutes of 50 miles or more imply a reconsideration of job site, home site, or both.

(13) The most explosively growing personal and corporate opportunities will be found by figuring out what will be breaking down in 10 years because of these developments, and inventing means of supplying fixes. The accuracy of one's perceptions can be checked against the relative average rates of growth of earnings per share in different economic sectors in the U.S. now. To illustrate, if energy prices are going to explode in ten years, movement of information between computers will be substituted for movement of people or goods, which is going to become extremely expensive. Already, we find that the corporations engaged in that substitution are one of the fastest growing parts of the economy. For people living in the U.S., another way of identifying new economic opportunities is by noticing differences in government and corporate policies between the U.S., on the one hand, and Japan and West Europe on the other. Rapidly growing new economic sectors will be those now being pushed in the latter. The vigorous efforts to enlarge the high speed train network, and increase service on existing lines in Vienna is illustrative. The shift from automobile to rail will create an explosion of new types of economic activity, and have a profound effect on spatial patterns of real estate development.

Prologue

The significance of information

By August 1992, "information" and the procedures for handling it were becoming major topics in the popular media. For about 18 months up to that time, the picture of recent economic history presented by government, executives and researchers for brokerage houses, and the media had gone like this:

> *There had been a short, shallow recession in the fourth quarter of 1990 and the first quarter of 1991, and since then there had been weak, but progressive growth. Within a few months, the economy would be once again growing vigorously. Retail sales would pick up, the unemployment rate would go down, and the future would look bright for as far ahead as we could see.*

By August 1992, however, six different sets of evidence were making it increasingly obvious that that picture was a statistical artifact, resulting from the way in which information was collected, processed, and then disseminated or sequestered.

- The first, and principal stimulus for this concern was the "unemployment" rate statistics. Many newspapers and some national media noted that the official government statistics did not measure what they appeared to measure, and were low by 40 percent or more. In fact, if only 10,000 people in the United States had jobs, and everyone else had become convinced of the futility of seeking employment, the unemployment rate would be zero. The unemployment rate only measured the percentage of the people with jobs, plus those still seeking employment who were not employed. This scarcely conforms to a common sense conception of "unemployment rate." An uncharitable observer might even argue that this bizarre definition was politically motivated, and designed to conceal the magnitude of the joblessness problem.
- A second type of discrepancy showed up between U.S. government economic statistics and the data collected independently by state governments. To illustrate, in 1990, the U.S. Dept. of Commerce estimated that non-wage income in California increased by 7 percent. The actual change in California was a drop of 3 percent. The U.S. Dept. of Commerce estimated that the incomes of New York State residents rose 3.4 percent between the first quarter of 1991 and the first quarter of 1992. New York state tax receipts show that the actual figure was a 2.3 percent drop in income.
- A third problem, with startling implications, was that optimistic initial estimated federal government economic statis-

tics were sharply revised downward, long after the fact. On August 2, 1992, the *New York Times* reported that the federal government had just revised third quarter, 1990 percentage change in gross domestic product downward from plus .2 percent, to minus 1.6 percent. This means that **the government literally does not know the true state of the economy until about two years after the fact**. This implies that a gradually deepening depression could be perceived as slow growth out of a short, shallow recession until we were about four years into the depression. This is not wild speculation: in the same release, first quarter 1991 growth rate was also revised downward, from -2.5 percent to -3.0.

- The fourth warning flag was the discrepancy between consumer confidence and some other economic statistics. The former suggested that the economy was slipping downward, not growing out of recession. This is worrisome, because consumers would be influenced by what they saw around them, as well as optimistic pronouncements from government and the media. Other, more optimistic statistics could result from purchasing agents for wholesale or retail houses ordering from manufacturers on the basis of their own optimistic projections, based on experiences with past recessions. **The 1990–1992 recession, however, was unlike anything since the 1930s**.

Consumers saw the economy slipping downward, not growing out of recession.

- A fifth reason for concern about "information" was the growing perception that "research" from Wall Street brokerage houses was affected by a "Pollyanna" world view. Indeed, the whole perspective surrounding the stock market was surreal. The argument that lower interest rates would be stimulating to the economy overlooks the fact that that didn't happen in the 1930s. It also overlooks the fact that the motive to lend out money is eroded by very low interest rates.

- A sixth reason for concern about information was the **gradual deletion of particularly revealing statistics from the annual *Statistical Abstract* of the United States**. "Cash, balances with banks, etc." was still being published in "Table No. 797. Insured Commercial Banks- Assets and Liabilities" in the 1989, 109th Edition. By the following, 1990 edition, that item had been dropped from the corresponding table, number 805. That item is critical in projecting the likelihood of depressions. Similarly, in Table 1219 of the 1990 edition, available in mid-1990, the last statistic given for proved domestic reserves of crude oil was for *1986*. The estimate for 1987 was (NA), meaning not available. To a person doing systems analysis of U.S. society, "proved domestic reserves of crude oil" was one of the absolutely most important measures of the status of the U.S. economy. Of course, that number could be be obtained from other sources; however, deletion of the number from the annual statistical yearbook of the U.S. meant that the number of people who would know the status of the nation with respect to oil reserves (and who could be

Deletion of "proved domestic reserves of crude oil" from the statistical yearbook meant fewer people who would know the status of the oil reserves—and who could be a political embarrassment to the government.

a political embarrassment to the government) would be smaller.

A democratic society cannot make rational political decisions if it does not have accurate information.

The significance of these examples is that a democratic society cannot make rational political decisions if it does not know accurate information about its recent history or its present state. The more time-consuming it is to find that information, the smaller will be the number of people who know what must be known in order to make rational political and economic decisions.

Further, information must be made available in a sufficiently timely fashion to be news, rather than history at the time of its release. At present, there is at least the appearance that accurate information is being made available so long after the fact that it will not be a problem for re-election of the party in power.

Chapter 1.

Forecasting: A sick field and the necessary cure

Everyone uses forecasting

All people, all governments, and all institutions base crucial decisions on their vision of the future. Much of human planning is based on assumptions about the state of the world 10–50 years in the future.

- Individuals and families decide whether to buy a house or rent.
- Investors decide to invest in stocks, bonds, or precious metals.
- Corporations decide whether it's better to purchase or rent capital equipment like airplanes and oil tankers.
- A utility company decides that demand for electricity will continue to grow enough to justify building nuclear power plants.
- Metropolitan areas plan new regional rail transportation systems.

Forecasting helps us foresee the ultimate consequences of bold, innovative, and historically unprecedented policy decisions, such as the communications and subsequent opening of economic trade with Russia and China initiated by President Nixon and Henry Kissinger in the early 1970s. A goal was to increase the market for U.S. agricultural commodities, so as to obtain foreign exchange to pay for sharply increased oil imports. This decision had a wide variety of large-scale economic effects on the United States.

From 1972 to 1974, domestic wheat inventories dropped to about a third their previous level (SA79 Table 1236).

- Wheat prices increased to $2\frac{1}{3}$ times their previous level (SA79 Table 1232).
- From 1970 to 1974 the value of private farmland increased 73 percent and the value of private non-farm land increased 58 per cent (SA79 Table 777).

In effect, the United States had been confronted with two policy options:

① 1. Effect an enormous increase in the efficiency of energy use so as to decrease the demand for oil imports, or

② 2. Allow a huge increase in oil imports that would have a pervasive effect on the general level of prices and the inflation rate.

Few people were concerned that the increased energy and soil nutrient use required to grow export crops could be associated with a net drain on U.S. resources, or that the agriculture export/energy import process would combine to delay the industrial world's recognition of the resource limitations they would have to confront in the (increasingly immediate) future.

Classic historical blunders

Napoleon took his Grand Army of 453,000 men into Russia in late June, 1812. When he left Russia in November, he only had 10,000 survivors fit for further combat.

Just 129 years later, June 22, 1941, Hitler sent a much larger army into Russia. Its losses were even more terrible. It is astonishing to discover the similarity between forecasting blunders made by Napoleon and those blindly repeated by Hitler. Both decisions to invade failed to consider the possibility of Russian fall and winter temperatures being below average. Both leaders were unlucky: 1812 was an extraordinarily cold year, and November 1941 to March of 1942 was far colder than normal in the Soviet Union. The average temperature for January, 1942 at Moscow was -4.4°F. Both armies were tragically ill-prepared in terms of clothing and equipment.

Hitler ran into another forecasting error. Compared with Napoleon, he operated in a time of much greater energy availability and use. This was the very core of his *blitzkrieg*, or lightning war. Because blitzkrieg involved self-powered, motorized vehicles rather than animal power and trains, Hitler had more power to cause destruction and move his forces. This also meant he had to rely on a larger, more complex and fragile system of logistics, with many more critical places that could fail. In other words, while blitzkrieg meant bringing trouble to the enemy faster than ever before, it also meant he could get into greater trouble faster.

Making any of these decisions ought to assume some knowledge of future energy prices, the volume of demand for transportation, the number of computers that are likely to be purchased, and so on.

To illustrate, from 1926–1929, interest rates went up and share value of industrial corporations increased rapidly at the same time that the average value of Aaa corporate bonds decreased slightly. This *opposite response* to interest rates is typical of the performance of stocks and bonds. Indeed, one investment strategy is to shift between stocks and bonds in response to changes in the economic environment. Knowing when to do this implies an ability to forecast that environment.

Specific decisions based on assumptions about the behavior of the system can, however, be wrong for several reasons.

- All industries experience long-term downward or upward trends.
- The trends don't move in straight paths through time. If they did, predicting the behavior of the stock market would be easy. Instead, there are cyclical oscillations—ups and downs—around long-term trends.
- The cycles for different types of investments are not synchronized with respect to each other.

Accurate forecasting avoids calamities

For lack of realistic forecasting capability, individuals, families, corporations and governments make decisions that do not support their interests. The costs of bad decisions based on unrealistic forecasts can run to tens or hundreds of billions of dollars, sometimes associated with the loss of millions or tens of millions of lives.

If mistakes concerning the best path are very wrong or made too late, they may permanently exclude the possibility of picking a wiser option later.

What could we do to prevent wars or depressions? The mode of settling a war can set the stage for the next war. (For example, look at the different consequences of the way World War I was settled compared with World War II.) We may chose a new energy technology unwisely. When we unwisely overinvest capital, energy and material in one technology, sometimes there's not enough of each of these to enable a switch to another technology that seems preferable after the fact. In general, if mistakes concerning the best path are very wrong or made too late, they may permanently exclude the possibility of picking a wiser option later.

Having a sufficient forecasting capability is a prerequisite for the continued survival of any people. All previous civilizations ultimately disintegrated because of phenomena they failed to use their capacity to foresee what lay ahead. In fact, four morals occur repeatedly in history (see side bar).

- Progressing blindly into the future without the benefit of realistic forecasting can be catastrophic.
- The lessons of history are more relevant to the present than most people recognize, because human experience is more cyclical than most people have noticed.
- While advances in technology increase our capacity to achieve goals, they also increase our vulnerability to error.
- Extraordinary, often knowable, forces affect processes that appear to be mysteriously cyclical.

The period just before World War I provides a compelling example of the disastrous outcome of using an obsolete vision of the future to develop policy. From 1880 to 1914 there was a vast amount of writing about a possible future major war.

> *"All such works precisely described what battles would be like: there is virtually no connection with reality. Essayists and military writers thought in Napoleonic terms—infantry charging in serried ranks, cavalry winning the decision, the whole thing lasting no more than a day. It was almost a sporting event....Illusions were virtually universal—only the 'wild' H.G. Wells, the designer Albert Robida, the Russian theorist Ivan Bloch appreciated that war would be industrialized, with millions of deaths and entire nations mobilized."*
>
> *(Ferro, 1987)*

Because of massive destruction of cities and their records, particularly in Russia, the total cost of the first world war is difficult to enumerate; however a minimum estimate of dead and wounded is over 20 million people (Ferro, 1987).

Identifying the biggest impact for the policy buck

Another motive for forecasting is to identify which high-leverage switches controlling the flow of inputs to systems have the greatest effect in regulating their outputs. The highest-leverage switch is the one with the largest impact on the rate at which output flows out of the entire system. Of several available actions we could take to have a beneficial effect on our future, which ones have the largest effect per dollar spent? For example, how would an airline increase profits most?

- Invest an additional $10 million on advertising?
- Rent one more plane?
- Improve passenger or baggage handling facilities at an airport?

The dismal state of forecasting

Models used in all fields for forecasting, planning, management and optimization are presented to the public as systems models, which they are not. These models do not produce surprising or unpleasant results and are therefore not counterintuitive. **Counterintuitivity, however, is a key characteristic of both the real world and of genuine systems models**, which incorporate the cross-linkages and feedback loops characterizing the real world.

Increasingly in the early 1990s, conventional wisdom realizes that something is wrong. To illustrate, the July 20, 1992, *Business Week* (p. 102) noted that "...deep-seated structural problems are throwing up barrier after barrier to growth." The conventional wisdom has not yet identified the root problem as an unrealistic, non-systemic paradigm.

Conventional wisdom has not identified the root problem as an unrealistic, non-systemic paradigm.

Given its great potential benefits, it is surprising to discover that forecasting and the related activities of policy, planning, and management (FP) are undeveloped in all fields, and in all countries, particularly when compared with what could be developed. A great many recent books and articles show that forecasting has very low predictive utility in many fields, from political and military intelligence to forecasting of population and economic trends, and demand for energy and transportation.

Further, the predictive utility of modern forecasting is actually getting worse. The reason is that FP has evolved as a servant of politics rather than as scientific activity. Following a long series of embarrassing, gigantic, highly visible and heavily-reported disasters, FP is currently in ill repute. These failures in forecasting are more the result of distorted individual and institutional machinations than of actual failures in our ability to look into the future. I will document that contention and show why it is justified.

A goal of much forecasting is to keep the procedure as secret and mysterious as possible.

To put it bluntly, FP has not been developed on the basis of objective research on the forces that drive historical trends, but rather to provide a client with a mountain of technically intimidating documents describing a desired fantasy future. The purpose of the documents is to justify policies that had already been selected by the clients for political reasons. The documents are designed to appear technically intimidating in order to impress clients with the work done and to discourage opponents of the proposed course of action from digging into the details of the forecasting method. That is, a goal of much forecasting is to keep the forecasting procedure as secret and mysterious as possible. The extreme complexity of forecasting models is used to obscure the connection between the model and reality—and to ensure that the model is incomprehensible.

The appearance of technical complexity does not reflect the sophistication of the underlying science; often the actual process generating the results can be written out on the back of an envelope. A recent book by a panel sponsored by the Social Science Research Council of the United States reviewed the status of forecasting; it explains the situation:

> *"In my opinion, the competitive, politically charged environment of transportation forecasting has resulted in the continuous adjustment of assumptions until they produce forecasts that support politically attractive outcomes. The mathematical models used are complex, and this complexity obscures the fact that the forecasts are more critically dependent on assumptions than they are on the mathematical manipu-*

lations that dominate technical reports and briefings. Citizens are told that 'scientific' models were used to estimate the cost and patronage of future transit systems. The complexity of the models, however, merely disguises the fact that assumptions and parameters are continually adjusted until the intended choice is justified by the forecasts."
(Wachs, 1987)

Models are ideologically driven.

Modern forecasting models are not only far more complex than necessary; they are also ideologically driven. For example, they are typically based on the world view that permeates all our institutions—that complex reality can be understood and managed by splitting it into its constituent fragments (the philosophy of reductionism). State-of-the-art systems analysis teams conclude, however, that the dynamic properties of systems (the way they change through time) are far more influenced by the causal connections between system components, than by processes within each of the separate constituents.

Predictions typically forecast that variables will go up or down indefinitely. The fact that all variables fluctuate constantly is rarely mentioned.

One of the most striking features of the real world is cyclical, oscillatory, or wavelike behavior of almost everything around us: the birth rate fluctuates, the rate of growth in the economy fluctuates, and sales of virtually everything fluctuate, from houses to cars. Indeed, our language and our culture are full of phrases acknowledging this fact: Kondratieff Waves, the business cycle, cycles of romantic and classical artistic and musical styles. Yet predictions typically forecast that some variables will go up or down indefinitely. The fact that all variables fluctuate constantly is rarely mentioned when forecasts are made.

Wars and depressions are predictable consequences of normal operation of modern societies.

More generally, because they don't consider wars and depressions, most forecasting models project a future that is qualitatively different than any past that has ever occurred. Instead, forecasting models are tuned to historical data series for the relatively stable periods between wars and depressions. It is rarely mentioned that such perturbations are predictable consequences of normal operation of modern societies, as they presently function.

Another curious and almost universal feature of modern forecasts is that we are told nothing about why we should have confidence in the forecast. Think of the effect it would have on us if the forecaster said,

> *"This is the twenty-first forecast I have made of the direction of the stock market. In my previous twenty attempts, I invariably predicted that the market would go the opposite direction to that in which it actually moved."*

In general, we are provided no information demonstrating that the forecasting procedure could account for past history, and we are not told how we can reproduce the results of the forecasting procedure for ourselves. That would be worthwhile because a high proportion of the population now owns computers on which forecasts could be checked.

In short, modern civilization has no well-developed and usually reliable forecasting capability. It is like flying an airplane without any navigational aids through mountain passes in a blinding snowstorm. This book explains a new system of radar.

The ruling paradigm

We need to make explicit the paradigm on which current forecasting is based. These notions are so fundamental to the way we think about the world that we rarely notice them or examine them, any more than fish notice or examine the water in which they swim. They describe hidden assumptions that underlie, to one degree or another, practically all our forecasts. Thus, as our forecasts show a widespread pattern of failure, we can look to these and other basic assumptions to discover the cause for error. They even contradict each other, a further indication that they don't describe reality.

Societal events and processes occur in response to policies adopted by government, and not to powerful systemic forces

The assumption is that people in general, but especially governments have complete control over the course of history. This belief makes it easy to overlook natural forces operating through long-term effects of changes in resource availability, birth rates, migration of the labor force from one economic sector to another, or switches in the allocation of investment capital from one sector to another.

Policy changes produce the desired results in a short time

This notion is surprisingly pervasive throughout thinking in all fields. The short terms in office of politicians are based on the assumption that they can effect changes of the type they and their supporters seek, within their terms in office. It is certainly not a widespread view that the full consequences of their decisions would not appear for 40 years. Some of our leaders expect a drop in interest rates to improve the economy within a few weeks.

If we have sufficient knowledge of the recent past, we can predict the future

With this belief, what we discover too late is that these immediate events were merely symptoms of far greater and persistent forces reflecting much longer-term influences—for example, the effect of nutrient depletion in the Tigris-Euphrates river systems.

Phenomena that appear complex must have been produced by causes of great complexity

Therefore, complex mathematical models must be required to forecast the behavior of systems that appear complex. Nevertheless, very simple mechanisms can produce highly complex patterns of behavior in space and time. I will show that extremely simple forecasting models have the highest possible predictive reliability. If very simple models work best, then in fact anyone with a computer can do realistic forecasting.

In fact, anyone with a computer can do realistic forecasting.

Complexity is a persistent factor but is within the working capacity of intelligent leaders

The fact is, a telephone repair person with a wiring diagram is better prepared to address the complexity of their jobs than are most policy makers and managers.

We either do not have, or must make exorbitant investments in the data required to make effective forecasts

Associated with the preceding two items, not only do forecasts often require far fewer data than conventional wisdom suggests, but better forecasting methods and procedures provide ways of obtaining specific data at much less cost and to greater advantage.

There are no predictable economic or societal ups-and-downs around trends

"Long wave" oscillations about steady states imply that our wise, "fine-tuning" government and economists failed to respond adequately to signals that the system was malfunctioning.

That is, conventional wisdom holds that there cannot be predictable "long wave" oscillations about steady states, because that would imply that our wise, experienced, "fine-tuning" government and economists had failed to respond adequately to signals that the system was malfunctioning. This is, of course, a direct contradiction of the assumptions listed above relating to complexity. (Obviously the system has to be complex enough to explain the failures of policies, but not too complicated, so that government can be trusted to fix it.)

The behavior of society can be forecast, planned, managed and optimized by manipulating policy levers related to money

The consequence of this view is that much that influences our lives, such as the non-market-valued work of ecosystems and the varying effect of concentrated resources, are either ignored or under valued.

Unregulated free-market competition is the optimal strategy to produce optimal short-, intermediate-, and long-term societal system behavior

Equity and wise allocation of capital investment over sectors and activities need not be major concerns. The free play of the market will produce optimal performance of all state variables in the long run.

Societies do not undergo fundamental transformation as they develop

In fact, wars and depressions have in the past been predictable consequences of normal system operation, rather than random "acts of God."

This belief causes conventional forecasting to miss major turning points in trends and shifts of wavelength in oscillations around trends. In fact, wars and depressions have in the past been predictable consequences of normal system operation, rather than random "acts of God." Experience demonstrates repeatedly that the same policy could have opposite effects at different stages in the evolution of a society, a company, or a family.

Effects of one type tend to be produced by causes of the same, or a closely related type

Thus, we believe that economic effects tend to be produced by economic or political causes. We don't expect economic effects to have demographic and ecological origins. This is consistent with the way we are taught in schools and universities, and the way all our institutions are organized. We learn about and manage reality by fragmenting it into compartments; economics, politics, history, geology, climatology, agronomy, ecology, demography and epidemiology are all taught as separate subjects. Our governments have separate departments of Commerce, Agriculture, Defense, Transportation, Interior, Health, Education, Welfare, Housing and Energy, with little integration and coordination between—and often with—them.

Our historical experience adequately prepares us to deal with the future

Modern history, particularly as it pertains to the U.S., has few of the immediate limitations that brought on traumatic change to other people in the past. Our approach to future energy supplies and water shortages in California demonstrates how little experience we have with real limitations and how willing we are to take unnecessary gambles with our resources and their use.

Forecasting efforts use the best concepts and science available

Contrary to conventional wisdom, there is virtually no rigorous assessment of the capabilities and comparative merit of forecasting methods and processes. This reflects the reductionist, difference-oriented bias of practically all western knowledge. Most forecasting services evolved out of narrow academic frameworks in which growth was the assumed direction of the economy under investigation.

Most forecasting services evolved from narrow academic frameworks that assumed the economy was growing.

Most forecasts are carried out to determine probable future circumstances

In fact most contemporary forecasts are carried out to popularize, legitimize, and perpetuate preexisting policies and points of view. Many examples (e.g., the experience of "whistle blowers" in government and private industry such as the Challenger space shuttle, nuclear weapons plants, and issues dealing with available resource limits) demonstrate that if a particular forecast did reflect the most likely reality, the forecaster was likely to lose his or her job.

With the collapse of Communism in most countries, the world now moves toward management by this paradigm, which emphasizes:

- The rate of growth in the money supply.
- Interest rates.
- Unregulated competition.
- The utility of markets in achieving optimal societal system performance over the long run.

The paradigm does not put much stock in evaluating outcomes of strategies over the next 50 years. Indeed, "forecasting" and "planning" have often been applied to activities that were actually thinly-disguised propaganda on behalf of special interests. That is, most forecasting and planning models work backward from future scenarios desired by clients to assumptions and models that will generate those scenarios.

The worst failure is that we are dropping into a depression that the dominant paradigm could not foresee.

Because this same paradigm is fundamental to all FP, these activities are constantly plagued by mysterious failures. The worst failure is that we are dropping into a depression that the dominant paradigm could not foresee.

The nature of a new paradigm

We can make FP much more realistic by using methods that are more complete, timely, cost-effective, and open for critical review and refinement. When this approach is applied to a wide range of social problems, new and intriguing interpretations result. Novel solutions to persistent problems arise.

These new approaches have not been widely adopted for reasons deeply embedded in our culture and the structure of our institutions.

That is, all our institutions—from corporations, to the Department of Defense, to a high school—deal with and manage complexity by fragmenting it into subcomponents. Instead of learning about the real world in educational institutions, we learn about discrete subjects—European history; the international trade and monetary system; climatology; or the physics and engineering of transportation, weapons, and energy production systems. That is part of the reason why so many of Napoleon's and Hitler's soldiers died of frostbite.

Long time lags

Wars and depressions are primarily driven by causes up to 40 years ago, not in the recent past.

The models I use are based on statistical analysis of very long historical data records, not just the recent past. Contrary to what common sense would suggest, my models demonstrate that major societal events and processes, such as wars and depressions, are primarily driven by causes up to 40 years ago, not causes in the recent past. That is, a major characteristic of modern societies is the very long time lags in cause-effect pathways. Later chapters will demonstrate that this phenomenon is widespread.

In order to understand why there are long time lags, it is necessary to think about the nature of systems. We may visualize all forms of systems in the modern world, from a refinery to a nation, as involving three types of components—storages, flows, and valves—and a set of operating principles described below.

The surprises in modern societies occur just after some storage has been completely filled or emptied.

The long time lags found throughout the modern world occur because systems consist of storages, as well as flows (see side bars). It is the long length of periods to fill up or deplete storages that explains the long time lags in systems. Many of the "surprises" in modern societies occur just after some storage has been completely filled up or emptied out. The time lag required to produce the surprise depends on the size of the storage; that is, the time lag is the number of years it took to make the storage as large or small as it was when it produced the surprise.

These long time delays in societal system control mechanisms necessitate the long look into the future required for planning major projects.

The role of energy

With the models described in Appendix A, we discover that energy is one of the resources that appears to have a very significant effect on everything else in society. Other storages, in addition to energy storages, account for the dynamics of the societal system. Money measures the flow across various subsystem boundaries (i.e between storages).

Internal (self-regulatory) forces

The self-regulatory forces pull a system down when it gets too far above its long-term equilibrium trend line, and shove it up when it gets too far below its equilibrium trend line. The self-correcting downward motion tends to overshoot the equilibrium trend, and so does the upward motion. It is this overshooting that produces the cyclical appearance in long-term behavior.

Systems are most predictable when their behavior is dominated by these cycle-generating, self-regulatory mechanisms. The goal of forecasting is to identify and mimic the cycle-generating mechanisms responsible for the main features of past and future trends.

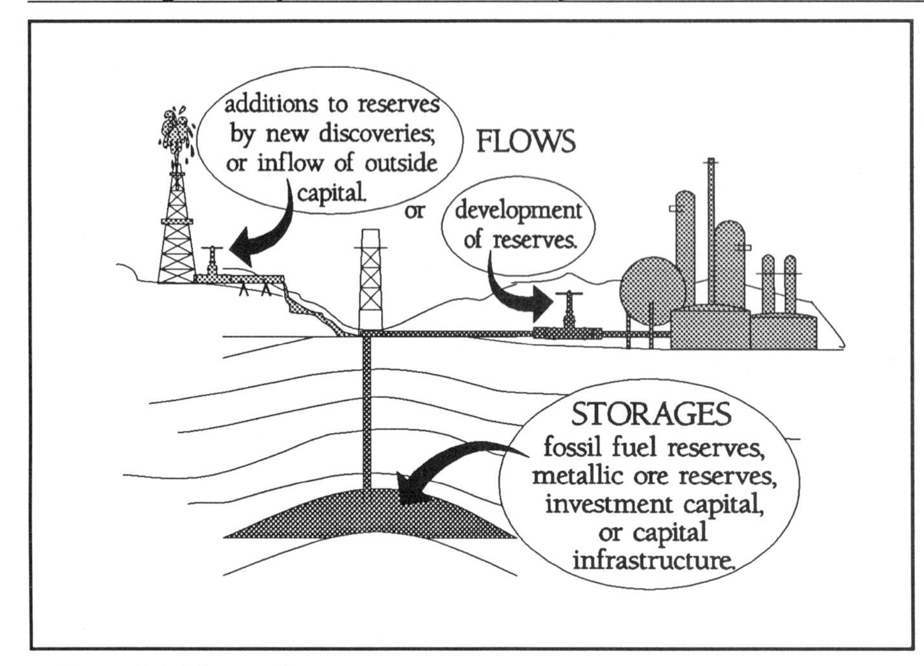

Figure 1-1. Flows and storages.

Effects of external forces

A small proportion of year-to-year change is caused by less predictable, external (exogenous) forces, such as volcanic eruptions and less predictable geopolitical decisions. Nevertheless, a proportion of year-to-year variation sufficient for forecasting is caused by self-regulatory forces internal (endogenous) to the system of interest.

The less a system is affected by exogenous cycle-generating mechanisms, the higher will be the proportion of year to year variation explained by the model.

Wars, depressions, and other surprises

The conventional wisdom would hold that wars and depressions are huge surprises. Our labelling of anything as a "surprise" may only mean that we do not yet understand how the system operates. The big shocks throughout history were often predictable outcomes of normal system operation. That is, major perturbations, such as wars and depressions, are produced by causes far back in time, causes that are themselves normal outcomes of cyclical system behavior. **Anyone who had understood the connection between cause and effect would have known almost exactly when wars and depressions would arrive, years in advance of the fact**. Clearly, this opens up the possibility of preventing such nasty "surprises."

The precise timing and severity of volcanic eruptions, major earthquakes, and certain geopolitical decisions are less predictable in principle, although we can develop models showing when there is an increased probability of such occurrences (e.g. Winkless and Browning, 1972). We cannot predict, however, the exact day of a Krakatoa-sized volcanic eruption at a particular location. Forecast accuracy and precision depends on the frequency and size of these less predictable occurrences, and how sensitive to them the system is.

Storages

Storages correspond to the liquid in a tank or the electrical charge in a condenser. As used in this book "storage" refers to the quantity stored, not the capacity of the container in which it is stored. Storages are exemplified by the size of inventories, as for automobiles or houses. The number of people still alive who were born in a particular year represents a storage. The amount of oil, coal or gas remaining in the ground in a nation is a storage. Our models assume that the size of such storages is an important characteristic of the current state of a nation or an industry.

Our labelling of anything as a "surprise" may only mean that we do not yet understand how the system operates.

Another surprising finding is that society gradually evolves, or develops so that its sensitivity to certain classes of stimuli either decreases or increases through time. Thus society is somewhat like a living organism, in which the sensitivity to hormones, drugs, alcohol or medicine changes through age, from the earliest stages of the fetus to extreme old age.

Economic cycles are closer together than they used to be.

To illustrate, when any nation is passing through the Industrial Revolution, it is much more sensitive to types of perturbations that have their greatest effect on primary industries, such as agriculture, mining and smelting. Once a nation is in its post-industrial phase, different types of perturbations are relatively more important. This *change in relative sensitivity* of societies to different classes of perturbations at different stages in their evolution explains some otherwise inexplicable phenomena, such as the fact that the wavelength of long economic waves have grown shorter recently (i.e., economic cycles are closer together than they used to be).

The computer revolution

As I mentioned above, it's a shock to discover that models able to project far into the future are very simple. Anyone with a knowledge of the history of a particular type of business or industry, an understanding of how people in executive positions make decisions, and a personal computer can make these models. Appendix A will explain in detail the structure of these models, and how they can be used for forecasting.

Wide use of the microcomputer thus allows for more effective forecasting—with very important side-benefits.

- Much more distributed use,
- More efficient access to data with commonly agreed upon reliability,
- Easier ability to generate consensus, and
- More effective processes for managing complexity as it relates to the planning, policy, and management process.

The procedures will be derived from analysis of historical records, and their accuracy will be checked against those historical records. Thus the models used for forecasting also reveal many new insights into forces that shaped the past. We see the real reasons why history unfolded as it did, so we avoid repeating types of decisions that had unfortunate consequences in the past. Putting it differently, research to identify the fundamental system drivers of the future is also research on the forces that drove historical forces in the past. Therefore, a side-benefit of research to improve forecasting is a reexamination of the forces that shaped history.

Finally, the widespread use of computers means that as more effective forecasting is developed, a larger body of people with their diverse interests can become involved in understanding the future. The value of this to the democratic process is expressed by no lesser sources than Thomas Jefferson and the Bible.

"I know of no safe depository of the ultimate powers of society but the people themselves; and if we think them not enlightened enough to

Flows

Flows correspond to movement of liquid through pipes or electrical currents along wires. Flows represent rates of addition to, or subtraction from a storage. Typical flows are birth rate, which measures the rate per 1,000 women at which babies are added to the number born in that year, a storage. Another flow is the rate at which crude oil is produced, and therefore removed from the quantity stored in the ground.

There are also valves on pipes, or resisters in electrical circuits, which control the rate of flow. For example, the average wage controls the rate at which people are removed from the unemployed storage and added to the employed storage. Higher wages lower that rate.

It takes many years to completely fill a storage (or build up or construct an inventory), such as the oil discovery and refining capital infrastructure large enough to supersaturate world demand for crude oil. (This of course says nothing about the geological time it take to build up the initial storage of oil.) It takes many years to use up a storage. An example is the number of years required before retirement of all the farmers who were 45 years of age in 1933.

exercise their control with a wholesome discretion, the remedy is not to take it from them, but to inform their discretion."
Thomas Jefferson, September 28, 1820

"In the multitude of counselors there is safety."
Proverbs XI, verse 14

Another approach to forecasting

I advocate an approach to forecasting in many respects opposite to those of FP as typically conducted. The FP models I advocate are extremely simple, not extremely complex. The causes of processes and events are treated as simple, not complex. I will demonstrate that a small number of very fundamental forces, or fundamental system drivers (FSD) have effects that pervade society. These effects are responsible for almost everything that happens in modern societies. There should be an absolutely transparent relationship between the structure of the forecasting model and the resultant forecasts.

In my opinion, the whole goal of the forecasting profession should be to completely demystify the subject and to make forecasts something that all individuals and families can work with, like the telephone or television set. Further, forecasting models should be accompanied by details on how anyone can check them against historical data, and use them for their own investment, career selection, and purchase decisions.

Forecasting models must be accompanied by demonstrations showing how they would have worked if applied to historical data, preferably over very long spans of history. How can we possibly have any confidence in a system for predicting the future if it can't even account for the past? Even so, people repeatedly present forecasts in the media without giving any evidence whatsoever as to why we should treat the forecast as credible.

Forecasts must project a plausible future. Thus, for example, a projection of indefinite future growth in anything, free of cycles, simply isn't plausible. We haven't seen anything like that in the past. Why should it occur in the future?

What realistic forecasting models should be able to do

I will demonstrate that we need a revolution in the way we think about how all systems in modern nations function and evolve. This book explains the problem and outlines a solution. One of the many compelling reasons to take the message seriously is the widely noted decline in competitiveness of the United States with respect to other nations. More generally, our deficient forecasting has contributed to a rapid decline in the U.S. standard of living, obscured recently by massive reliance on debt and a short-term world glut of crude oil that has held its price down.

Deficient forecasting has contributed to a rapid decline in the U.S. standard of living, obscured recently by massive reliance on debt and a short-term world glut of crude oil that has held its price down.

I believe that forecasting models should be completely consistent with everything we know about how the system works. Every assumption underlying the model should be testable and should have been tested against historical data. This would give us an objective measure of the confidence we should place in our forecasting procedure. Therefore, we must be able to demonstrate that the forecasting model can account for changes over a long period of history so as to include a very wide range of past conditions.

We would like also to be able to predict unusual events. The logic is inescapable: no forecasting model has any chance of predicting unusual events such as depressions, wars, major new business opportunities, or any other event in the future unless it can account for all such events or changes in the past.

The model should give us the longest possible look ahead into the future. This is necessary, because long times from project initiation to completion characterize large scale projects. For many large scale projects such as new regional transportation systems or new energy generating systems, we must begin action now to achieve some goal 10–20 years in the future.

The forecasting model should allow us to predict using variables that are widely available in documents published by government, central banks, international organizations, or business or industrial organizations. We will discover that there are problems with many of these variables. This book demonstrates, however, how we can use widely available statistics to construct new measures that are far more revealing of the actual state of systems than are measures that are routinely published.

Summary

The forecasting models explained in this book are built on several key ideas.

We need a good understanding of the actual history of the industry or activity being modeled.

Of particular importance is a knowledge of how key decision-makers respond if prices become very high or very low. Extremely high prices tend to occur just at the end of wars or at times of inventory depletion. Extremely low prices characterize the bottom years of depressions or deflationary periods, when money supply is so low that demand can't absorb (buy) the supply of commodities and goods on sale.

Many models put primary emphasis on flows, and tend to underestimate the significance of storages.

The models I will describe assume that storages, particularly the remaining reserves of fossil fuel in a nation, are extremely important in determining everything else going on in a system. This includes, surprisingly, the behavior of government and the status of popular and "serious" culture. The preeminent importance of energy is a widely-held view by scholars of systems behavior (Hall et al., 1986; Odum, 1983), and there has been a long history of some of the most powerful thinkers in society holding that belief (Martinez-Alier, 1987). This has never been the "dominant paradigm" view in any society, however, and it certainly is not a dominant view in this society now. The focus on money and overlooking of the significance of energy is one explanation for many previous forecasting failures.

Fluctuations through time are explained by time lags in control mechanisms operating throughout society.

We assume, however, that these control mechanisms are in three different classes, depending on the lengths of the time delays in their control mechanisms.

- **Very fast-acting mechanisms that produce business cycles**, as characterized by the automobile industry. These have wavelengths of only a few years.
- **Capital investment cycles have intermediate time lags** of around 14 years or more.
- **Long time delays resulting from movements of laborers out of primary industries to other sectors** of the economy have delays of 30 to 40 years. These are the very long lagged mechanisms that generated the "Kondratieff Waves" of a roughly half-century duration that have intrigued so many scholars.

We assume also that causal pathways flow between different components or sectors of the economy previously thought of as unrelated or unconnected. That is, energy availability affects wages and hence, consumer purchasing power, as well as demand for agricultural land and hence, city density.

Chapter 2

Failed Visions of the Future

A major FP study can cost millions, or tens of millions of dollars, yet poor forecasts with enormous consequences are routinely made. Academic literature, business publications, and the popular press often discuss this problem:

> *"In retrospect, 1982 appears to be something of a watershed year for the major firms. It was a recession year, and many clients closely examined their consulting expenditures. As it happens, the big firms had done so poorly in forecasting that recession that many clients found their services expendable."*
>
> *(Hiltzik, 1985)*

> *"Let's face it. Strategic planning, as practiced by most American companies, is not working very well."*
>
> *(Hayes, 1986)*

> *"With the devastation of one U. S. industry after another, serious questions have been raised about the competence of American management."*
>
> *(Steele, 1987)*

Not only can't we understand the present or project the future, we still don't understand the past.

The implications are provocative. Because the universal modern method for projecting the future is to use computer models based on analysis of past history, forecasting failures imply that not only can't we understand the present or project the future, we still don't understand the past. The reader may find this assertion incredible, but a number of simple, fast checks validate it. The simplest test is to compare past predictions in business magazines or newspapers with what actually happened. Save newspaper and magazine forecasts and review them every two or three years; you'll be astounded.

Peter Temin's (1976) book and many others shatter one's faith that economists understand what caused the Great Depression or what causes business cycles. Books by Fay (1930) and Taylor (1948) show how much secrecy and mystery veil the origins of World War I, a topic that has received an immense amount of research.

A first step in developing a new approach to FP must be to identify and describe the forces that actually drive historical processes.

The search for patterns

A great many scholars have been struck by patterns in human affairs that are only partially explicable, from the half-century economic waves first popularized by Kondratieff (1925), to the 50–year cycle in world wars noted by Dyer (1985). Long waves, or repeating cycles, have been discovered in an astonishing variety of fields from metaphysical poetry to political speeches (Namenwirth, 1973; Weber, 1981, 1983). Recent research suggests that the waves in different phenomena may be linked (Goldstein, 1985, 1988).

This chapter suggests a variety of reasons for faulty FP. In comparing a number of cases involving large scale errors, a ubiquitous pattern emerges of fundamental flaws—both conceptual and methodological.

Linkage between forecasting and planning

Forecasting and planning both specify visions of the future. If events don't turn out as expected, then the vision of the future must have been unrealistic. When some activity conducted in accord with a forecast or plan doesn't meet expectations, then forecasting of the activity or the environment in which it was conducted, or both must have been defective.

Failed visions everywhere

Very serious problems in FP occur in all fields and in all countries. The dismal laundry list of FP failures runs through all fields: population and birth rate forecasting, economic forecasting, transportation and energy demand forecasting, and estimation of the cost of major public works (Ascher, 1978; Ascher and Overholt, 1983; Hall, 1982; Land and Schneider, 1987; Lee, Ball and Tabors, 1990).

Other recent large-scale surprises include an economic collapse in the United States farm sector (Volume 4), and a wave of bank and savings and loan industry failures.

There has been immense worldwide overinvestment in oil drilling and production facilities, electrical power generating plants, and real estate.

U.S. nuclear power program

> *"The failure of the U.S. nuclear power program ranks as the largest managerial disaster in business history.... The utility industry has already invested $125 billion in nuclear power, with an additional $140 billion to come before the decade is out, and only the blind or the biased can now think that most of the money has been well spent."*
>
> *(Cook, 1985)*

A proximate cause was excessively optimistic forecasts of growth in electrical energy demand, which led to over-investment in electrical production capacity. Construction cost overruns on nuclear power plants caused increased utility costs and rate increases. These rate increases, in turn, decreased growth in demand for electricity. The utilities became trapped in a squeeze between lower income and higher overhead, a situation that creates the potential for large scale economic problems.

The Washington Public Power Supply System stopped work on two units it had under construction, and canceled two others. For a time there were fears that this could have a serious ripple effect on the nationwide municipal and regional bond market (Dolan, 1983).

Space shuttle Challenger

The explosion of the space shuttle *Challenger* on the morning of January 28, 1986, was produced by the effect of freezing temperatures on the tightness of the seal provided by rubbery O rings between sections of the booster rockets. These low temperatures were far outside the range of environmental conditions for which the rocket was designed:

> *"Plans to protect shuttles from cold here with a $15 million heating system on the launching pad were scrapped in the early 1980s because it was considered not cost-effective in the usually warm Florida climate."*
>
> (Broad, 1986)

How is it that nobody in NASA management had noticed that average January temperatures in northern Florida had dropped so much in the last 40 years that in four years out of five, it was too cold to grow citrus?

Energy consumption forecasts

As recently as 1982, a review of energy consumption forecasts by a number of well-funded projects with large staffs showed that they all expected world energy demand to grow at between 2 and 4 percent, compounded annually, for the foreseeable future (Perry, 1982). In fact, world production of energy only grew at an annual average rate of .46 percent from 1980 to 1985 (SA [1987] Table 1409).

Energy price forecasts follow events, they do not lead them.

Energy forecasters have difficulty forecasting what will happen shortly after the forecasts are made, let alone the energy demand several decades into the future. One of the most comprehensive recent analyses of energy policy makes it clear that energy price forecasts follow events, they do not lead them (Lee et al, 1990). That is, energy price forecasts simply extrapolate exponentially growing price trends, beginning with very recent prices (see fig. 2-1). **None of the forecasts reveal any understanding of the forces that caused recent energy price fluctuations.**

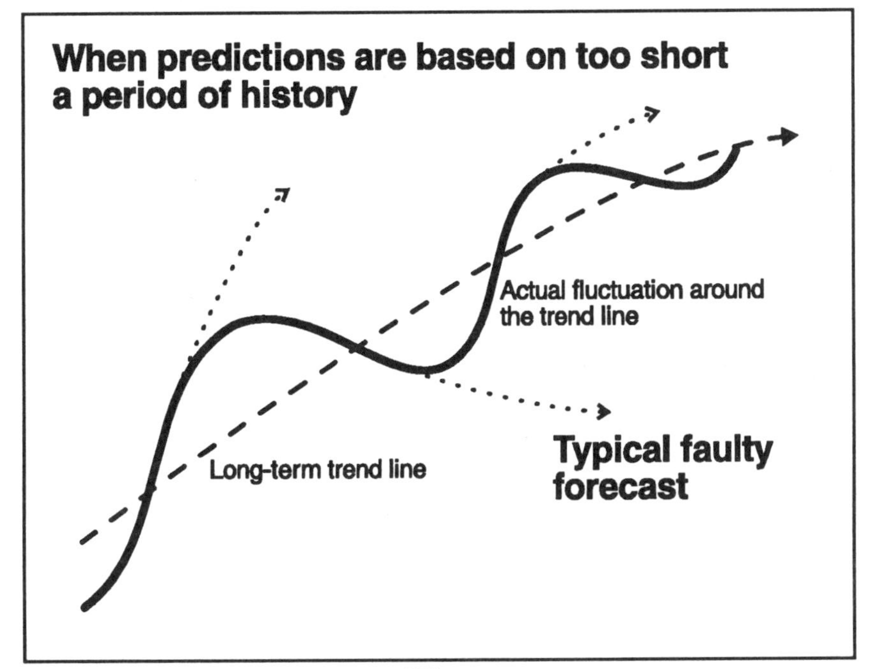

Figure 2-1. In this hypothetical example the dashed line is the long-term trend line. The solid line shows actual fluctuation around the trend line. Dotted lines, illustrative of most forecasts, are made by projecting ahead from too short a period of history.

The "oil price shocks" of 1973–1975 and 1979–1981 came as great surprises.

> *"In 1972, before what came to be known as the energy crisis, forecasts of energy consumption reckoned on the continuance of a declining trend in relative oil prices until 1980–1985. The present economic crisis is evidence, if that is still necessary, that errors can render forecasts misleading rather than useful"* (Godet, 1979).

Nuclear power demand

The declining demand for nuclear power in the United States has come as another great surprise.

In spite of a huge effort by many corporate, national, and international energy forecasting groups, there have been two consecutive major errors: failure to forecast the price increases from 1973 to 1980, then massive overinvestment in oil, gas and nuclear production facilities, failing to recognize that large increases in energy prices would depress demand for energy.

Collapse of resource stocks

In a totally different field, there has been a surprising series of collapses of major fish stocks, from the California sardine to the Peruvian anchovetta (Murphy, 1977). In many cases, the fisheries represented such large proportions of the national or regional economy that the consequences were devastating. The Peruvian anchovetta fishery was the largest single-species fishery in the world, and made Peru the world's major fishing nation. The destruction of fish stocks, one after the other, occurs in each instance as if the industry were completely unaware of the facts and circumstances of previously overexploited stocks.

California salmon fisheries have collapsed in the mid-1990s. Again, warning signs and comparable experience have been ignored.

Political and military intelligence failures

> *"When the Shah of Iran was deposed, there was an almost immediate postmortem to determine why the many intelligence operations of the United States and other Western governments had not predicted this outcome. Private corporations, many with vast holdings in Iran, were similarly shocked."*
>
> (Ascher and Overholt, 1983)

Curiously, many of the world's great thinkers have perceived history as a process resulting from powerful systemic forces whose effects pervade all aspects of society, rather than the consequences of decisions by great political leaders. This point has largely escaped attention. One passage in Tolstoy's *War and Peace* provides a particularly compelling illustration of this.

"From the time that the first person said and proved that the number of births or of crimes is subject to mathematical laws, and that this or that form of government is determined by certain geographical and politico-economic conditions, and that certain relations of populations to soil lead to migrations of peoples - from that time the foundations on which history had been built were destroyed in their essence.

"By refuting these new laws, the former view of history might have been retained, but without refuting them it would seem impossible to continue studying historical events as the results of man's free will. For if a certain form of government was established or certain migrations of peoples took place in consequence of certain demographic, ethnographic, or economic conditions, then the free will of those men who appear to us to have established that form of government or to have brought about those migrations can no longer be regarded as the cause."

(Tolstoy, 1869).

The list of military and political FP failures is much longer than anyone has pointed out yet because most were incorrectly perceived as terrible accidents, rather than predictable events.

The transportation industry

The supersonic Concorde built by Britain and France was estimated to sell 400 copies by 1970; it sold 9 (Hall, 1982). Failures of FP are ubiquitous throughout the transportation industry. Astonishingly, only about six models out of more than 20 commercial jet transports manufactured have ever sold enough copies to make the model profitable to the shareholders. At least a quarter of the roughly 6400 jet airliners flying in the non-communist world have been sold at a loss (Economist, 1985). The *appearance* of profitability is created by computing overhead per copy on the assumption that enough copies will be sold over a period of years to render the model run profitable. Clearly, though, the size of the model run is never known with certainty until manufacturing ends, which may be eight years into the future.

Only about six out of more than 20 commercial jet transports models manufactured ever sold enough to be profitable.

Plans for metropolitan rapid transit consistently fail to predict acceptance and use by the public. Riders in the eastern U.S. (e.g., Washington D.C.'s Metro system) use Metro *more* than predicted by planners, while in the west (e.g., BART in the San Francisco Bay Area) low ridership continues to baffle planners.

The Swiss overestimated the gasoline tax revenue they would obtain to pay for their new border-to-border freeways, because they overlooked the fact that many foreign travelers could drive right through Switzerland on one tank of gasoline purchased just before they entered the country.

The Vietnam War

The Vietnam war was one long series of surprises for the United States (Tuchman, 1984). Many wars have been huge surprises for many of the nations involved, and they still are, for reasons that were understood by a few people decades ago.

Construction

The economic consequences of some of the FP errors is quite mind-boggling. For example, as of 1986, there were 290 million square feet of office space for rent in 12 large North American cities (Koon, 1986). This is the equivalent of 290 empty office buildings, each 224 by 224 feet on each side, and 20 stories high. Many people have never seen that much office space in any one place, utilized or unutilized. The actual cost of the Sydney opera house was 14.2 times the original estimated cost (Hall, 1982).

Why conventional models fail

Enormous FP errors were invariably produced by large teams of experts, on well-funded projects, using large to extremely large computer models and the most "modern" mathematical and statistical procedures. The computer models are very rich in detail and based on a high level of technical information and understanding.

A curious phenomenon is that—repeatedly—large-scale FP projects have not benefited from errors of previous projects. Wars and battles were lost for exactly the same reasons that previous wars and battles were lost. Fisheries collapsed from the same management errors that ruined previous fisheries. Nuclear power plants and other major public works had the same cost overruns as previous projects. Economic forecasts erred for the same reasons that previous forecasts failed. Retrospective analyses of FP failures are typically presented as isolated instances completely dissimilar to other failures in the same, or different areas of activity, or different countries.

Whatever the problem, it is much more widespread than previously noted. A few scholars have pointed to systemic, widespread deficiencies in planning (Hall, 1982), forecasting (Ascher, 1978; Ascher and Overholt, 1983; Land and Schneider, 1987) or political judgment among powerful leaders at different times and places (Tuchman, 1984). A few authors have pointed out patterns of repeated managerial failures in particular areas, such as fisheries (Murphy, 1977) or the United States nuclear power program (Cook, 1985).

Economic forecasts err for the same reasons that previous forecasts failed.

What has not been noted, however, is that some very fundamental error or errors are found in all FP in all classes of activity, and in all countries. Further, the severity of the problem has been underestimated, because the largest FP errors have been perceived as terrible, gigantic, unforeseeable and probably unavoidable accidents. The Great Depression and a long series of wars fall into this class. Nevertheless, **they were FP errors, because a few people found it possible to foresee them** (Chapter 3). Therefore, they were foreseeable in principle, and consequently, avoidable.

There are several possible explanations for FP errors in large projects. Perhaps all such errors are related in some fundamental way; for example:

- Real-world systems of high complexity may be less predictable than we think. Interruptions of continuously evolving processes by periods of chaotic system behavior and by discontinuities in historical trends may be more frequent than we believe. If so, the assumption underlying FP—that events are unfolding in accord with unchanging rules, laws of nature, principles, or relationships between variables and processes—is a delusion.

- The problem may originate in the observer-system interaction. We may have been measuring systems incorrectly, or using meaningless measures. Chapter 18. demonstrates that this problem is more serious and widespread than recognized: from average annual temperatures to indices of the money supply, or leading economic indicators, widely used and trusted measures may be far less useful than they are believed to be, and refinements may be required.

- Errors may originate in the relationship between forecasters and planners and their clients or employers. The latter may make it clear that the purpose of the FP projects for which they pay is advocacy, political influence, or the provision of political and economic advantage to powerful interest groups, not objectivity. Advisers of the powerful have never wanted to be messengers blamed for providing truthful, rather than desired messages. This tradition extends back to the earliest writings, as in the fate of Laocoon, who Homer tells us warned the Trojans that the Trojan Horse might contain enemy soldiers (Tuchman, 1984).

- Another problem is that after the work is done everyone tends to forget the circumstances under which FP was conducted. Even the people who ordered unrealistic FP may forget their motives for commissioning the study and come to believe the results, with calamitous impacts.
- FP failures may originate in the interaction between managers and the systems they manage. The systems may be so complex that there are countless ways for failures to occur. Avoiding all possible failure sequences could be beyond the best efforts of any managers.

If any of these explanations accounts for most FP errors on large projects, the basic problem is simply a very low probability of FP success.

Fundamental flaws in conventional FP

I argue that the real error is more basic than any technical problem, and rather, lies in the mode of conceptualizing real-world systems that underlies most FP. The set of implicit assumptions underlying computer or planning models simply don't correspond to the way complex systems work. The problem is a genuine failure to understand certain ubiquitous features of complex real-world systems.

One might assume that a large number of technical errors would tend to cancel each others' effects on forecast accuracy or the managed system; so they would—**unless they were all biased in the same direction**. The fact that many errors have been enormous suggests a different kind of problem.

Large increases in complexity of conventional FP models don't make their predictions more accurate.

One revealing clue is that large increases in complexity of conventional FP models don't make their predictions more accurate. Rather, models of small to intermediate complexity have the highest predictive utility (Armstrong, 1978; Klein and Burmeister, 1976; Makridakis et al, 1984). Indeed, among scholars doing retrospective, comparative analyses of FP projects and models, a consensus is developing that large increase in the number of variables or equations does not improve the predictive utility of the model (Ascher, 1978; Ascher and Overholt, 1983; McClean, 1977; Odum, 1983). So the problem may not be that FP models are insufficiently large, complex, or rich in detail.

The real problem is systematic flaws in conceptual models of reality underlying all FP projects.

Rather, there must be **something incorrect about the usual way variables and equations are selected** for addition to the model and about the way we attempt to mimic behavior of complex systems. In technical jargon, a marginal increase in richness of detail isn't producing a corresponding marginal improvement in the realism of the model. This observation suggests that the real problem is one or a series of systematic flaws in conceptual models of reality underlying all FP projects—basic flaws in:

- The techniques of selecting variables for inclusion in a model,

- Linking the equations describing dynamic system behavior, and
- The detailed and overall structuring of the model. It is these procedures—and not their richness of detail—that determine the predictive utility of FP models.

This leads us to propose a tentative hypothesis:

Processes and events are produced by fundamental forces, but a different set than those assumed by the conventional wisdom.

Is it reasonable to conclude that widespread problems in FP originate in something so fundamental?

Hidden assumptions in conventional forecasting

All FP conceptual models are based on assumptions about the main characteristics of the future (proposed in Chapter 1). Also, all FP models are based on additional hidden assumptions that our desires and decisions have overriding importance in shaping the future of the managed system.

- The future will be a constantly growing, unsurprising extrapolation of recent trends, free of oscillations, fluctuations, major discontinuities or perturbations, and unconstrained by limits.
- The way we won the last war will win the next one for us.
- Nuclear power will be the wave of the future because of the economies of scale made possible by gigantic electrical generating plants.
- A particular fish stock is too abundant for us to wipe it out, and in any case, the fishing fleet is the only major source of mortality for the fished stock.
- Factors relating to money are considered overridingly important in influencing the system.

Other types of factors are excluded from the model. They are assumed to be, collectively, an unchanging "environment" for the system.

Our culture assigns a much lower relative importance to the influence of natural forces, such as:

- The availability of natural resource inputs to the system.
- The effect of wide-amplitude demographic waves on wages, and hence the effect of consumer purchasing power on prices.

Also, hidden assumptions about the maximum possible length of system time lags on system stability pervade our conceptual models for FP. Short time lags imply that if we decide to affect some process or system, we can obtain our desired goal quickly. Long time lags imply that even after we start to shove the system in an appropriate direction, our patience may be cruelly strained while we wait for our reward. The subconscious worldview basic to all our planning is that civilization, and human decision-makers have the power to override the operation of natural forces. We are omnipotent heroes. (Becker, 1971)

All conceptual models are influenced to some extent by a vision of the future that their authors would like to see, as well as by what objective reality suggests they are likely to see. That is, conceptual models of reality are influenced by mind-brain systems that edit and filter the incoming stream of sensed information as well as by reality itself. In Volume 4 we will see that the anatomy and physiology of the brain influence our judgments about the future in ways known only to a few neurophysiologists.

Forecasting business as usual

The recent record for FP projects is mixed at best, and there is no evidence of improvement over time (Ascher, 1978). Examining a wide range of activities in many countries, we see that FP as presently conducted at the least represents a major threat to sustained economic growth, and at worst, a potential hazard to the continuation of civilization. Case studies throughout the book will suggest that this is no exaggeration. The problem will be traced to a set of specific defects in the almost universally accepted procedures for forming conceptual models of complex systems.

Is it possible that a phenomenon of such importance, affecting matters on such a large scale, and in so many countries and areas of activity could have escaped notice for so long? In fact, many people have become aware of parts of this problem.

Case study: World War II

Winston Churchill (1949) described the salient features of the fall of France in 1940, where there had been widespread confidence in the planning capability of the French general staff. He also explained how they succumbed because their enemy was operating on a new conceptual model of warfare.

> *"Hitler and his generals...were not at all deterred by the physical difficulties of traversing the Ardennes. On the contrary, they believed that modern mechanical transport and vast organized road-making capacity would make this region, hitherto deemed impassable, the shortest, surest, and easiest method of penetrating France and of rupturing the whole French scheme of counter-attack".*

The error of the French planners was not on matters of detail, but on the underlying conceptual model of war appropriate for 1940. With respect to the significance of the underlying conceptual model,

> *"...all evidence points to the essential importance of the validity of core assumptions antecedent to the choice and application of methods. Behind any forecast, regardless of the sophistication of methods, are irreducible assumptions representing the forecaster's basic outlook on the context within which the specific trend develops."*
>
> *(Ascher and Overholt, 1983)*

Case study: the airline industry

From 1950 to 1970, revenue passenger seat miles in United States scheduled airlines grew at an average annual rate of 13.7 percent on domestic trips, and 13.4 percent on international trips (SA [1974] Table 972). Extrapolating those astonishingly high growth rates, about 1970 it was widely believed in the airline industry that business would continue to grow at about 10 percent per year until 1980 (Watt, 1974). On the strength of that optimism, 12 new models of jet airplanes for use on regularly scheduled airlines were designed and manufactured in various countries, with sales beginning in 1969.

From 1970 to 1986, however, the average annual growth in airline revenue passenger seat miles was only 6.9 percent for domestic trips, and 5.4 percent for international trips (SA [1987] Table 1024). As would be expected, therefore, only about six of the more than twenty new models of jet transports being sold starting in 1969 made money for shareholders or taxpayers (*Economist*, 1985). Amazingly, the widespread expectation of a post-1970 growth rate in airline business roughly double that which actually occurred was based on a simple logical error that could be detected in 1972 by an observer external to the aerospace and airline industries (Watt, 1974).

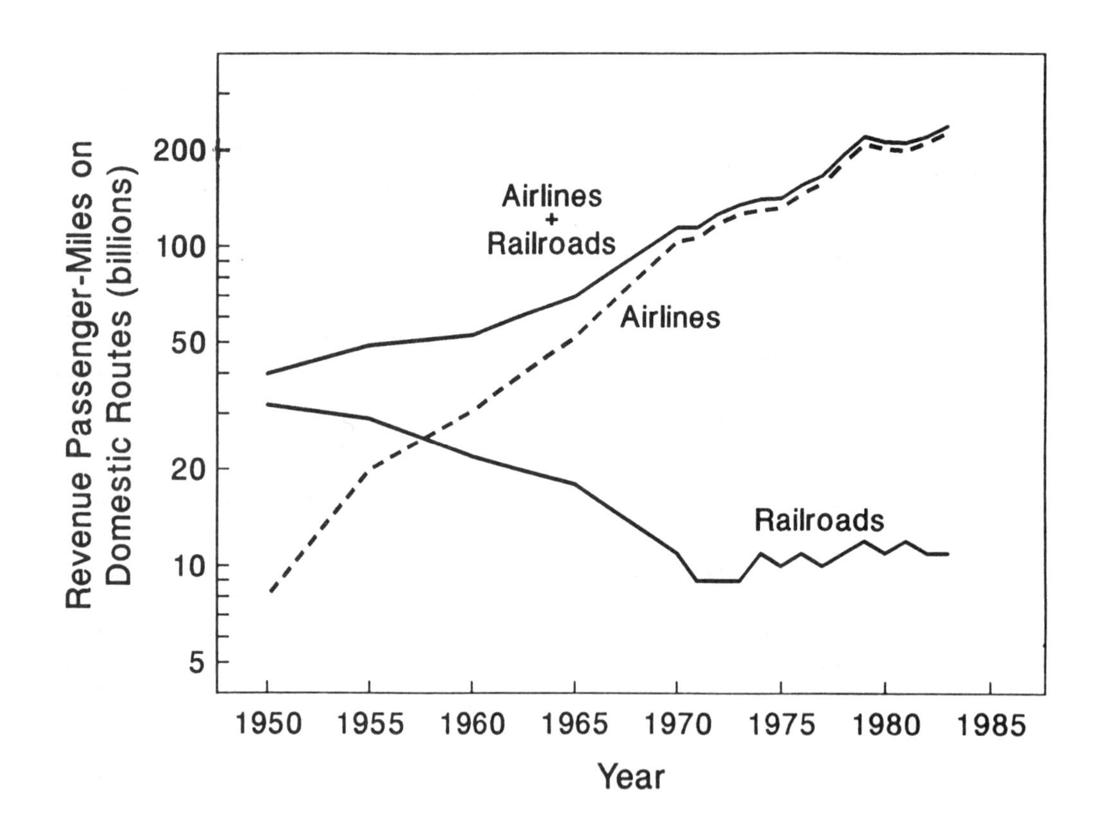

Figure 2-2. The growth in passenger miles on U.S. domestic routes for airlines and railroads combined (top line), airlines only (dashed line), and railroads only (bottom line). (SA, various years) Note that much of the growth in airline travel occurred when railroad travel declined.

Their error is explained in fig. 2-2. Airline planners and aerospace manufacturers looked only at the past trend *in their own business* as the basis for projecting its future growth. It did not occur to them that from 1950 to 1970, much of that growth occurred because passengers switched from trains (on domestic trips) and ocean liners (on international trips). The growth in the airline business is the growth in the total volume of all travel, multiplied by the proportion of that total volume captured by airlines. Prior to 1970, the airline growth rate was very great because a growing proportion of all travel was on airlines. That proportion would not continue to grow after the proportion captured by ships, trains and buses had dropped to a very low level, however.

Fig. 2-2 shows that from 1950 to 1970, the very rapid growth in airline travel was accompanied by a rapid drop in train travel on domestic trips. When travel by both modes is added, the total growth in revenue passenger miles from 1950 to 1970 was only 5.4 percent a year, a figure much closer to the 6.9 percent a year growth rate in air travel by scheduled carriers after 1970 than the 13.6 percent a year in scheduled air carrier passenger growth for 1950 to 1970. The inability of Douglas, Lockheed and other companies to make a profit on the new generation of jets, and the extraordinarily poor sales of the Concorde were all predictable before the fact.

The industry assumed that demand for airline seats was unaffected by processes external to the air travel business.

What characteristics of the FP conceptual models used by airlines and aerospace companies around 1968 made it impossible for them to forecast accurately when it was obvious to others at that time? The industry assumed that demand for airline seats was unaffected by processes external to the air travel business. Simply by shifting to a conceptual model assuming that airline passenger volume is driven by *all* the factors influencing the entire volume of passenger travel, the proportion captured by the airlines yields a more realistic demand forecast. One could guess that demand growth for scheduled air carrier seat miles is governed by population growth and age structure, the average level of affluence and propensity to travel by air of each age group, the portal-to-portal speed and cost of competing transportation modes, and the factors driving transportation costs, such as fuel prices.

We could imagine two different strategies for formulating an FP conceptual model of the factors regulating demand for airline passenger seat miles. The model might be constructed using several variables from one interrelated cluster of causal variables: measures of past trends in volume of passenger travel on various airline routes. A conceptual model might also be formulated using only one or two variables from each of a number of different factor clusters: population characteristics being one factor cluster, fuel prices being another. As explained in Volume 2, logic and experience with modeling complex systems suggests that the latter strategy would have far higher predictive utility.

Estimated sales for the Concorde were 400 planes; in fact, only 9 planes have been sold, at a total cost of 2 billion pounds.

The basic error of airline and aerospace planners was in assuming constancy of the "environment" surrounding the system of their immediate interest, when a variety of changes of immense and immediate importance for their system were anything but constant. One well-documented example indicates the enormity of the economic consequences of investing in research, development, and tooling up for manufacturing of many different models of planes for which the need was illusory. In 1962, the estimated cost of R & D for the Concorde was 150 to 170 million British pounds, and estimated sales were 400 planes. In fact, while only 9 planes have been sold, the total cost of the Concorde program to Britain and France has been 2 billion pounds—over 222 million *each* (Hall, 1982).

High technology costs are widely underestimated.

Another component of the problem in this and many other cases has been the widespread tendency to underestimate the cost of all new high-technology R & D, tooling up for manufacturing, and manufacturing itself. Still another component is the high inherent operating cost for very high-technology systems: up to twice as much per seat mile for the Concorde as the Boeing 747.

Hidden deep in the core of this problem is the ramifying effects on inflation of a gradually depleting world fossil energy resource.

There is an even more basic flaw in the airline demand forecasting case: a **philosophical bias against perceiving the reality of market saturation in particular, or the concept of limits to growth in general**.

All the FP errors of the airline demand case show up in the next case study.

Case study: nuclear power

There were two reasons why many nations turned to nuclear power. The situation in the United States was typical: demand for electricity grew at an annual average rate of about 6.5 percent from 1940 to 1973. The kind of FP conceptual models used by electrical utilities expected that growth rate to continue indefinitely. Also, while the capital costs for nuclear plants were higher than for coal or oil-fired electrical generating plants, the fuel cost was lower, so that the overall costs of nuclear power appeared competitive.

After the first few plants were built, it became apparent that the power they generated would be more expensive than expected. To maintain the competitive edge of nuclear over coal-fired plants, it seemed reasonable that moving to very large nuclear plants would exploit economies of scale and decrease unit costs.

In analyzing conceptual FP models of decision-makers for electrical utilities at the time commitments to the nuclear option were being made, we find two important factors operating.

- It appeared around 1970 that simply extrapolating trends to that time, an enormous growth in both kilowatt hours used per capita, or total kilowatt hours used would be likely (Gandara, 1977).
- Also, board members of such regional utilities as the Washington Public Power Supply System (WPPSS) were concerned that energy might run out. They were given to understand that the hydroelectric installations in their regions would not be able to supply enough power by the early 1980s (Dolan, 1983).

Construction of state-of-the-art very high-technology large capital projects is characterized by cost overruns.

Those boards experienced two major surprises. Construction of state-of-the-art very high-technology large capital projects is characterized by cost overruns. For the five nuclear generators planned by WPPSS the cost would have escalated from $4 billion to $24 billion, if all five had been completed. The industry-wide phenomenon discovered through statistical analysis is that **architect-engineering firms could only learn how to keep costs down if they could build several consecutive plants of identical design** (Mooz, 1978). The nuclear power industry in the United States, however, has been characterized by constant innovation in designs. Thus each plant built has too high a component of its overhead due to innovative research and development (and often manufacturing).

The other surprise resulted from the same type of error that plagued airline and aerospace forecasts: ignoring some of the relevant factor clusters. To illustrate, forecasts erroneously predicted that demand for electricity would continue to grow at 6.5 percent per year in the United States from 1940 to 1970 (fig. 2-3). The models assumed a continuation of the crude oil price environment that had fostered that growth. Residential electricity price had remained constant throughout the period (bottom panel of fig. 2-3). Because wages had risen steadily throughout that period, the ratio of residential electricity cost to consumer purchasing power had declined steadily throughout the interval. It should have come as no surprise that demand for electricity had grown steadily.

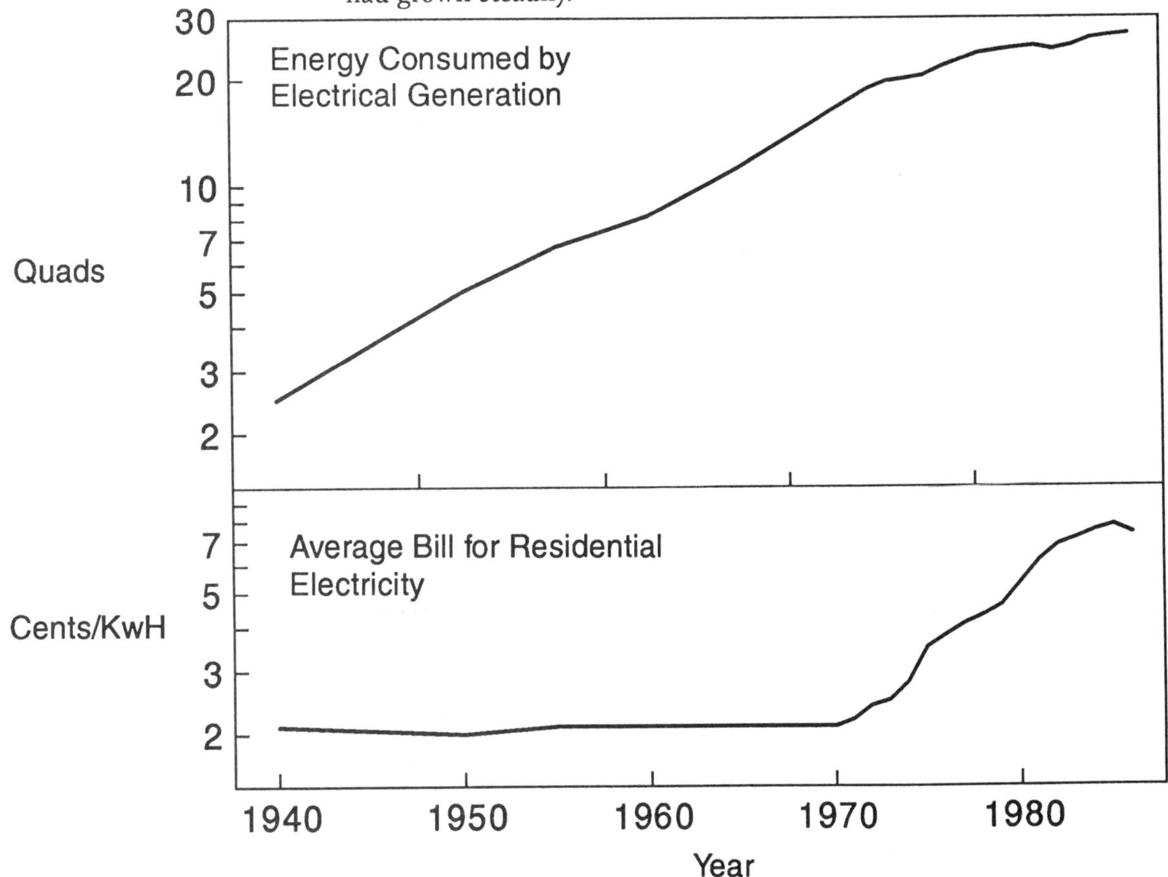

Figure 2-3. Growth in the energy consumed by electrical generating plants (top panel) and in the average bill for electricity to residential customers (bottom). (SA, various years.) Note that growth in demand (top) slackens markedly when electricity bills go up (bottom).

If, however, anything happened to increase the retail price of electricity, demand growth would slacken or stop altogether. Electricity demand forecasters in the 1960s overlooked two factors that were bound to increase electricity costs.

- The first was increased costs of the fuel for fossil-fuel-fired generating plants, as U.S. fossil fuel resources became scarcer and more costly to discover and produce, as was being predicted by some analysts (Chapter 3).
- The second was the impact on nuclear plant construction cost of high frequency of breakdown due to the great increase in technological novelty, complexity, and scale (Mooz, 1978).

Again, the key planning error was an incomplete conceptual model. The "environment" for electrical utility systems was treated as if it would remain constant, when it could not, as fossil fuels became depleted. A realistic, complete conceptual model needed to include variables from several different types of factor clusters, but most of these were overlooked. For example, the impact of technological novelty, complexity and project scale on unit costs is a widespread phenomenon that ought to have been well known: it has shown up in all major projects in the last twenty years, from rockets and military systems to the Sydney opera house, mass transit projects, and nuclear reactors.

An incomplete conceptual model treated the "environment" for electrical utility systems as if it would remain constant, when it could not, as fossil fuels became depleted.

It is noteworthy that no long-range FP models allow for serious recessions or depressions. It is always assumed that, even though they have occurred in all prior history, they will never occur again. In fact, a characteristic of modern industrial nations is susceptibility to powerful long economic waves (Chapter 7). More generally, energy demand and price projections appear unaffected by any sense of limits to growth. Again, this attests to the powerful subconscious role of ideology underlying FP conceptual models.

Will we squander precious capital investment?

The following is an imaginary tragic scenario in which the modern world may be involved, again through treading along a path pointing towards an obsolete vision of the future.

Peace breaks out everywhere, and the public in all countries demands a massive reduction in military spending. In the United States, the public sends a great volume of mail to legislators demanding its expected "peace dividend". Politicians resist this pressure for awhile, but after the first significant economic downturn, the pressure to make major cuts in military preparedness becomes overwhelming. The budgets of aerospace corporations who make airplanes and missiles are devastated, and most of their staffs are laid off.

Within ten or fifteen years, most countries discover that the key to being economically competitive in a peaceful world is to have a very technologically sophisticated infrastructure. This would include extremely efficient transportation systems, which waste far less traveler time, agricultural land, energy and minerals than at present. Then people begin to realize that there is a need for a type of corporation that can build radically new types of ground transportation systems, with almost miraculous operating characteristics. Nations would then be searching for very large corporations with experience in managing armies of high-technology staffs so as to accomplish miraculous objectives within very limited time schedules.

What type of corporations can routinely produce large-scale miracles? The corporations that could build extremely fast bombers and fighters; the corporations that had just been disbanded.

Case study: the space shuttle Challenger

The design of the space shuttle Challenger, which exploded on January 28, 1986, contained a hidden implicit assumption of an approximately constant environment. That is, climate and other environmental factors could be assumed to be the same as at the time the shuttle was being planned. Therefore, the material of which the booster rocket O-rings was manufactured was not based on knowledge of how cold Cape Kennedy was likely to be in the future. In fact, the average January temperature for the weather station at Titusville, just 18 miles from Cape Canaveral, had declined markedly during the four decades prior to the year of the launch (Volume 4). January temperatures for the five years prior to the shuttle launch were an average of 9.5° lower than those for the five years 1949–1953. Extrapolating that trend forward suggests that very cold temperatures would increasingly pose a threat to future launches unless the shuttles were modified with that threat in mind.

The trend in Titusville January temperatures could be discovered in about half an hour in any large library. Further, the effects of unusually cold weather in the 1980s on the citrus crop in Florida were well known. Given the enormous budget for the National Aeronautics and Space Administration ($7.3 billion in 1985), it is astounding that nobody seems to have thought to investigate this issue. This omission is a commentary on the conceptual model used for managing the shuttle program. A complete conceptual model for shuttle FP would have recognized that climatic trend was a relevant component of the "environment" for the program.

On July 27, 1988, it was announced that a panel of experts warned that NASA would require better weather forecasts to avert future disasters or delays in launching the space shuttle fleet (Boffey, 1988).

Patterns in unrealistic FP models

They don't allow for revolutionary change or even a downward bend in the trend.

We frequently find the assumption of a world at equilibrium, or at least following a trend that grows indefinitely at a roughly constant rate. The implicit assumption is that fluctuations are of small amplitude and return quickly to that equilibrium trend. A method common to all FP models with this implicit assumption is forward extrapolation of recent trends. This type of conceptual model doesn't allow for revolutionary change or even a downward bend in the trend.

This is curious, since even our common language explicitly recognizes the possibility of revolution, or structural transformation of systems: "Industrial Revolution", "Information Revolution," "Demographic Transition". Given such transformations, it is clear that comprehensive FP models need to be based on long enough data time series to identify and explain the fundamental forces that cause system transformations.

Failure to identify the fundamental system drivers and hidden assumptions

Models for FP typically fail to identify the necessary and sufficient set of fundamental system drivers (FSD) that govern the dynamic behavior of the system of interest. Thus airline planners and energy demand forecasters failed to notice the effect that consumer purchasing power for energy had on trends in demand for transportation and energy.

FP models are characteristically plagued by hidden implicit assumptions. The assumption that economies of scale would never become diseconomies of scale for very large scale projects is an example.

Using the wrong data

In order for FP models to be realistic, they must be based on accurate, recent data that measure what experts think they are measuring. These and many other assumptions about the information used for FP models are typically violated (Volume 4).

Perhaps the single most serious problem with all FP models is that they are constructed using many variables from one or a few factor clusters, rather than a few variables from several factor clusters. In addition, the environment surrounding the system of interest is assumed constant.

Ignoring time lags

Most FP models assume that real world systems are either free of lagged effects, or that time lags are of a few years duration at the longest. The idea that there might be very long time lags operating in systems is rarely recognized. Yet it is obvious that wages in a particular year for those 20–24 year olds attempting permanent entry into the labor force must be affected by the supply of people of that age relative to the demand for them. That supply to demand ratio, in turn, is primarily the result of birth rates 20–24 years previously. Thus, wages are under control by a system of causal pathways with a 20–24 year lag. Important causal pathways with time lags many years long are characteristic of complex modern societies.

Few models treat complex systems as being made up of many subcomponents that differ markedly from one to another and compete with each other

This suggests conceptual models with hierarchical levels of organization, with many subcomponents on each level determining part of the dynamics at the next higher level. A common example is separate nations, each of which is influenced by behavior of constituent regions and interacts with other nations to determine the behavior of the system of international trade in commodities, manufactured goods, and the international flow of money.

World views shape conceptual models

Scientists, scholars, technical experts and managers involved in FP are now operating off several distinct conceptual models as to how the world works. Holling (1986) has presented sharply drawn portraits of some of these views.

"Nature Constant"

This world view supplies the underlying assumptions and mathematical machinery for most FP models. Complex systems are modeled as if they undergo minor, temporary oscillations about long term equilibrium states, or constant-growth-rate, long-term trend lines. It is assumed that if the variables measuring the state of the system depart from their steady state or growth trends, then self-regulatory or homeostatic forces will quickly force them back to equilibrium.

These equilibrating forces increase rapidly in intensity, the greater the departures from equilibrium. This world view does not recognize the existence of forces strong enough to move the system away from the present equilibrium state toward one or more new equilibrium states. No matter where in the universe of possible states that the system travels, it will return quickly to this one and only (and therefore, "global") equilibrium state or growth trend.

A body of theoretical and mathematical baggage is inexorably linked to this idea. A system of that type can be modeled by equations implying that the probability of return to the equilibrium state increases with the size of the departure from the equilibrium system state. Therefore, we need not postulate breaks in system behavior.

There is no room in this world view for: limitations on system behavior, structural transformation, discontinuities, or major perturbations.

That, in turn, contains the hidden assumption that the system can be conceived of purely in terms of flows. The "Nature Constant" world view does not require the assumption of any storages. Including storages in addition to flows in a conceptual FP model implies that limits can be reached, either when a storage is completely depleted or completely filled up. Corresponding phenomena in the real world are complete depletion of a crude oil reserve at oil prices people are currently willing to pay or complete supersaturation of a housing or office space market. The "Nature Constant" conceptual system model views reality as a complex system of flows controlled only by the settings of valves or switches throughout the system. There is no room in this world view for limitations on system behavior, structural transformation or evolution, or discontinuities, or major perturbations.

This model has been very useful. It works well in periods between major perturbations or structural transformations, when the system state does stay near a particular equilibrium domain or follows a smooth trend, free from breaks in rate of change or direction.

The distinction between a "flows only" and "flows and storages" view of the world has far-reaching implications. If a container is filled to the maximum possible, saturation level, the rate at which it can be filled per unit time decreases, and approaches zero as saturation is reached, due to the backpressure of the contents already in the container. Similarly, if a storage can be completely emptied, the rate at which it can be drained approaches zero as complete emptiness is approached. Zero rates of change imply asymptotes, thresholds and limits. They further imply mathematical models with different structure than those that assume no storages, only flows.

Completely filled or empty storages are found throughout the real world—in saturated transportation corridors, energy markets, office or residential real estate markets, or resources completely used up—but they find no place in the "Nature Constant" conceptual FP models.

"Nature Constant" can be described by mathematical models in which the flow rate can be expressed as a simple proportion or multiple of a valve or switch setting. Linear models suffice to describe this world view, because with no storages to be depleted or saturated, there is no need to include either nonlinear equations or constraints on rates of flow.

It is the most common type of world view used as the conceptual foundation for FP models. It is the absence of storages, and hence the limits imposed on flow rates that generate the embarrassing mismatches between model and reality—and account for much of their low predictive utility. A model without storages cannot simulate limits being reached.

One strategy for retaining the "Nature Constant" world view commonly employed is to attempt to model only periods of history between discontinuities. Thus, many models only attempt to describe the period after World War II, which was free of major wars or a global depression. Such models will not explain why world wars or depressions arise, however, and they certainly couldn't predict either.

Such models will not explain why wars or depressions arise, and they certainly couldn't predict either.

Similarly, a FP model of a corporation that eliminated data on collapse of corporations in the past would have limited utility in showing how to avoid the collapse of a corporation. A map cannot tell us anything about the territory external to the territory being mapped.

"Nature Resilient"

In "Nature Resilient" models (Holling, 1986), systems can jump to new equilibrium steady states or growth trends without undergoing internal structural transformation. That is, there are multiple "local equilibria" or "local steady states" within the universe of all possible system states. This, in turn, implies that as a system travels further away from a recent steady state or long-term trend line, forces could come into play with gradually increasing intensity to force it into a new "local equilibrium" or long-term trend line. In either case, there might be several such equilibria in possible.

"Nature Resilient" includes the possibility of nonlinearities. Because nonlinearities imply stocks that can be supersaturated or depleted, this is a conceptual model of "flows and storages" as well as flows. Such a world view mirrors real-world situations in which a storage (such as an inventory of houses or the national reserves of crude oil) is completely used up.

Another type of limit occurs when borrowers have borrowed as much money as they can possibly afford to borrow, because their interest payments are consuming the maximum possible proportion of their monthly incomes; no increase in the money supply will induce them to borrow more. In this model, nonlinear equations are required to describe situations in which rates of change with respect to time or some other independent variable drop to zero.

The "Flows only" and "Flows and storages" FP models are different views of how the world works. Their corresponding mathematical models appear quite dissimilar and make different forecasts as they reach limits to growth. "Nature Resilient" models tend to be more accurate and yield more realistic forecasts. They are also unpopular, because they suggest the possibility of major system discontinuities.

Such models challenge some of the most fundamental beliefs and paradigms of a society predicated on the assumption of never-ending growth in everything.

"Nature Evolving"

In Holling's third world view, the system of flows and storages undergoes structural transformation:

- Relative sizes of parts of the system change;
- Parts of the system disappear and new parts appear;
- System components are hooked together in new ways; and
- Old linkages are broken.

In the corresponding mathematical model, the system of equations gradually or suddenly loses or adds terms or relationships. The relationship between two variables might change in response to the values taken by a third variable, for example.

"Nature Constant" implies a world that retains its character or grows to be more of what it always was: more population concentration in large cities, more miles of flying in airplanes per person every year, constant growth in electricity consumption per household, and nuclear power plants that become ever-greater in average size, for example.

"Nature Resilient" implies that there can be major short-term departures from equilibrium regions or trends experienced during lengthy depressions, revolutions, droughts or wars. The system retains its structural integrity and the ability to return to former system states, however, and ultimately it does, as when the U.S. economy returned to its previous growth trend at the conclusion of the Great Depression.

"Nature Evolving" implies permanent change to a completely different state. The "Industrial Revolution" was a social transformation from a world of horse-drawn carriages and bulk goods movement by barge canals to a world of railroads, then cars, trucks and airplanes. The shift from railroads and streetcars to cars and trucks, in turn, implied a world no longer organized along straight lines, but around the leapfrog development pattern made possible by road networks.

Cheap fossil fuel stimulates a pattern of centralized control of resources.

Future radical changes in the whole pattern of social organization are possible. Cheap fossil fuel stimulates a pattern of social organization concentrated around a small number of point sources of massive amounts of energy: coal mines, oil derricks, refineries, electrical power generating plants and gasoline stations. Society, therefore, evolves towards great centralization of social, political, and economic control over resources. Centralization, in turn, fosters enormous capital accumulation and a centralized spatial distribution pattern for population, most of which lives in a small number of very large metropolitan regions of very high population density.

A switch from this integrated system structure to a society organized about renewable power (solar, wind, small hydroelectric stations) would evolve towards great decentralization of social, political and economic power and population distribution. It would be more difficult to accumulate great stores of capital, or it would have to be done in new ways. The tremendous pressures towards great population concentrations in a few very large cities would be replaced by evolution towards a large number of small towns because the energy sources would be diffuse, not concentrated. The strength of powerful central government would weaken, since it would have less to provide that was worth anything. Vast military might, a crucial benefit and justification for enormous concentration of political power is only necessary when there are important large targets and transportation corridors to be defended. These are the oilfields, mines, sea lanes, and transportation and port facilities required to obtain and move fossil fuels. A world of solar or wind energy provides only a very large number of very small targets, each of minimal attractiveness to either foreign powers or terrorists.

It is noteworthy that one of the most rapidly-growing sectors of the U.S. economy consists of corporations developing methods for moving information around in computer networks. One need no longer live in a big city in a world of lightening information transfer over great distances through such networks.

A rapidly-growing sector of the economy is developing ways to move information in computer networks.

This brief discussion of different world views only hints at the magnitude of the effect they could have in shaping FP models. If we wish to improve performance in these activities, it is the world view that lies hidden deep underneath our implicit assumptions that must be examined and corrected.

Chapter 3

Realistic Visions of the Future

If all FP were shown to be wrong, a logical conclusion might be that the behavior of systems is too chaotic and discontinuous to predict. On the other hand, if among a sea of inaccurate forecasts we find some that are accurate, this may demonstrate that accurate forecasting is possible, provided that one uses alternative methods of logic.

This chapter describes five remarkably prophetic forecasts. From these we draw two conclusions: accurate FP is possible in principle, and accurate forecasts share a process that ensures realism.

What is an "accurate forecast"?

Throughout history, failures by "conventional wisdom" FP to perceive a future threat coincided with unheeded warnings from a few people who foresaw danger. People make forecasts all the time; the tabloids are full of them. By chance alone, some of those are correct. The fact that a small proportion of all forecasters are accurate does not in itself prove that forecasting accurately is possible.

Five forecasts not only showed remarkable foreknowledge, but also demonstrated understanding of the mechanisms that produced the actual outcome.

I selected five "accurate forecasts" that not only showed remarkable foreknowledge, but also demonstrated understanding in advance of the underlying mechanisms that produced the actual outcome. This criterion of "accurate forecast" shifts emphasis away from event prediction to understanding forces that control historical processes. It also focuses on the features of the conceptual models used for FP that enhance realism.

This line of argument leads to a rigorous definition of FP error.

An FP error has occurred when at least one person, in advance of an event, has identified the fundamental forces that produced the actual scenario, rather than the scenario projected by other recognized experts.

For each of the five case studies, there is no question that the "conventional wisdom" erred, after the history is examined. In each instance, one or more people clearly understood, in advance, that the actual scenario was more probable than the one expected by "conventional expert wisdom." Further, the accurate forecasters correctly identified fundamental forces that would produce the future that surprised most other experts and knew which data were most critical for analysis of those forces. *The correct forecasts were not freak accidents*. Rather, they resulted from a fundamentally different conceptual model of complex systems behavior than that used by conventional expert wisdom.

Case 1: World War II

Retrospectively, World War II can be viewed as a horrendous series of FP errors. Six examples illustrate the typical error, and expose the distinction between realistic and unrealistic FP models.

① The **fall of Poland** in September 1939 illustrates key features of military situations found repeatedly, up to the bombing of Libya by the United States in 1986. Previously, warfare had involved relatively static confrontation between opposing forces. The fall of Poland was the first example of three innovations in warfare:

- The use of large numbers of dive bombers (over 1500 aircraft were used against Poland);
- Surprise, with a large proportion of Poland's 900 military aircraft being destroyed on the ground; and
- Close integration of fast-moving tank columns with tactical fighter and bomber air cover.

Variations on this tactic continued to prove successful for Germany, then Japan, until well into 1942.

② **France** met the same fate as Poland. By May 14, 1940, the French had proved unable to resist the combination of tanks

Mitchell's remarkable vision

Study of Mitchell's writings is mindboggling, given subsequent events. Passages such as the following (published in 1925) leap off the page.

"The Hawaiian Islands, due to their remoteness from the continent, should be equipped with an air force of three hundred airplanes...In addition to the air force units, there should be a unit for the local defense of the Island of Oahu of one hundred planes and accessories for defense against aircraft...Alaska should be provided with an air force of three hundred planes...It takes our own defending pursuit aviation at least twenty minutes to take to the air and rise to 15,000 feet....They should be up there a few minutes before the hostile formation arrives so as to be entirely ready to launch a concentrated attack against the enemy...Listening posts are not enough, because modern airplanes do not necessarily make a noise; therefore, surveillance aviation has to be kept constantly in the air where they can not only see but hear the enemy aircraft...The older means of transportation, vessels and railways, have followed the parallels of latitude, through the temperate Zone. The new means of transportation through the air will follow the meridians, that is the shortest routes, straight across the poles....By going directly across the top of the earth... via...Nome, Alaska...the trip ...from New York to Peking, China...may be made by air in from sixty to eighty hours...instead of...four to five weeks....As air power can hit at a distance, after it controls the air and vanquishes the opposing air power, it will be able to fly anywhere over the hostile territory....The role of armies and their way of making war will remain much the same in the future as it has in the past, if air power does not entirely prevent them from operating." Mitchell demonstrated by a series of experiments in 1921 that even "unsinkable" battleships could be sunk by bombs from aircraft."

(Mitchell, 1925)

and dive-bombing. Winston Churchill specifically identified the key role of an outmoded conceptual model.

> *"Not having had access to official information for so many years, I did not comprehend the violence of the revolution effected since the last war by the incursion of a mass of fast-moving heavy armor. I knew about it, but it had not altered my inward convictions as it should have done."*
>
> *(Churchill, 1949)*

His memoirs made clear that by the fall of Poland a second factor had become critical: the use of air power to achieve surprise. Still the Allies failed to grasp the significance of surprise attack by air.

③ On Sunday, December 7, 1941, in 110 minutes 105 Japanese aircraft from 6 aircraft carriers sank 4 United States battleships at **Pearl Harbor** and heavily damaged three others. As in Poland, United States planes were surprised on the ground, and 475 were converted to burning wreckage before they could take off.

④ In the **Philippines**, beginning December 8, the same scenario was repeated: United States airplanes were destroyed by enemy aircraft before they could take off.

⑤ Then on December 10, 84 Japanese bombers and torpedo bombers surprised and sank in about 140 minutes 2 British battleships without protective fighter air cover, near **Singapore**.

⑥ A World War II incident of immense potential geopolitical significance was the temporary **seizure by Japanese landing parties of the Western Aleutian islands** of Attu and Kiska in June, 1942. These were the first moves in a program by which the Japanese could have used air armadas to leapfrog down the west coast of Alaska and British Columbia until they had seized airfields in the western United States for conducting bombing raids against the 48 coterminous states.

Every one of the six incidents mentioned came as a complete surprise to the conventional military wisdom of England, France, Poland, the United States, and many other countries. Up to three weeks prior to Pearl Harbor, the American public was being bombarded with assurances such as, "Germany and Italy cannot send myriads of planes to bomb London," and "As for Japanese air power, it is almost nonexistent" (Gauvreau, 1945). Why had very few people outside the German and Japanese military grasped the significance of surprise attack by aircraft: because it was impossible?

Mitchell's predictions

In fact, a few Americans had understood the new conceptual FP warfare model since around 1900. One person in particular had tried to spread understanding of the significance of surprise attack by air: Billy Mitchell, the general heading the U.S. air force in France at the end of World War I (Gauvreau, 1945; Hurley, 1975; Levine, 1958).

Mitchell's foreknowledge of the fundamental forces that would shape events in World War II was in print and widely available by 1925; the war would have been very different if his FP conceptual model had been adopted by all Allied military planners prior to 1943. More astonishing, by 1935, Mitchell had conceived a detailed realistic scenario of much of the war that was still four years in the future. To illustrate, he made the following remarks before five witnesses at a dinner shortly before his death in February, 1936.

> *"Hawaii, for instance, is vulnerable from the sky.... Yet we bring our Navy in at Pearl Harbor and lock it up every Saturday night so that the sailors can spend their week's pay to please the merchants and politicians who have arranged that routine because they think it's good for business. And Hawaii is swarming with...spies. As I have said before, that's where the blow will be struck—on a fine, quiet Sunday morning."*
>
> *(Gauvreau, 1945)*

And this is exactly what happened—on Sunday morning, December 7, 1941.

Mitchell's conceptual model

What were the differences between the conceptual FP model used by Mitchell (see side bar), and all the other military experts and politicians who could not foresee what was so clear to him?

- His forecasts were not simply extrapolations of recent trends; he had identified and understood the fundamental forces that would cause revolutionary system transformation of warfare. Air power would ensure victory, if used wisely. The striking force would be fast, freed from existing transportation corridors, and therefore able to exploit the surprise inherent in sudden arrival at completely unexpected locations. He realized that air power would represent a major discontinuity in the method of conducting warfare over vast distances, by using great circle routes that followed the shortest distance between two points on the surface of the globe, rather than the route suggested by plane representations of that surface on flat maps.

- He understood that the silence and speed of modern airplanes allowed very little warning of their arrival. He understood that attack from the air would demoralize and disorganize ground forces, a fact grasped by almost no famous and respected military leaders at the outset of World War II, in any theater. Mitchell always projected on the basis of accurate, recent technical data, of which other planners were often unaware.
- He understood that realistic FP models must be based on key forces from a diversity of types of factors: economics, geography, technology, logistics, operations research and other fields were combined in his conceptual model.
- A central feature of Mitchell's thinking was his grasp of the significance of time lags in complex systems. He realized that it was irrelevant how many military airplanes a nation had or

how technologically advanced they were relative to other nation's air forces, if they had inadequate time to get airborne and protect their own airfields against an enemy air force.

- Basic to his thinking was the notion that there are limits to what is possible. If a military airbase is about to be attacked by enemy aircraft, there is a limit to the delay in getting one's own fighters into the air, if destruction of the base is to be prevented. Given the time for a large number of defending fighters to roll down the runway, ascend to a sufficient altitude to be above the invaders, and move far enough away from the base to minimize risk of some bombers penetrating to it, that minimum time might be an hour.

Case 2: Oil price shocks of 1974–5 and 1979–81

Motorists in the United States became accustomed, over the period 1950–1972, to a remarkably constant gasoline price. Because wages rose rapidly through that period, their purchasing power with respect to gasoline increased rapidly, and total national consumption of gasoline in land vehicles increased by a factor of about 2.62 times. Suddenly, in association with the Arab-Israeli War and limitations of oil supply by the Arab states of O.P.E.C. (The Organization of Petroleum Exporting Countries), retail gasoline prices jumped sharply from about 38¢ a gallon in 1972 to 55¢ in 1974, then from 66¢ in 1978 to $1.31 in 1981.

The notion that these price hikes were "caused" by O.P.E.C. operating as a cartel to limit world oil supply can only be a proximate, but not an ultimate explanation for the price increases. If there had been no more fundamental cause, then as the price increased, other nations, such as the United States, would simply have increased their crude oil production so as to exploit the higher prices. The fact that this did not happen indicates that it could not happen. That, in turn, suggests that the fundamental cause was decreasing availability of crude oil in other countries relative to world demand. The O.P.E.C. price increases were made possible by an increase in the constant dollar marginal cost to discover one new barrel of oil in the United States, the principal world oil consumer. The increasing discovery cost resulted from decreasing reserves, so that new barrels discovered were in deeper, more inaccessible strata, for which locating drilling sites and drilling were more expensive per well (e.g. SA87, Table 1168).

The true ultimate cause of U.S. gasoline price increases since 1973 is declining domestic reserves.

To summarize, the true ultimate cause of U.S. gasoline price increases since 1973 has been declining domestic reserves relative to domestic demand. Without that, limitation of supply by O.P.E.C. would have been irrelevant.

It is still true that few Americans understand the causal connection between United States costs for domestic crude oil exploration and the price they pay for gasoline. This is not surprising: the statistics one needs to understand the role of domestic crude oil reserves in regulating the energy market in particular, and more generally, the entire economy, are not available in the appropriate form for clarifying causal connections. The required statistics must be computed from other data published by the government and the petroleum industry. Chapter 4 exposes the linkages between energy and other aspects of society.

Because few people had any knowledge of the status of United States fossil fuel reserves, the oil price increases of the 1970s came as "oil shocks." To one man, however, they came as no surprise at all.

Hubbert's predictions

M. King Hubbert is an internationally respected geologist who worked with the Shell Development Company, then for the U.S. Geological Survey, then as a visiting professor at various prestigious universities. Beginning in 1956, he published a prophetic series of analyses of the U.S. and world energy situations and likely future scenarios. As Chairman of the Energy Resources Study of the National Academy of Sciences–National Research Council he wrote about U.S. crude oil as follows:

> *"...the peak of production is expected to occur by about 1967 or earlier...Due in large measure to petroleum imports, which have been building up since World War II and now amount to approximately 20 percent of domestic production, the present rate of production is somewhat less than full capacity....This discrepancy between the actual rate of production and a hypothetical maximum productive capacity, therefore, allows some latitude in the exact year at which the peak of production could occur. Conceivably, if, for some reason comparable to the Suez Crisis, the production were to be at the maximum capacity for some given year, then in whatever year this may have occurred between 1962 and possibly 1975 the peak of production would occur."*
>
> *(Hubbert, 1962)*

It occurred one year after the middle of this range, in 1970 (SA87, Table 1165).

It was inevitable that shortly after U.S. production peaked, a sharp increase in the long-term trend in wholesale and retail energy prices would begin. The reason was that after that time, the unit discovery cost for U.S. oil reserves would begin rising rapidly, which would allow foreign oil suppliers to begin increasing their oil prices rapidly, as already explained.

Hubbert's conceptual model

Hubbert's forecast was based on a conceptual model of the way current reserves of fossil fuel in the U.S. and other countries were determined by long-term trends in cumulative proved discoveries and cumulative production. This theory employed estimates of the ultimate recoverable size of the resource in each category (oil, gas, coal, uranium) and in each country. These estimates came from two independent sources that serve as checks on each others' accuracy: enumeration, from geological surveys; and statistical fitting of curves for the growth of discovery and production year by year, which provide estimates of ultimate recoverable total production for each resource.

Hubbert assumed an S-shaped curve for the long-term increasing trend in cumulative oil production, with the fastest growth in cumulative production occurring when the ultimate recoverable reserves were somewhat more than half gone. The curve for the long-term trend in reserves would have a bell shape, with the peak occurring when reserves were half gone.

Several unusual features characterize Hubbert's conceptual FP model.

- The distinction between a "flows and storages" and a "flows only" conceptual FP model.
- The notion of limits: he perceived the crucial significance for any nation of having limited geological storages of fossil fuels.
- He was sensitive to the critical significance of time lags. He recognized that the curve for cumulative U.S. oil production must lag that for cumulative discoveries, and he discovered that the year of peak production rate lagged the year of peak discovery rate for U.S. oil by about 10.5 years. Thus he recognized that *a curve for cumulative proven discoveries was a leading indicator for a curve of cumulative production*. A leading indicator is a variable that gives advance warning of subsequent changes in other variables.
- Hubbert is one of a handful of thinkers in many fields and countries over the last century who have realized that energy, and not money is the ultimate determinant of industrial development, human population growth, and the standard of living (Martinez-Alier, 1987).
- He recognized the fundamental interrelationships between energy, population growth, and economic development. Thus his conceptual model recognized the linkages between variables from very different factor clusters.

Case 3: The Great Depression

Galbraith (1961) makes clear that the Great Depression of 1929–1939 came as a surprise to almost everyone. There are many indicators that warn of depressions long in advance (Chapter 4), but in 1929 few people knew what they were. One man, however, knew many of those indicators by the early 1920s: the Russian economist Nikolai D. Kondratieff. A series of his papers in Russian published between 1922 and 1928 documented the existence of roughly 50-year economic "waves." One of the most important of these papers has only recently been published in English; it is truly astonishing (Kondratieff, 1984).

Kondratieff's long wave theory

By 1922 he had become convinced that the economies of the capitalist countries were characterized by a long, wavelike pattern of fluctuation. This wave had a nadir about 1785, rose to a peak about 1814, dropped to a nadir about 1847, rose to a zenith about 1873, dropped to a nadir about 1893, then rose to a zenith about 1917. He referred to "The probable downward wave of the third cycle beginning in the period

1914–1920." Kondratieff was not precise about the dates of the nadirs and zeniths; they were typically defined in language such as "the period 1844–55."

He presented an elaborate theory accounting for these waves, involving interactions between the rate of technological innovation, and demand for and supply of raw commodities, including gold. He understood that wars, revolutions, agriculture, and trends in supply relative to demand for capital were implicated in the wave-generating process.

His theory argues that a long upswing begins after a depression, when there has been sufficient capital accumulation so that capital can be invested profitably in creation of basic productive capacity and a new generation of technological improvements. These investments set in motion a series of economic growth-stimulating processes that gradually increase the demand for capital relative to its supply. Ultimately, a downturn results when capital demand outstrips supply, and this coincides with the beginning of a depression.

A critical test for Kondratieff's hypothesis is provided by trends in interest rates. If capital shortage was one of the forces leading to depression, then the years just prior to depressions would be characterized by a sharp increase in interest rates. The prime commercial rate on 4 to 6 month commercial paper in the United States increased from 3.98 percent in 1924 to 5.85 percent in 1929.

The dynamics of this wave-generating process will be dissected and documented in subsequent chapters. Here, the important point is that by 1925, Kondratieff had a conceptual model of how economic long waves worked, had recognized that two previous waves had already been completed, and that the world in 1925 was probably in a downward wave and approaching a depression that would terminate the third wave. The contrast between his assessment of the economic situation in 1925 and that of virtually everyone else making pronouncements about it at that time is truly astonishing.

Kondratieff's conceptual model

As with Mitchell and Hubbert, the key issue is identification of the characteristics of Kondratieff's FP conceptual model that allowed him to formulate a realistic vision of the future when others could not.

- Central to his worldview was a "flows and storages" model of complex systems behavior, rather than just a "flows only" model. He understood that capital investments were storages that can be created or used up, and that they have persistent effects on society for decades or centuries after their creation. Therefore, limits to what is possible is a basic notion in his thinking: the size of storages at any point in time imposes limits on what is possible at that time.

- Kondratieff did not simply extrapolate recent trends, did consider the linkages between diverse clusters of factors, and had an intuitive grasp of the significance of time lags.

Case 4: Demand for nuclear power

A series of well-funded, large scale national and international energy research projects in the 1970s and early 1980s projected that world energy use would increase in compound interest fashion at average annual growth rates of 1–5 percent for several decades into the future (Perry, 1982). It came as a great surprise when world total energy production actually declined from 1980 to 1983 (SA85, Table 1489). Also, rapid growth rates in nuclear power plant construction were forecast by all the conventional wisdom, energy-demand forecasting projects. In fact, one of the great surprises of recent years has been the economic problems of the nuclear power industry and the attendant slowdown in nuclear power plant construction.

Lovins' predictions

One group of people not surprised by these slowdowns in growth of energy demand was Amory Lovins and his associates. They had studied interactions of the various systemic forces that would shape the development of energy systems in the future, and they considered it unlikely that we'd see the great growth in demand for energy and in the number of nuclear power plants expected by the "conventional wisdom" of energy forecasting experts. Lovins and his associates believed that the most likely scenario was a marked shift to energy conservation, a diversity of innovative alternate energy technologies, and a decline in world energy use. They developed a scenario in which world primary energy demand declined steadily starting some time after 1975, to a world demand in the year 2080 about 46 percent that of 1975.

Lovins' conceptual model

The books by Lovins and his colleagues had several unusual features (Lovins and Price, 1975; Lovins, 1977; Lovins et al, 1981). They were all based on an extraordinary technical grasp of the engineering, physical, and economic aspects of many different kinds of energy generation and conservation technologies. Their data were extremely accurate and up-to-date. The FP conceptual models they used were completely interdisciplinary, and they deliberately and explicitly focussed on the linkages between different kinds of factors, rather than the separate impacts of different types of factors considered in isolation. Their future scenarios were based on interplay between technological, logistical, economic and political factors (Lovins and Lovins, 1980).

- The work by Lovins and associates was based on an extraordinarily sophisticated understanding of the role of time lags. Price introduced a novel theory showing that if a population of nuclear power plants grew too rapidly in a crash program of construction, there would be a lag of many years from the initiation of the program to the time when any net energy would flow from the entire population of plants. The explanation was that for several years, more energy would go into construction than would be produced by the small proportion of the ultimate total population of plants already completed.

- Running through all the work by Lovins was a sensitivity to the notion of limits to what is possible. The selection of energy generating systems to be constructed is ultimately limited by profitability and energy output relative to energy input.

Case 5: Peruvian anchovetta fishery

One of the world's great success stories since the end of World War II was the growth of the Peruvian anchovetta fishery. From 1951 to 1970, the landed catch increased by about 300 times (fig. 3-1). Peru evolved from being a minor fishing nation to having the world's largest fish-catching and fish meal processing industry. The anchovetta fishery became a major vehicle for upward social and economic mobility in Peru, and an important source of protein for the world. Suddenly, after 1970, the fishery collapsed, and since then annual catches have oscillated about a level roughly a quarter that of the 1970 catch.

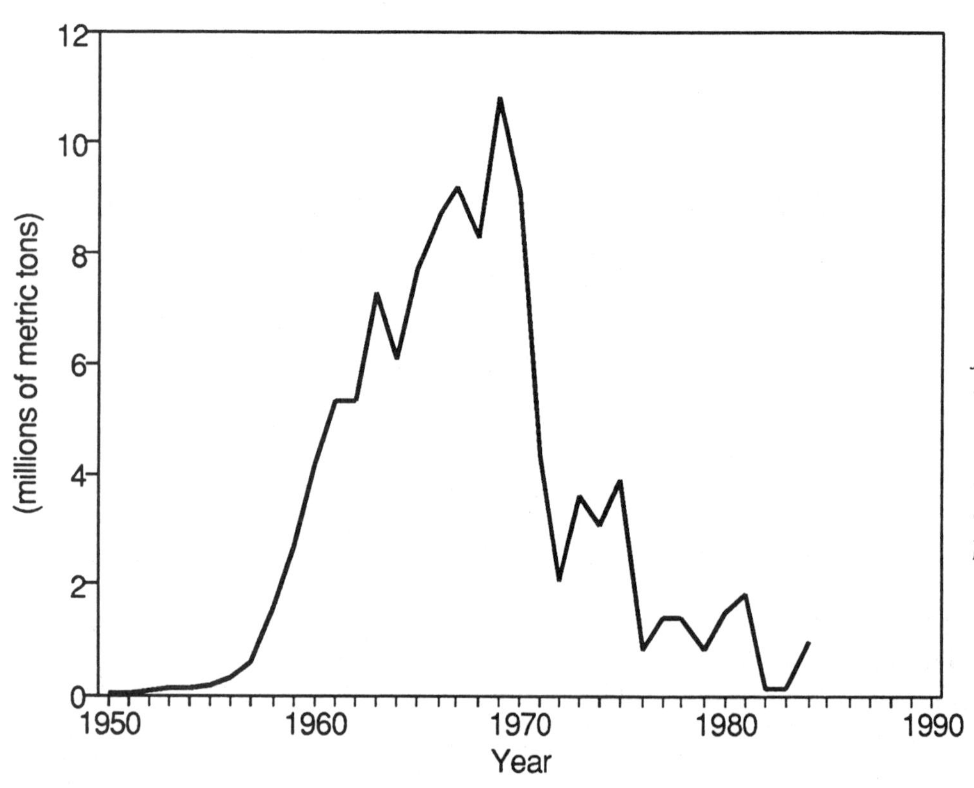

Figure 3-1. The Peruvian anchovetta catch, in live weight landed catch. Statistics from a variety of sources were collated and converted to a common measure using conversion factors computed from various published data.

Paulik's predictions

Gerald Paulik (1971), in an essay for which the most recent data were from 1968, wrote,

> *"Thinking about unthinkable catastrophes is one way of preventing them. Destruction of the world's greatest single species fishery is unthinkable. Could it really occur?"*

He outlined a detailed scenario for collapse of the fishery, based on a completely interdisciplinary FP conceptual model that involved virtually every type of factor known to regulate the dynamics of the fish stock and the behavior of the fishing industry.

Paulik's conceptual model

- A characteristic feature was his grasp of the significance of time lags. If there is a lag of a few years from the time a fish is hatched from the egg until the age at which it can first reproduce, then fishing out almost the entire stock before it was old enough to reproduce itself would ruin the stock, and the effect would not show up until after remedial action would be too late to be effective.
- Buried deep in his conceptual model was the notion of limits. For example, no matter how much the anchovetta population was decreased by heavy fishing and competition for food in the remaining population was diminished, there was a limit to the speed with which anchovettas could become mature enough to reproduce and replace the stock lost to overfishing.

Differences between realistic and unrealistic FP models

Chapters 1–2 identified the character of the underlying FP conceptual model as the critical determinant of success or failure for FP projects. Now using the five case studies just presented, we seek the key characteristics that distinguish realistic from unrealistic FP models. These differences fall into four categories: the influence of political, economic and sociological forces on development of the model, the basic thought patterns of the modelers, the characteristics of the data used in constructing the model, and the structure of the model itself.

Influence of political, sociological and economic environment

A pattern running through the five case studies is that realistic FP is more likely when the practitioners are able to free themselves from influence of prevailing paradigms and the current conventional expert wisdom. Scholars have noted throughout history that people making accurate forecasts have had to be able to do independent thinking, even when this resulted in being highly unpopular. This pattern has been startlingly consistent throughout cultures and civilizations, and has a profound significance. History is full of instances of scorn heaped on "bearers of bad news," "Cassandras," or "doomsayers." Indeed, *doom-and-gloom* is an effective epithet used to discredit visions of the future that challenge existing centers of power.

Not only are counterconventional visions of the future greeted with enormous resistance at the time they are made, but the two ways popular wisdom remembers them long after the fact are revealing.

- Either they are surprisingly widely forgotten, particularly noteworthy in a case such as Mitchell, where his foresights would be useful for perpetuity, or
- The people and their innovations are remembered, but there is selective mass forgetfulness about the opposition the idea met at the time, as in the case of the steam engine and the steam locomotive. To remember the opposition would remind the popular wisdom of its poor historical record.

Of the period just prior to the 1929 market crash, Galbraith noted concerning people who warned that there was no economic basis for the giddy stock market rise,

"Almost without exception, those who expressed concern said subsequently that they did so with fear and trepidation."

Barbara Tuchman (1984) noted the association between power and poor FP: "power breeds folly." The power to command often appears to carry with it a failure to think. What this may actually mean, however, is that people politically astute enough to understand the sources of power realize the peril of being frank about their thoughts.

Even when accurate forecasters were not actually punished, they were typically less successful than they should have been as a consequence of their FP. We need to examine this curiosity with some care.

Billy Mitchell

Mitchell was convicted of insubordination at a U.S. Army court-martial in December, 1925. He was sentenced to suspension from rank and duty for five years, and he resigned from the army. This followed his accusing the U.S. War and Navy Departments of "incompetency, criminal negligence, and almost treasonable administration of the national defense." Given subsequent events at Pearl Harbor, the Philippines, Alaska and elsewhere, it is scarcely any wonder that the conventional wisdom is not constantly reminding us of his visions of the future.

Kondratieff

Never widely recognized as an important thinker outside Russia, an unabridged English translation of his critically important 1925 paper was not published until 1984. The Russian secret police arrested him in 1930 as the alleged head of an illegal antigovernment Peasant's Labor Party and shipped him without trial to Siberia, where he died. In Russia, he was scorned because orthodox Marxists were not receptive to a theory arguing that major downturns in capitalist economies were part of a cyclical self-corrective, negative-feedback homeostatic process that would result in an upward correction after several years. Marxists preferred to believe that capitalism has inherent defects such that any depression would trigger a collapse of the capitalist system.

M. King Hubbert

Although he worked within easy walking distance of the Senate and House office buildings in Washington, Congressional Committees were reluctant to invite him to testify about the status of energy resources. Other energy experts were flown in at government expense from thousands of miles away, even when they protested that they had learned from the writings of Hubbert and that he was the pioneer and internationally most respected expert on energy resource assessment and forecasting.

Lovins

A 1982 publication comparing various energy demand forecasting studies, of which only that by *Lovins* and his colleagues was correct, said of their work,

"This scenario is startling and unconventional in projecting future energy requirements substantially lower than present consumption, notwithstanding continued economic development."

(Perry, 1982)

Ironically, by the time that assessment was in print, up-to-date data had already shown that actual energy consumption was following the scenario of Lovins and his colleagues, not the scenarios of the nine recent well-funded and highly-regarded energy forecasting studies with which it was compared. All of them incorrectly forecast continued exponential increase in demand.

Retrospectively, it is clear that by the time he was 28 years of age, Lovins was by far the most realistic and well informed energy analyst alive. Despite a 12-year record of consistently more realistic assessments than anyone else, he has never been asked to head a major, well-funded national or international energy forecasting study. His most long-lasting institutional affiliation was with Friends of the Earth, an international environmental advocacy organization noted for a high level of literary elegance and mastery of technical issues, and a much lower level of financial support.

Paulik

Gerald Paulik died suddenly and prematurely, coincident with the collapse of the Peruvian anchovetta fishery in 1971–2, an event he had clearly understood was imminent.

People discover early in life that seeking the truth tends to get in the way of seeking power.

The meaning of this history is that people discover early in life that seeking the truth tends to get in the way of seeking power, or seeking power does not appear compatible with seeking and broadcasting the truth. To obtain power, one must be prepared to accept the beliefs of current power-holders, and "rocking the boat" is unacceptable behavior.

Implications for the design of FP projects

Teams meant to produce realistic FP work should be housed in an administrative setting in which there is clear, broad-based and consistent support by superiors for realism—not optimism or adherence to the current conventional wisdom. Results should be announced and published with considerable fanfare and clear statements of support for the work by representatives of the client. This description matches the work environment for independent organizations such as The Worldwatch Institute and the publication announcements of Club of Rome reports. Promotion and tenure of FP teams must be linked to the realism of their output, rather than its acceptability to stakeholders whose personal power or wealth could be adversely affected by the output. All FP work should be examined carefully to ensure that it has not been influenced by covert self-serving interests, which introduced unrealistic biases into the analysis.

Basic thought patterns

Unrealistic FP typically projects growth and tends to be based on surprise-free extrapolations of recent trends. There has been no vigorous search for the fundamental forces that gave rise to recent fluctuations and that will shape the future. The possibility of novel developmental patterns is discounted. Realistic FP projects surprises, future changes in the direction of trends, and are based on an understanding of the identity and behavior of the forces that regulate historical processes.

- Conventional expert wisdom did not foresee that air power implied a revolution in the tactics and strategy of warfare. Consequently, many nations prepared for World War II as if it could be won by tactics and strategies out of date by 1919, let alone 1939. Mitchell recognized that the mobility and surprise resulting from air power meant that armies, battleships, and even enemy airforces were vulnerable to quick destruction.

Similarly, conventional expert wisdom expected that economic growth, Peruvian anchovetta catches, and demand for energy, nuclear power, and jet transports would all increase at a roughly constant growth rate indefinitely.

- Hubbert understood that the key determinant of all scenarios affected by the status of fossil fuel reserves was the proportion of the ultimate recoverable total still left in the ground. Once about half of the ultimately recoverable total had been produced, production curves had to start bending down.

- Lovins and Price understood that net energy output would be the critical determinant of the relative attractiveness of different types of energy-producing systems. Very rapid growth of nuclear power plants implied low net energy output from the plants for many years, because of the high energy cost of constructing them. Alternative sources of energy would prove surprisingly attractive, in part because their heats of production matched the nature of their end uses (the nonsense counterexample would be using nuclear fusion as the source of electricity for heating homes in the winter).

- Paulik understood that the key system driver for anchovetta stocks was the average length of life of the fish relative to the age at which reproduction first occurred.

In each case, realistic forecasting was made possible by discovery and correct selection of the critically important forces shaping historical trends.

Incorrect FP models are plagued by hidden implicit assumptions that have gone unexamined and unchallenged. Battleships will be able to defend themselves against air attack, without fighter cover. Dive bombers will not seriously disrupt infantry movements. It is difficult to obtain population estimates for the large numbers of small alternate sources of energy, so we will ignore them in energy forecasting studies.

Out of sight, out of mind. It is safe to fish gigantic fish stocks as hard as we like, because they will always increase in numbers sufficiently rapidly to compensate for the catch by the fishery.

Correct conceptual FP models tend to be based on explicit statements of underlying assumptions; Lovins typically enumerates his.

The problem of ensuring that a conceptual model includes all key forces shaping trends is so critical that it requires a formal, structured approach in each FP project (Volume 2), just as the flight crew of a jet plane goes through a preflight checklist item by item.

Data base of the conceptual model

Unrealistic models are typically based on obsolete data. People who present realistic FPM often address this issue explicitly.

> *"Nations nearly always go into an armed conflict with the equipment and methods of a former war."*

The Germans and Japanese spent the late 1930s preparing for World War II. The Poles, French, British and Americans not only spent the same period preparing too little; they also prepared for World War I.

Distinguishing between the deleterious effects of obsolete world views and obsolete data is often difficult in retrospective analyses of case studies. In many instances, however, the relative roles of the two problems can be separated unambiguously. The problems unambiguously caused by defective information are touched upon in the Prologue and will be dealt with in Volume 4.

Right up until publication of this book, entire air forces have been repeatedly demolished on the ground.

From the history of World War II, it is clear that generals and admirals who had never been pilots found two new phenomena incredible until they had witnessed them personally: the inability of any military personnel or weapons systems to withstand intense surprise air attack, and that one's own aircraft were useless until they had reached cruise altitude, typically 20 minutes after starting to roll down the runway. Right up until publication of this book, entire air forces have been repeatedly demolished on the ground because they were parked in neat rows at airports, with inadequate warning of impending surprise air attack.

Lovin's visions of the energy future were always more accurate than anyone else's, because he had more current information on new technological developments in alternate energy generation systems. Kondratieff, Hubbert, Mitchell, Lovins, Price and Paulik all employed an exhaustive study of the available quantitative data on the phenomena of their interest. Most of them explicitly state that accurate conceptual models require meticulously thorough analysis of empirical data. After noting that nuclear energy has traditionally been represented as an energy source that could replace all fossil fuels, Lovins notes that nuclear power in fact only serves to replace coal (Lovins and Lovins, 1980).

Models of reality ought to be interdisciplinary.

The writings of all the authors mentioned appear remarkably free of ideological bias. Another explanation for their realism is that their standard assumptions differed from those of the conventional wisdom on such issues as the significance of limits on the range of possible human actions or on behavior of systems.

They may have had a shared philosophical conviction that where data and theory are in conflict, it is the theory, not the data that must be modified. Their results do not follow from deductive theory based on unchallenged assumptions, but induction supported by masses of data. Their publications are remarkably full of numbers, graphs, charts and tables based on actual measurements or observations. Apparently, accurate forecasters believe that theory must grow out of empirical observations, rather than a process of deduction beginning with assumptions unchecked by the traditional rigorous strong inferential hypothesis testing of science.

Where data and theory are in conflict, it is the theory, not the data that must be modified.

The character of the conceptual model

Unrealistic models describe real-world phenomena as if they were primarily regulated or driven by one factor cluster—i.e., surrounded by a constant "environment." Economic phenomena are assumed to be largely regulated by economic variables; energy demand is assumed to be largely regulated by factors endogenous to energy technologies. That is, it is assumed that growth in the availability of energy-generating systems will be accompanied by growth in an internal factor—demand required to use up the output of those systems.

Significance of factor clusters

Cultural values are overlooked in most kinds of models. Conventional FP models treat system subcomponents of types of variables other than those describing the system of interest as if they were, collectively, a constant environment. Thus, the model typically uses many equations linking a large number of variables from within only one interrelated cluster of factors, or "factor cluster." Variables describing the status of fossil fuel resources are drawn from a non-renewable resource factor cluster, variables measuring birth rates and the number of people in each age group are a demographic factor cluster, the size and recent rate of change of the federal government public debt is from a government factor cluster, and so on.

Many FP models err in two ways with respect to factor clusters.

- Not enough types of factor clusters are incorporated in the conceptual model, and
- Not enough attention is paid to the system-regulating consequences of the causal pathways *between* factor clusters.

The model may also lack sufficient interdisciplinary considerations. Unrealistic models don't scan all the factor clusters actually affecting the system being forecast. Economic models exclude the status of fossil fuel reserves or oscillations in birth rates. Energy models overlook: diseconomies of scale in very large power generating plants; the status of fossil fuels and hence the effect of increased prices on demand for energy; or the effect of higher prices on expected lower unit cost for new types of energy production systems.

Conventional wisdom has not been sensitive enough to the "externalities" associated with a particular production mode, as when the waste discharge from chemical plants kill most of the fish and shrimp in a bay. Realistic FP models explicitly recognize that real world phenomena are regulated by the interaction between variables from different factor clusters. Hubbert's FP model of energy demand explicitly included the interaction between economic variables and resource geology.

Mitchell discussed in detail the economic aspects of warfare, and their implications for strategy and tactics. The world had changed permanently when a naval ship was vulnerable to destruction by aircraft each of which cost as little as one thousandth as much. The "environment" for military or transportation FP models had changed drastically when airplanes travelled shortest-distance "great circle routes" over the globe, rather than parallels of latitude.

Paulik (1971) provides the best example for illustrating the diversity of factor clusters that must be scanned for possible inclusion in an FP model. Any complete model must begin with a preliminary scan of seven different types of factors. His Peruvian anchovetta model explicitly addressed all seven. We will review his laundry list of factor clusters, because this is the same list that serves as a template for FP model design for any type of system (Volume 2).

① **The physical environment**. Year-to-year fluctuations in the productivity of the anchovetta population are affected by ocean currents, which in turn affect water temperature and the strength of the upwelling that brings nutrient chemicals to the ocean surface where they are incorporated into anchovetta food by smaller organisms.

② **Non-renewable resources**. The chemicals in the ocean serve as the input nutrients to the community of organisms on which the anchovettas feed.

③ **Renewable resources**. Productivity of the anchovetta resource is affected by their population size and age structure. The anchovetta population is much more likely to go extinct if it is fished so hard that few individuals survive beyond their first birthday; the fishery destroys almost the entire population before it is old enough to reproduce. In addition, the survival of anchovettas in the ocean is affected by the size of the predatory fish and bird populations that also eat them. These predators in effect constitute an unseen second fishery that competes with the human fishery for the anchovetta resource, enormously decreasing the probability of survival of each anchovetta. If both human and predator fisheries increase rapidly in response to a short-term increase in the anchovetta population brought on by a change in upwelling of nutrients, and then the anchovetta survival decreases because of an oceanographic change, a reduced anchovetta stock is faced with two very large fisheries feeding off it. The human fishery is aware of only one of these.

④ **Demographic factors**. Size, age structure and growth rate of the Peruvian human population—along with their unemployment rate—was an important factor leading to a rapid buildup in the size of the human population engaged in fishing or processing the anchovettas, and hence, the collapse of the fishery.

⑤ **Economic factors**. A factor that could lead to overexploitation and subsequent collapse of the anchovetta resource was "the industry's creditors...clamoring for payment of short-term loans." Further, as fish get scarce, the unit price for fish meal would increase, providing a motive to wipe out the remaining stock.

⑥ **Government and political factors**. The fishing industry spawned a small but important group of newly rich and many new jobs for lawyers, engineers, boat-skippers, factory managers, and others. This created a well-funded constituency that could pressure politicians to oppose catch limitation regulations.

⑦ **Cultural factors**. The belief system lead to building a fishing fleet up to four times that necessary to remove the yield that could safely be harvested without ruining the reproductive capacity of the stock. This helped set the stage for disaster.

The Peruvian anchovetta fishery collapsed because of the interactions among these seven types of factors. Any FP model should begin with a preliminary scan of these seven to ensure that representative variables from each are included if relevant and necessary.

Unrealistic FP models tend to include very large numbers of variables and equations, as if sheer numbers would increase predictive accuracy.

A large number of publications attest that there is no evidence that this is true. Realistic models tend to be small or intermediate in size, with the ingenuity having gone into very careful selection of variables and inclusion of appropriate linkages between the variables in different factor clusters. Variables are only included because tests against historical data showed that they were each critically important determinants of the system change through time.

Kondratieff, Hubbert, Mitchell, Lovins, Price and Paulik had realistic visions of the future, not because their FP models included a very large number of variables, but because they had included the minimum necessary set of critically important variables. This selection was based on a preliminary scan of a very large number of variables to determine which were most important. Volume 2 explains how to systematize this selection process.

Visions of the future are realistic not because they include a very large number of variables, but because they include the minimum necessary set of critically important variables.

Unrealistic models visualize systems in terms of "flows only"; realistic FP models include "storages and flows."

Examples of storages are Hubbert's remaining geological reserves of fossil fuels, the 300 airplanes Mitchell saw as essential for the defense of Alaska, and Kondratieff's inventories of capital goods, for which over- or underinvestment caused the long economic waves. Paulik understood that the number of anchovettas old enough to reproduce is a storage, and if it falls below a critical threshold, the population of anchovettas will decline. Modern societies are replete with storages that have enormous impacts on the dynamic behavior of systems: the size of remaining geological reserves of fossil fuel, the inventory of land suitable for growing wheat or building airport runways, the inventory of residential and office buildings, and the number of people 20–24 years of age. None of these is a flow; all are storages.

Realistic FP models all deal with the effects of time lags in systems.

Mitchell grasped the significance of the 20 minutes required to get each plane off a runway and up to cruise altitude in order to protect the airport from enemy air attack. Price and Lovins understood the many-year lag before a rapidly growing population of nuclear power plants can contribute any net energy to a nation. Hubbert understood the significance of the 10.5 year lag from the time that oil was discovered until the time it was produced. This meant that 10.5 years after the United States oil discovery curve peaked, the oil production curve would also peak. There is a lag from the time of overinvestment in productive capacity until the time when all major markets are supersaturated simultaneously, and a depression results. Kondratieff (1984) explicitly recognized the role of very long time lags in producing wavelike system oscillations.

"Since the rising waves in these conditions occurs on the basis of a high intensity of accumulation and long-term investments of capital in basic and costly projects, a very long period elapses before that rising momentum is overcome and the downward wave sets in."

Unless FP models incorporate time lags and mimic their effects on stability and fluctuations (chapters 5 to 9), they cannot correspond accurately to the phenomena they purport to mimic.

Realistic FP models typically require a hierarchically-organized structure.

That is, causal pathways are perceived as flowing not only sideways between systems at a particular level of organization (i.e. between cities, or between nations), but also from micro levels of organization to macro levels, and in the reverse direction. For example, the macro-level (highly aggregated) system characteristics of national energy systems are affected by household (micro level) decisions about which kind of energy most efficiently delivers heat for end use in each different temperature range (Lovins et al, 1981). Nuclear fusion power plants are not required to heat a living room to 68°F.

Hence micro-level system decisions affect a meso-level system characteristic—the nature of the power-generating plant most suitable for providing energy for a large number of micro-level systems (single-family residences). Large number of meso-scale power plants, in turn, determine how many of which type of plant constitutes the national energy-generating system. That mix, in turn, determines system properties of the national energy system, such as the requirement for and economic efficiency of breeder reactors. The effect of the size of electrical power plants on the marginal cost of a kilowatt hour delivered to a residence affects the choice of energy type used in that residence. The sum of a large number of choices of that type in turn feeds back on the decision as to the size and type of power generating plant that will be built next by an electrical and gas utility company.

Whenever fundamental truths of this type have been understood for a long time, they become incorporated into the folklore of the popular culture. The system phenomenon just enunciated is passed down from generations long ago as "For the want of a nail, a horse was lost; for the want of a horse, a battle was lost; for the want of a battle, a kingdom was lost." We now know the set of characteristics required for any FP conceptual model to be realistic, and this analysis dictates the structure of subsequent chapters.

Chapter 4

Long-Term Trends

In chapters 1–3 we described fundamental problems afflict conventional FP. To establish forecasting and planning on a sounder footing, we need a completely new strategy. The various elements of this new strategy will be presented step by step in chapters 4–9. This process will reveal the structure of the system of forces that controls all system change through time, which we will verify with an analysis of history. Then we will use our knowledge of this system of forces to project into the future.

In this chapter we will:

① Determine if there is a discernible long-term trend in the historical data for systems that we wish to forecast. By "long-term trend" we mean a long-term pattern of growth or decline. We can imagine the long-term trend for any system variable as a smooth line about which fluctuations occur. (In the graphs that follow, long-term trends will be indicated by a dashed line.)

② Demonstrate that some trends show evidence of being limited by a controlling force.

③ Identify the forces driving those trends and the nature of the relationship between the forces and trends.

④ Present arguments that cumulative fossil fuel production in a nation is the most important single controlling force.

1. Proof that long-term trends exist

In systems theory, if a system shows no long-term trend, this implies that the system is trapped in a global stability region, or equilibrium. That is, whenever the system variables depart from their equilibrium, or steady state values, the probability of returning to equilibrium increases in proportion to the magnitude of the departure. This may be imagined as continually returning to equilibrium whenever the system drifts or moves away from that steady state.

A shift away from old methods of transport makes it more likely (not less) that the system will move even farther away from the old steady state.

For many systems of our everyday experience, however, it is hard to imagine why global stability regions should exist. To illustrate, transportation in 19th century England existed in a steady state around use of the horse, stagecoach and horse-drawn barge prior to construction of railroads. After that point, though, any shift away from the old methods of transport made it more likely (not less) that the system would move even farther away from the old steady state. People were likely to stick with the new methods of transportation once they'd started using them. Logically, then, we would expect to observe **changing**, not flat trends.

Types of trends

When we examine long-term trends in different data series, we discover three different types of trends:

- **Indefinitely rising at a constant rate,**
- **Rising at a gradually reduced rate**, and
- **Dropping at a gradually reduced rate.**

We find on examining many trends of all three types that their variation through time can be split into three components:

- More or less gradual variation due to the **long-term trend,**
- **Oscillation about the trend** with a wavelength of 30–60 years, and
- **High-frequency (short-term) fluctuations**, which we will call "**F**."

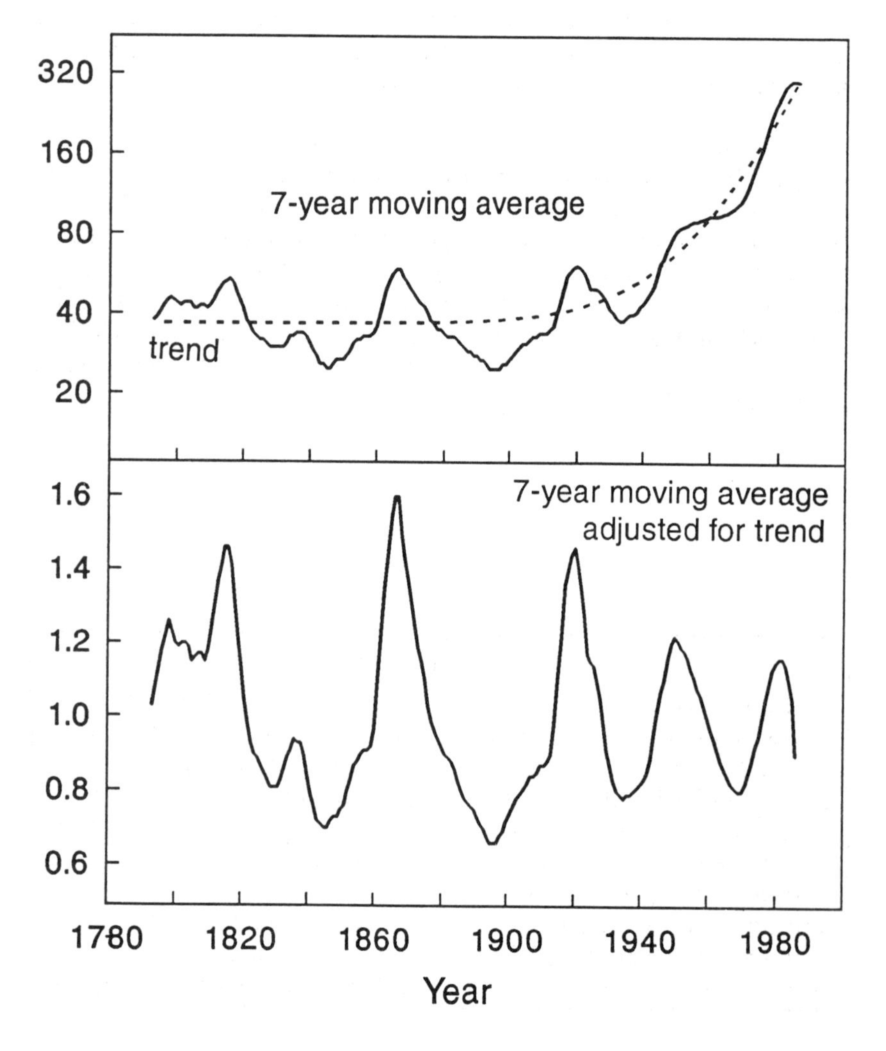

Figure 4-1.
Panel 1. The solid line is the 7-year moving average of the WPI, superimposed on a dashed line describing the trend. (E23,E52)

Panel 2. WPI 7-year moving average adjusted for trend.

(The equations describing this and other relationships in this book will be explained in Appendix A.)

Moving averages

An important concept used throughout this book is that we can eliminate the effect of **F** (short-term, high-frequency fluctuations around a trend) from any data series by use of moving averages. For example, in the wholesale price index series, the high frequency fluctuation appeared to have an average wavelength of 7 years. Accordingly, the effect of the fluctuation having this wavelength was eliminated by using 7-year moving averages in fig. 4-1.

For each year, we calculate this average by adding to that year's values the 7 values starting 3 years before that year and the 3 years after the year; then we divide by 7.

This procedure eliminates the effect of high-frequency, short-term fluctuation from the historical record and enables us to isolate and focus on the long-term trend and the fluctuation about that trend having a longer wave length.

It's important to understand this concept because we will be using many figures showing moving averages in this book.

The solid line in fig. 4-1 is the 7-year moving average of the WPI, superimposed on a dashed line describing the trend. For the moment, we defer identification of the force regulating the trend. Note that at this stage, we are simply demonstrating a long-term trend in a variable. **It is specifically not being argued that time causes the change in WPI. Rather, as we shall see, the trend is being governed by another variable that also increases gradually with time.**

Actually measured values depart from their long-term trend in association with wars and depressions.

Let's look first at growth continuing indefinitely at the same rate—that is, growth that shows no evidence of approaching a limit. The U.S. Wholesale Price Index, WPI, (E23,E52) is a typical example. Fig. 4-1 illustrates a pattern you will see repeated throughout this book: major inflection points (curvature changes, see Glossary) in oscillations about the trend are associated with wars (1812, the civil war and the two world wars) and depressions (1780s, 1840s, 1890s and 1930s). That is, actually measured values depart from their long-term trend in association with wars and depressions.

Federal Debt

The federal government debt moves far above its long run trend line during wars. After a war, the debt is gradually retired (except for recent decades). A long period of debt retirement implies that there has been a long period in which the capital available for investment has been shifted from the public to the private sector. At the end of such a period, there will likely be widespread market supersaturation in the private sector (apartments, office buildings, energy and agriculture), leading to layoffs, then a depression.

Too much public debt relative to the trend line implies war; too little sets the stage for depression.

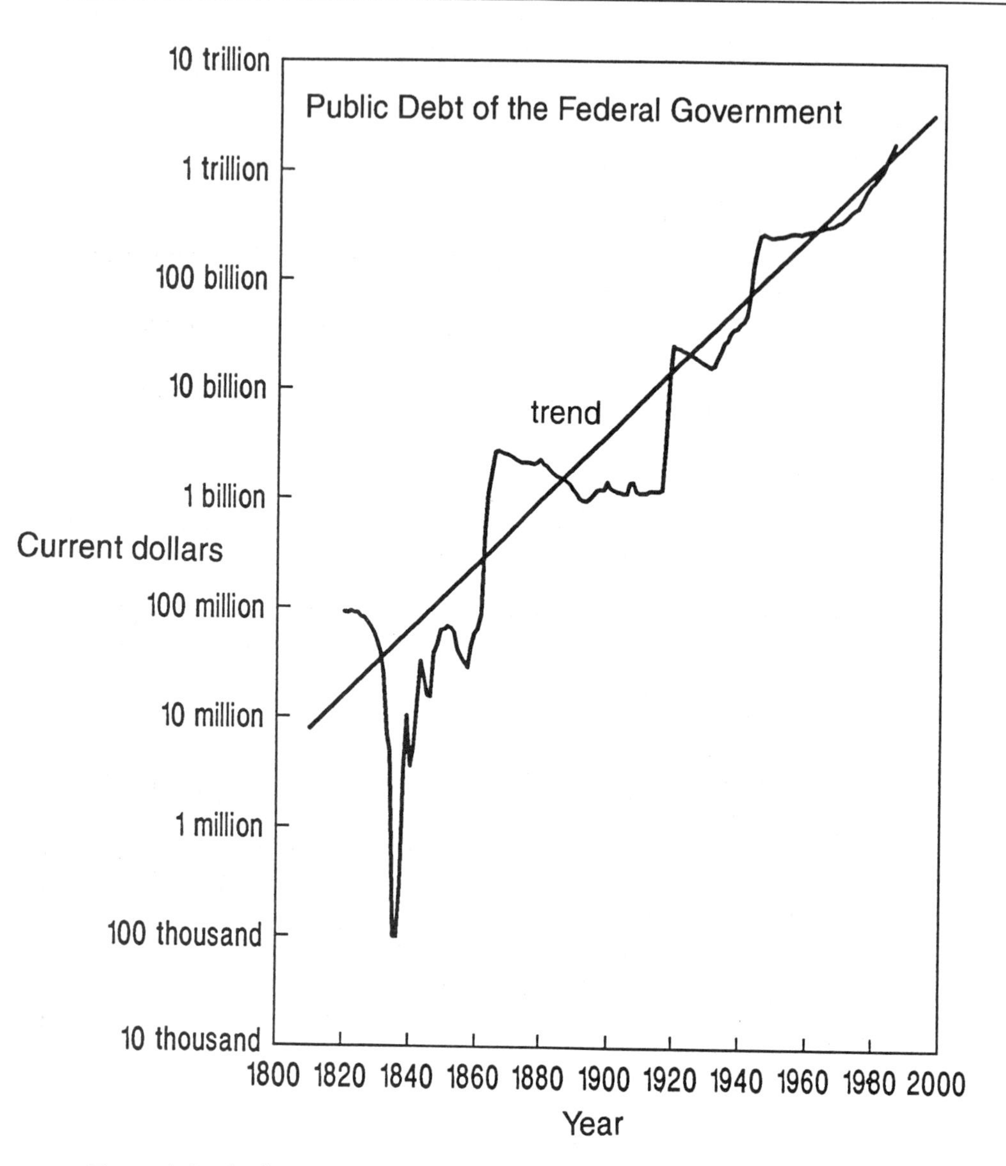

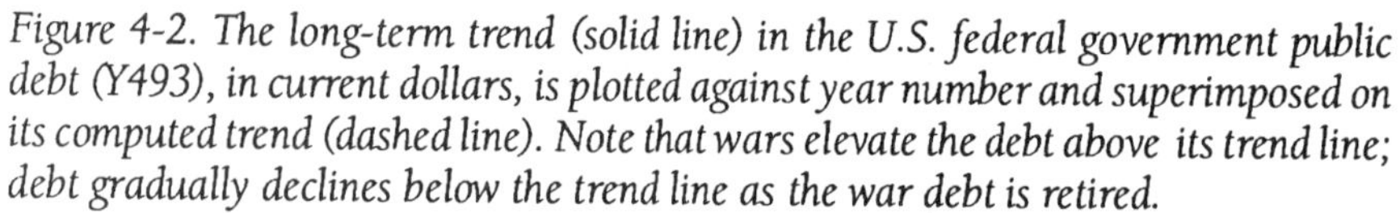
Figure 4-2. The long-term trend (solid line) in the U.S. federal government public debt (Y493), in current dollars, is plotted against year number and superimposed on its computed trend (dashed line). Note that wars elevate the debt above its trend line; debt gradually declines below the trend line as the war debt is retired.

The federal government public debt is another example of a variable that has grown with no evidence of a constraining force (fig. 4-2). The computed growth rates for the federal government public debt and the wholesale price index (fig. 4-1) are identical, suggesting that both are being driven by the same underlying process.

The federal deficit is another variable that has grown with no evidence of a constraint on growth.

2. Evidence for a force limiting growth

In other long-term trends, growth appears to be constrained by some limit. Fig. 4-3 depicts the pattern of fluctuation in the tonnage of pig iron shipped, superimposed on its computed long-term trend (dashed line). This trend is typical of many variables in modern societies: rapid growth at the beginning of industrialization, then growth at an ever-slower rate as society matures. One factor imposing the limit is increased cost per unit as the nonrenewable resources are depleted.

Also, once a bridge or skyscraper has been constructed, it is not necessary to replace it until decades or centuries have elapsed. That is, *market saturation* imposes a limit, too.

The argument presented to this point is a postulate, not an empirical fact. Now we examine the data, to determine if facts support the postulate.

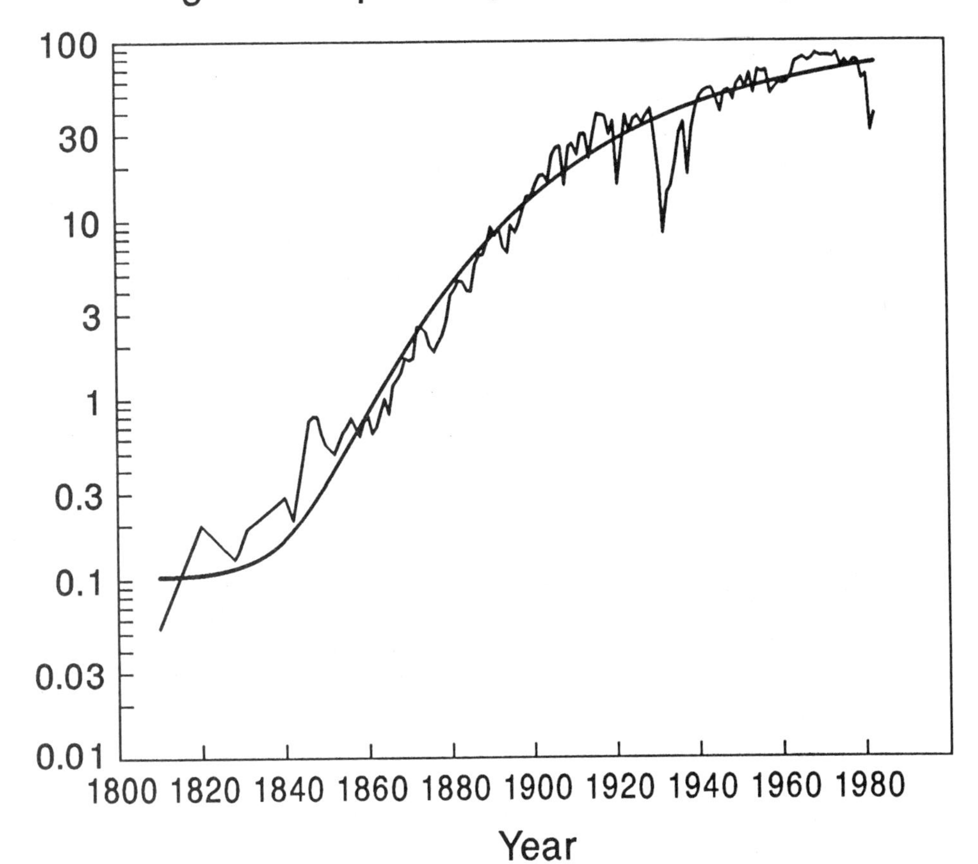

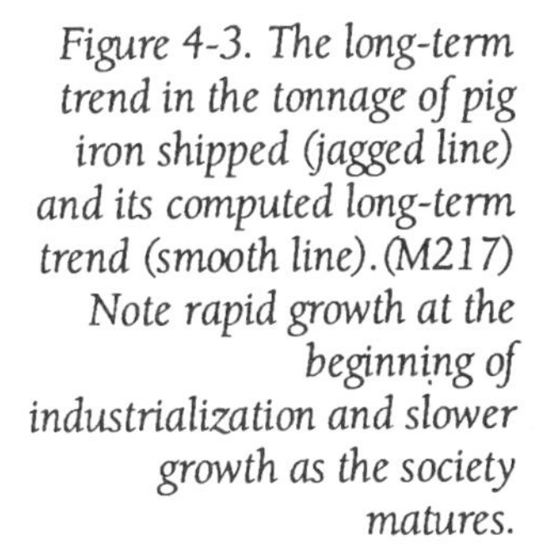

Figure 4-3. The long-term trend in the tonnage of pig iron shipped (jagged line) and its computed long-term trend (smooth line). (M217) Note rapid growth at the beginning of industrialization and slower growth as the society matures.

Two ancient civilizations have been studied particularly intensively and comprehensively: Mesopotamia, adjacent to the Tigris River in what is now Iraq, and the Mayan civilization of what is now the Yucatan peninsula of Mexico and northeastern Guatemala.

Mesopotamia

It is known from ancient records that progressive increase in soil salinity decreased crop yields and contributed to the breakup of past civilizations (Jacobsen and Adams, 1958). A measure of the change in soil fertility is the average yield of grain per hectare (fig. 4-4).

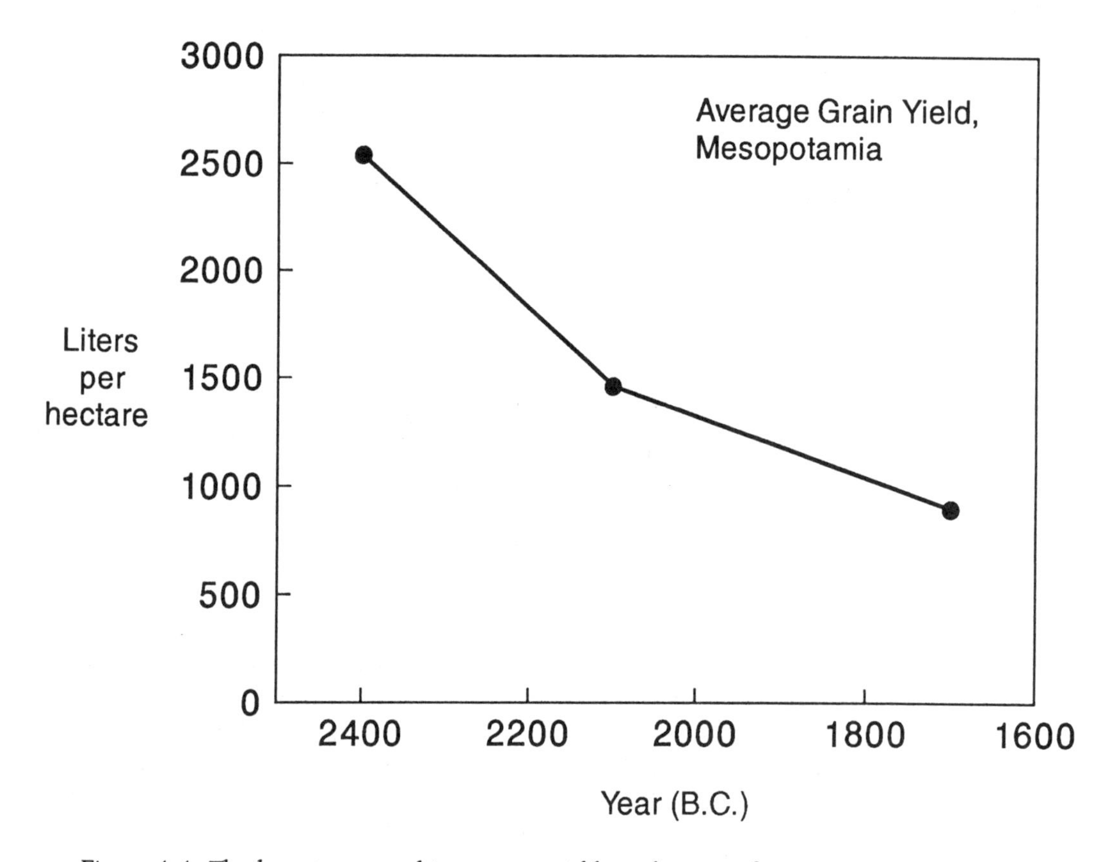

Figure 4-4. The long-term trend in average yield per hectare of grain in ancient Mesopotamia (data from Jacobsen and Adams, 1958).

Mayan civilization

Mass transport of soil resulting from forest clearing by the Mayans added phosphorus to lake sediments. Fig. 4-5 depicts the trend in the rate of transport of terrestrial phosphorus to lake sediments, as measured by chemical analyses of lake bottom sediment sections using a core sampler (Deevey et al, 1979). The buildup of phosphorus in lake sediments was correlated with population increase, and after the Mayan population collapsed, the rate of phosphorus addition to lake sediments declined markedly. A reasonable interpretation of the findings is that excessive phosphorus in the water of paddies for growing crops caused excessive growth of algae that choked off growth of the crops.

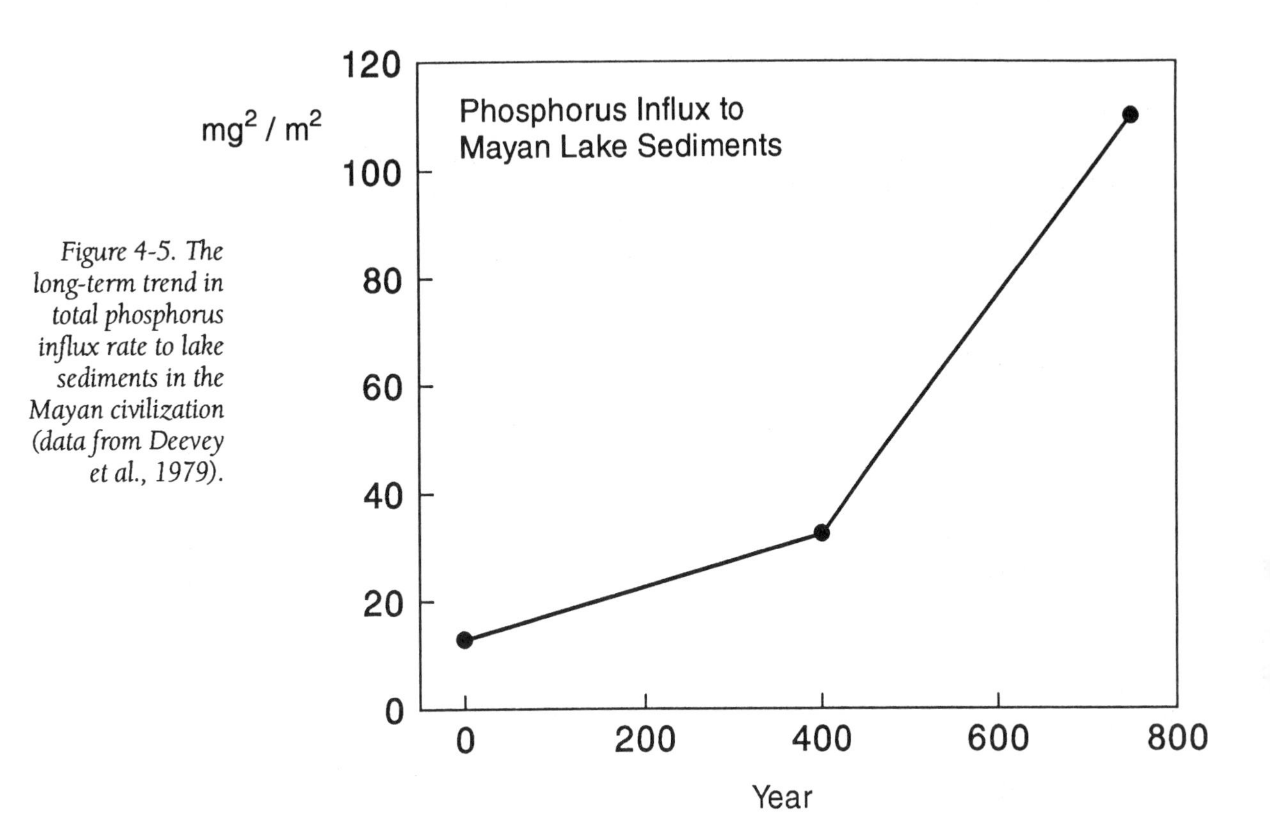

Figure 4-5. The long-term trend in total phosphorus influx rate to lake sediments in the Mayan civilization (data from Deevey et al., 1979).

Law of Limiting Factors

If variables show long-term patterns of growth or decline, this implies that the dynamic of the system is under control of some fundamental force—internal or external—that is itself undergoing long-term change.

In 1840 Justus von Liebig formulated the law of limiting factors. This argues that when either too much or too little of any single necessary nutrient is available, it may limit or prevent plant growth even if all other factors are at or close to their optimum values (e.g. Nebel, 1981, pp. 23–25).

A plausible extension argues that for any living system—including lakes, forests, or nations—during any given period there is some critical limiting factor, since all other factors are at or close to optimal. Decline or growth of any system results from a decrease or increase in availability of that currently limiting factor, depending on whether it had been too low or too high.

In a natural ecosystem or an agrarian civilization, growth limits are imposed by factors determining the rate at which the system can convert solar energy to plant tissue. That rate, in turn, would be set by how the availability (storage) of soil chemicals affects the nutritional level of plants and hence the rate at which plants convert incoming solar energy to green tissue. The yield of crops or naturally occurring plants, in turn, would be the fundamental system force determining all other rates in the system, including the birth rates of animals and humans.

Historians and economic historians have now identified a series of instances in which the critical limiting resource for economic development of a nation was some renewable natural resource.

- For Spain in 1600, it was oak timbers for construction of naval vessels and wheat to feed the population (Braudel, 1972, 1973).
- For England in the 16th century it was firewood (Nef, 1932).
- In late 18th century England it was shallow coal—further economic development only being made possible by invention of the two-cylinder steam engine (Smiles, 1865).

Before conversion to steel vessels, economic growth of Britain was also critically dependent on forests to build ships (Albion, 1926).

3. Fossil fuel reserves as system-controlling force

In an industrial society, solar energy has been largely replaced by fossil energy except as the primary source of energy for growing crops. Even in agriculture, natural soil chemicals can be supplemented by fertilizers manufactured using fossil fuels, so the natural nutritional status of soil is no longer limiting. It follows that the factor regulating all other rates in modern societies is a storage—a nation's fossil fuel resources.

Past use of fossil fuels, however, was invested in another storage—capital infrastructure that increases the rate of use of fossil or solar energy. That is, cumulative use of fossil fuels has been invested in our standing inventory of refineries, coal mines, oil and gas drilling rigs, hydroelectric dams, national electricity transmission systems, railroads, highways, pipelines, manufacturing plants, office buildings, etc. Therefore, the variable best expressing the effect of fossil fuel on current system fluxes is a measure of cumulative fossil energy use up to and including the present year, not annual flow of energy through the social system.

The factor regulating all other rates in modern societies is a storage—national fossil fuel resources, best expressed as cumulative fossil energy use up to and including the present year, not annual flow of energy through the system.

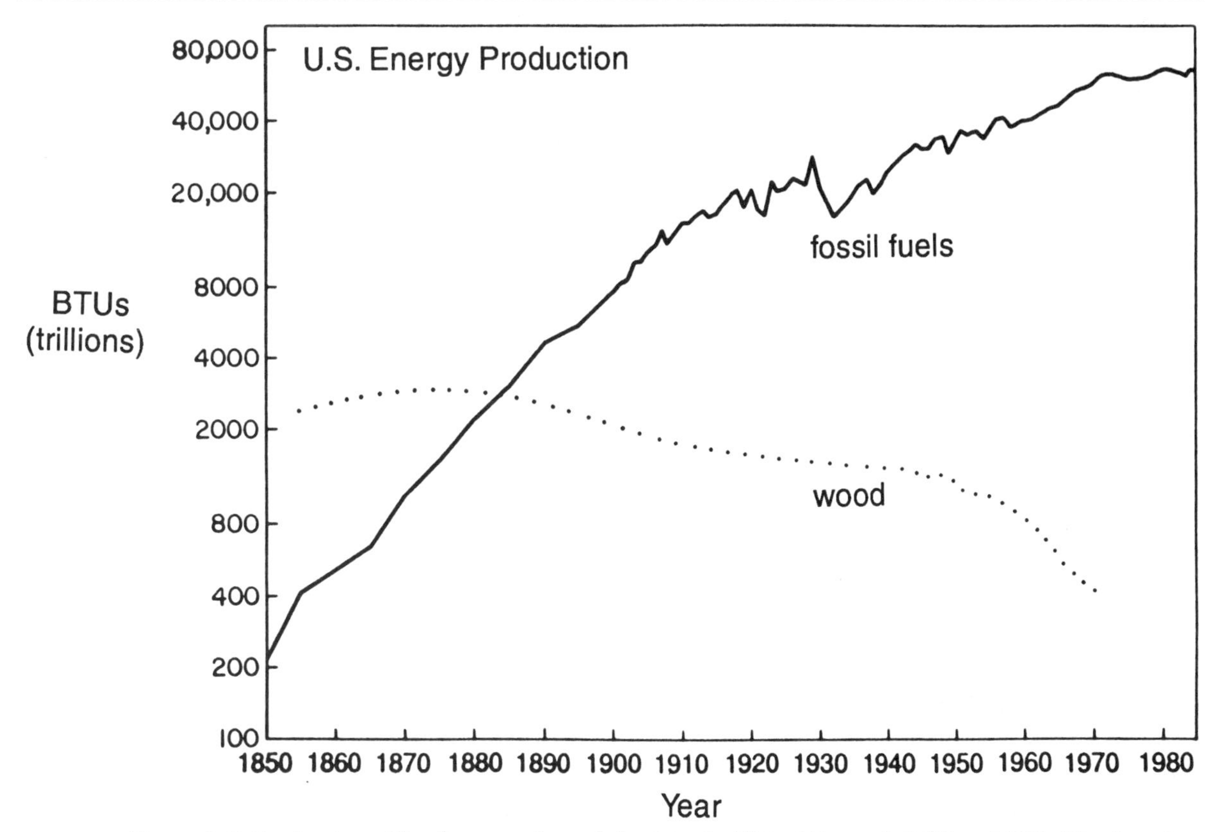

Figure 4-6. Production of fossil energy (actual data) in the United States (solid line, M76). The dotted line represents consumption of fuel wood (M92).

Fossil fuel (the solid line in fig. 4-6) had surpassed wood (the dotted line) as the stored energy source for the United States by 1885, so it is reasonable to postulate that fossil fuel is now the critical limiting resource for this country.

Energy costs and net energy

It's easy to recognize intuitively that it takes energy to produce energy. We call this *energy cost of production*. Simple examples are:

- Muscle energy to chop down a tree for firewood.
- Machinery, labor and fuel to raise coal to the surface.
- Machinery, labor and fuel to build and operate an offshore drilling platform.

Greatly simplified, the **net energy** benefit or value of the oil produced at that platform is its energy in BTUs minus the energy cost of producing it.

Without getting into the thermodynamics involved, we can say that **energy benefit** or **value** is a measure of the work that can be performed. It follows that the higher the energy cost of production, the lower the net energy value (i.e. a reduction in thermodynamic efficiency).

A substantial body of scientific literature describes energy values and *net* energy of many goods, from potatoes to infrastructure such as buildings and transportation systems. The notion that economic systems are ultimately driven by resource availability, particularly energy, was sufficiently widespread by 1989 that a new journal, *Ecological Economics* began to publish articles by scholars working on this idea in 15 countries.

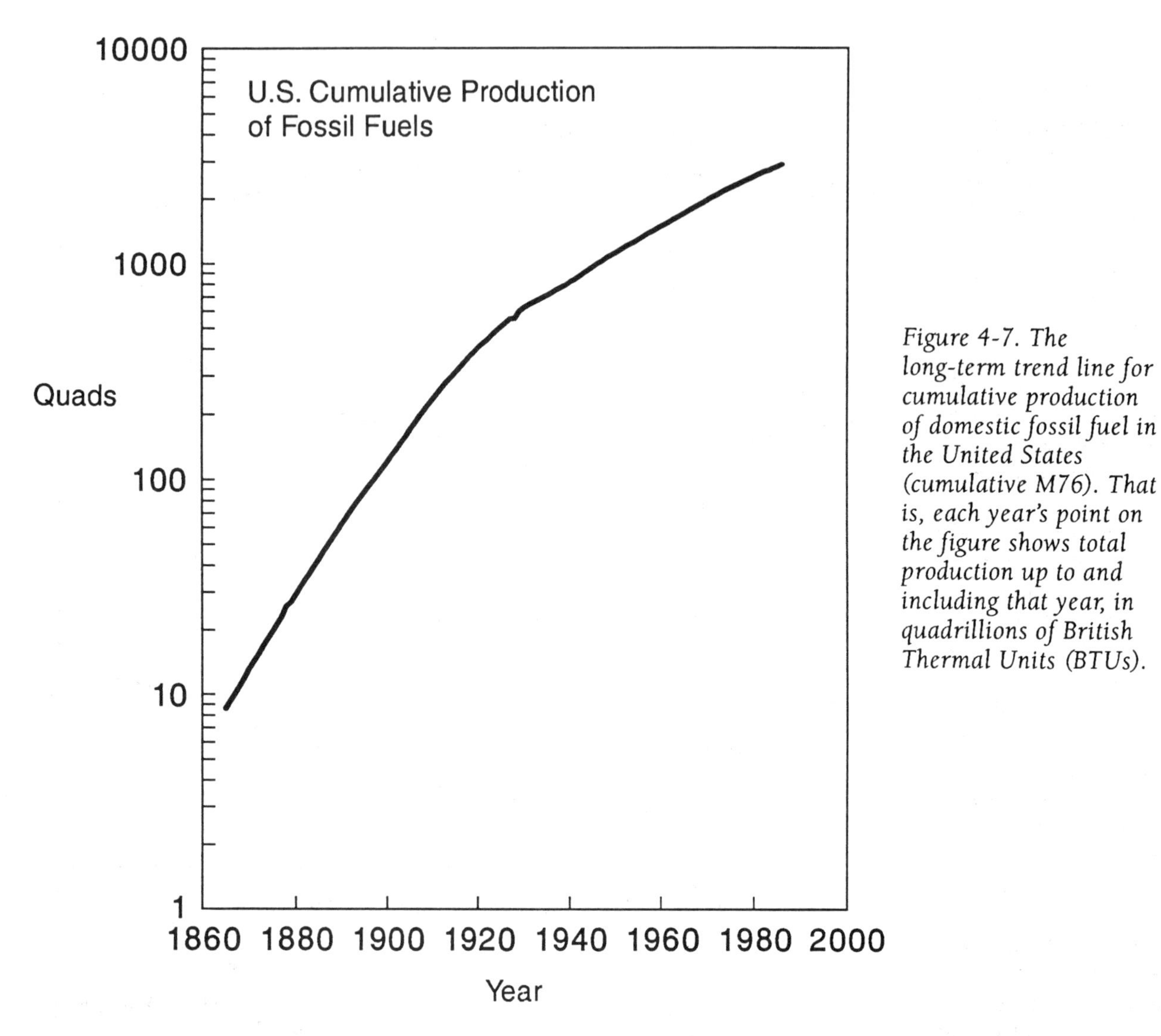

Figure 4-7. The long-term trend line for cumulative production of domestic fossil fuel in the United States (cumulative M76). That is, each year's point on the figure shows total production up to and including that year, in quadrillions of British Thermal Units (BTUs).

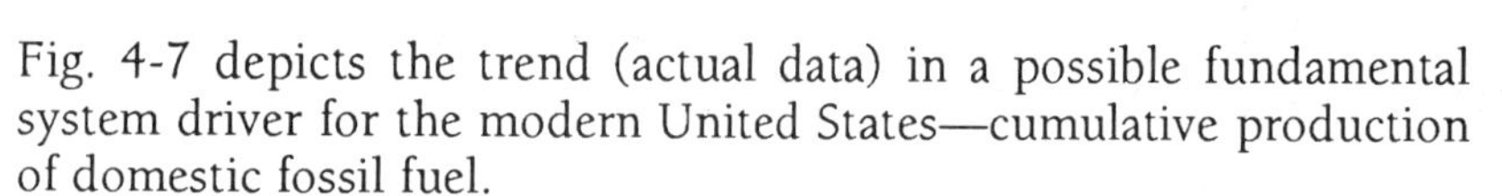
Fig. 4-7 depicts the trend (actual data) in a possible fundamental system driver for the modern United States—cumulative production of domestic fossil fuel.

4. Fossil fuel as the system driver

Many types of arguments support the hypothesis that fossil fuel is indeed the system driver for modern societies. We will consider five.

① Similar long-term trends

The first type of argument is illustrated by the long-term trends in fig. 4-8. In this composite figure, four different variables are plotted against cumulative U.S. oil production.

- The ratio of the average wage to the consumer price index: a measure of **consumer purchasing power**.

Figure 4-8. The trends in consumer purchasing power, or the ratio of wages to the consumer price index (panel 1), the wage index (panel 2), the consumer price index (panel 3), and the average oil discovery price per barrel in 1967 dollars (panel 4).

All are plotted against the cumulative U. S. domestic crude oil production in billions of barrels.

The wage index is the average annual wage of contract construction workers (D745); the CPI is 10 x E135. The oil discovery cost per barrel was calculated by dividing the total exploration cost (e.g. SA 1987 Table 1168) by the number of new barrels discovered in year Y. This statistic was computed using the relation:

discoveries in year Y = reserves at end of Y - reserves at end of Y-1 + oil production during Y

The data for that calculation are from tables such as 1166, SA 1987, and the deflating was done using the producer price deflator in SA 1987, table 729).

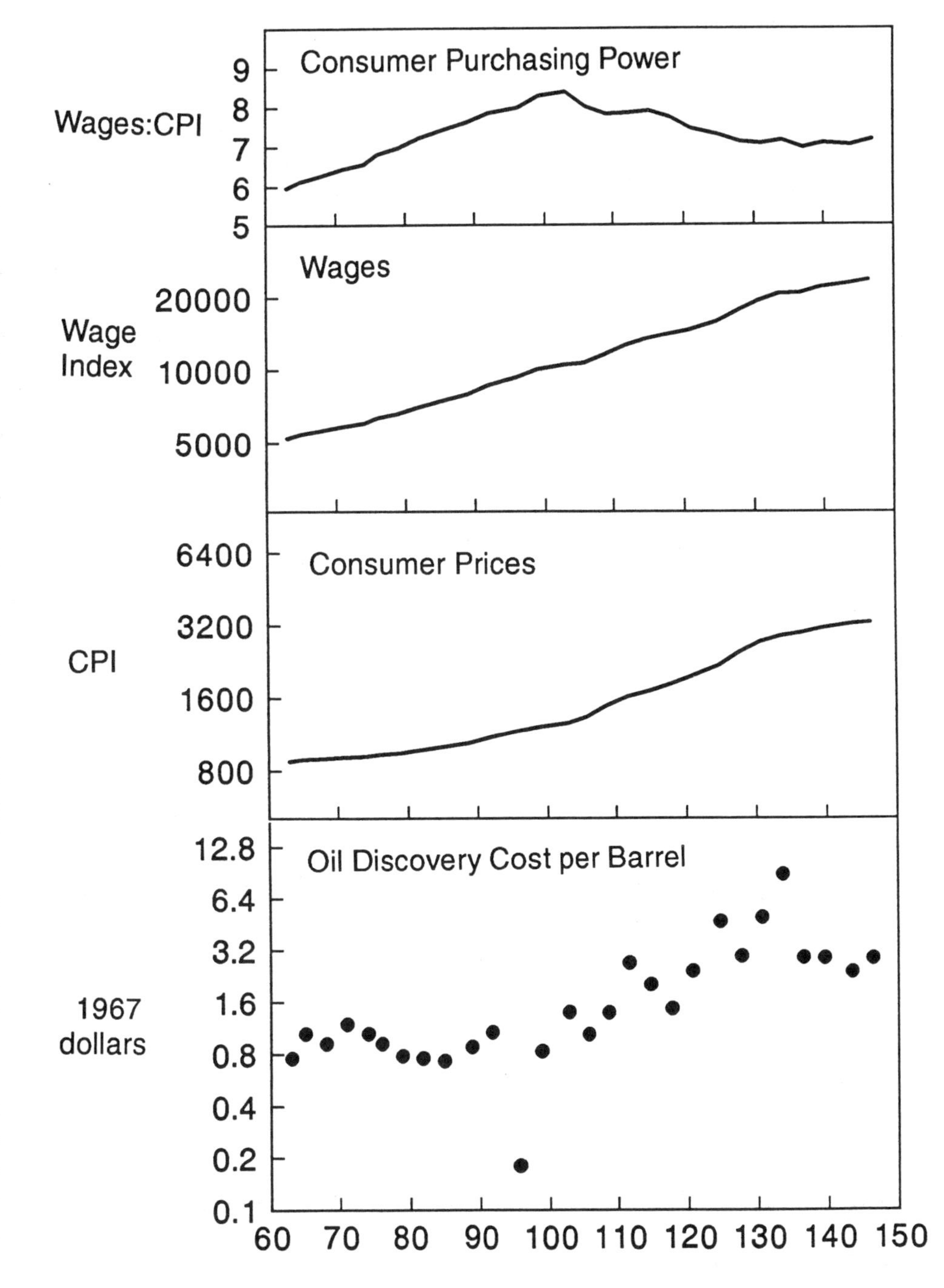

- The trend in **average wage** (annual wages of contract construction workers, in current dollars).
- The **consumer price** index.
- The average **oil discovery cost** per barrel in 1967 dollars.

Oil and gas discovery cost is multiplied enormously as it passes through the economy.

Note that the consumer price index began to increase at an increasing rate after the oil discovery cost began to increase markedly. As a result, the trend in consumer purchasing power (top panel) bent down when oil discovery cost rose.

A counterargument is that oil discovery costs could not possibly have that large an effect on the economy, because the increase in expenditures on all exploratory drilling for oil and gas was so small: only 37 billion current dollars for 1970—1982 (SA, 1987, Table 1168). The explanation is that this cost is multiplied enormously as it passes through stages in the economy from exploration to retailing; profit is extracted at each transaction. End use costs for energy in the U.S. increased from 83–441 billion current dollars from 1970–1985 (SA, 1987, Table 910). In the same 15 years, the National Defense budget only increased from 78–253 billion current dollars (SA, 1987, Table 510), yet the latter figure generated far more political discussion.

Some readers may find it difficult to accept that the system driver for trends in modern industrial nations is the status of their fossil fuel resources. After all, the cost of discovering and producing fossil energy only began to shoot up noticeably in the 1970s in the United States, whereas many of the long-term trends in other prices have been increasing since at least the industrial revolution. It's very revealing, however, to measure economic processes in terms of their net energy benefit relative to energy cost of production—instead of their monetary profit (see side bar). When we do this, we see that net energy cost has a very early effect on the growth in these other trends.

For example, in 15th century England, when coal could be found on the surface (sea coal) or a few feet below the surface, the energy cost of obtaining coal was small relative to its energy benefit when burned. As early as late 18th century, however, it required the more efficient two-cylinder steam engine invented by James Watt to pump the flood water from the depths then being mined. At that time, the energy cost of coal had begun to rise relative to its energy benefit. This reduced thermodynamic efficiency was reflected as a slight increase in all prices, since the cost of energy is an input to the cost of everything else.

The increase in the general level of prices then appeared as an increase in the inflation rate (which is the rate of increase in the money supply). In fact, the fundamental force driving prices up was the increasing cost of energy.

Whether or not activities are undertaken and continued ultimately depends on their net energy profit, energy output less energy input, not their net economic profit.

This argument about the energy efficiency of various economic activities being more important than their gross energy output is fully developed by Odum (1983,1988), Hall et al (1986), Gever et al (1986), and the history of the concept is in Martinez-Alier (1987). Cook (1976) and Slesser (1978) also present a comprehensive picture of the significance of energy for civilization. Odum points out that whether or not activities are undertaken and continued ultimately depends on their net energy profit, energy output less energy input, not their net economic profit. He also developed a thoroughly worked-out theory of the controlling role of energy in complex systems.

② Tracing causal pathways back to ultimate causes

We can also follow causal pathways backwards from ultimate effects to discover their ultimate causes. Every such pathway that we follow leads back to the cost of discovering and producing fossil fuels. Several examples follow.

Metals

The cost of metals is determined by their scarcity. The most accurate measure of that scarcity is the energy cost to mine and process the ore to obtain the pure mineral. High-grade ores are depleted first (some of them in prehistoric times), and the average grade of the remainder is lower. More and more ore must be processed to obtain a ton of pure metal, and that increases the energy cost of the product. The remaining ore is in progressively deeper and more difficult sites, increasing the energy cost to discover and mine new resources, as well.

Retail prices

Using similar reasoning, energy cost determines the retail price of every type of commodity, manufactured good, and service used in modern society: corn, canned tuna, jet aircraft engines, hospital care, the wage of a stockbroker or professor. The cost of energy determines the feasibility of any type of activity.

Whaling and fishing

High seas whaling or fishing great distances from port are only feasible if the energy cost is cheap, in the form of wind and sails—or cheap petroleum. If the price of crude oil increases sharply in the 1990s, long distance whaling and fishing will cease or there will be a return to sail and wind power.

Economic substitution processes

Because U in the equation **U = C + R** is a constant, unvarying through time, the other two variables are algebraically related by the equation

$$R = U - C.$$

That is, **R** is dependent on **C**. This is fortunate; it means that a great deal of political controversy about the magnitude of **R** becomes irrelevant (Wildavsky and Tennenbaum, 1981). We simply use **C** as a "surrogate" variable for **R**.

We now follow the chain of logic explaining how as a nation's fossil energy resources decrease, its energy production costs increase and drive down the growth rate of average wages.

Cumulative fossil energy production, up to and including the present, is related to the amount remaining. Each nation has an ultimate recoverable amount of fossil fuel, an absolute amount we may never actually reach. Beyond that amount, the energy cost to produce one more unit of fossil energy is higher than the amount of energy in the unit—the resource is simply too dispersed. At any point in time,

$$U = C + R$$

where **U** is the ultimate recoverable amount of fossil fuel, **C** is the cumulative amount already produced, and **R** is fossil energy reserves left.

The more fossil fuel has already been used up, the more likely the next unit to be produced will require very energy-expensive technologies

As **C** increases, the next units of fossil fuel to be produced come from deeper underground or less accessible sites, such as the arctic or under the ocean floor—often with harsh, violent environments. It takes more energy to obtain energy from such locations than from shallower or more accessible sites. The more fossil fuel has already been used up to a given date, the more likely the next unit to be produced will require very energy-expensive technologies: for example off-shore oil platforms that must be supported by helicopters, the most energy-intensive mode of transportation.

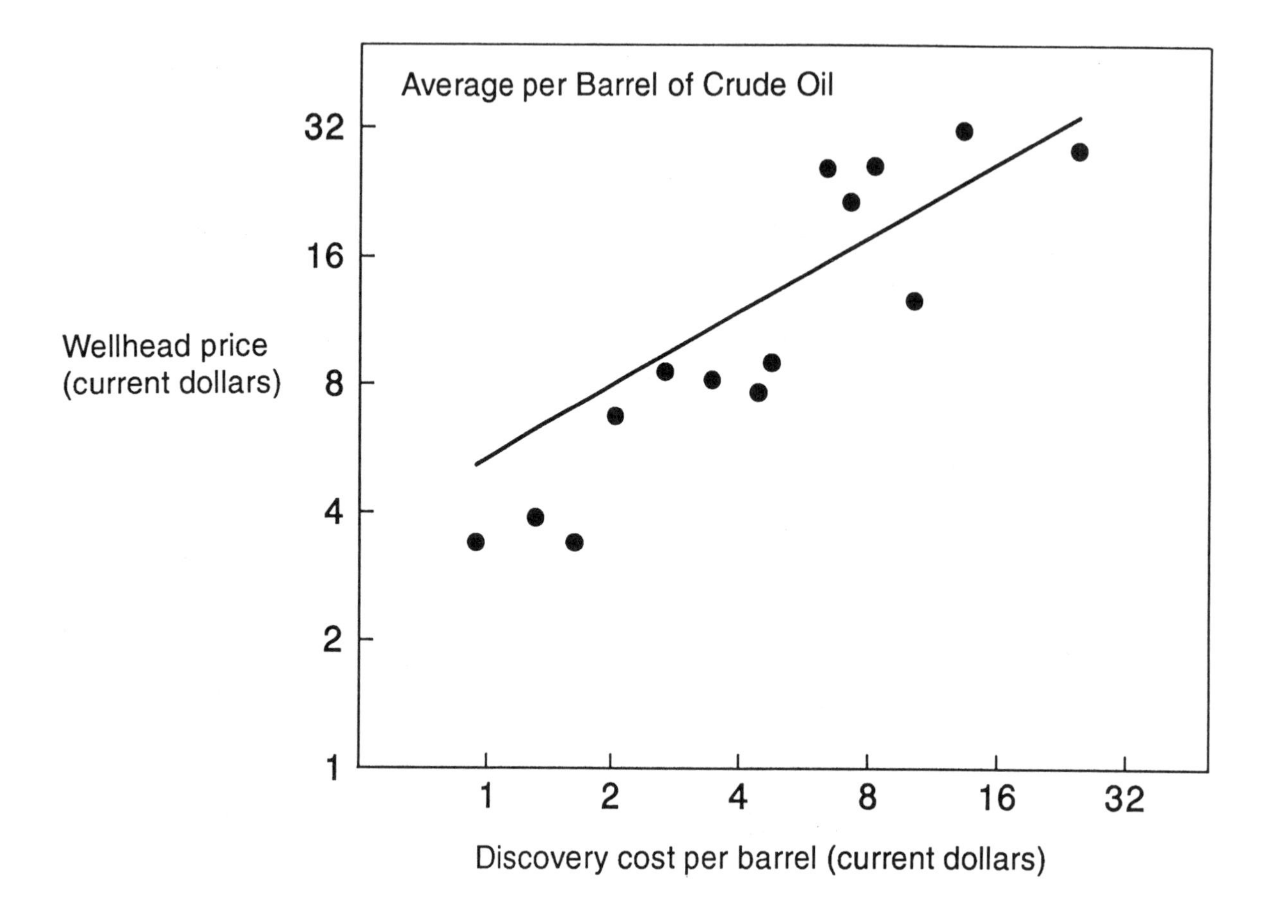

Figure 4-9. The relation between the average wellhead price of a barrel of crude oil and the current dollar cost to discover an additional (or marginal) barrel of oil. (See the explanation for fig.4-8 and, for example, SA 1987, table 1166.)

Once fossil energy resources have been so far depleted that technological innovations can no longer compensate for decreased availability, energy prices rise rapidly. Fig. 4-9 demonstrates that the increased cost to discover oil drives up the average wellhead price.

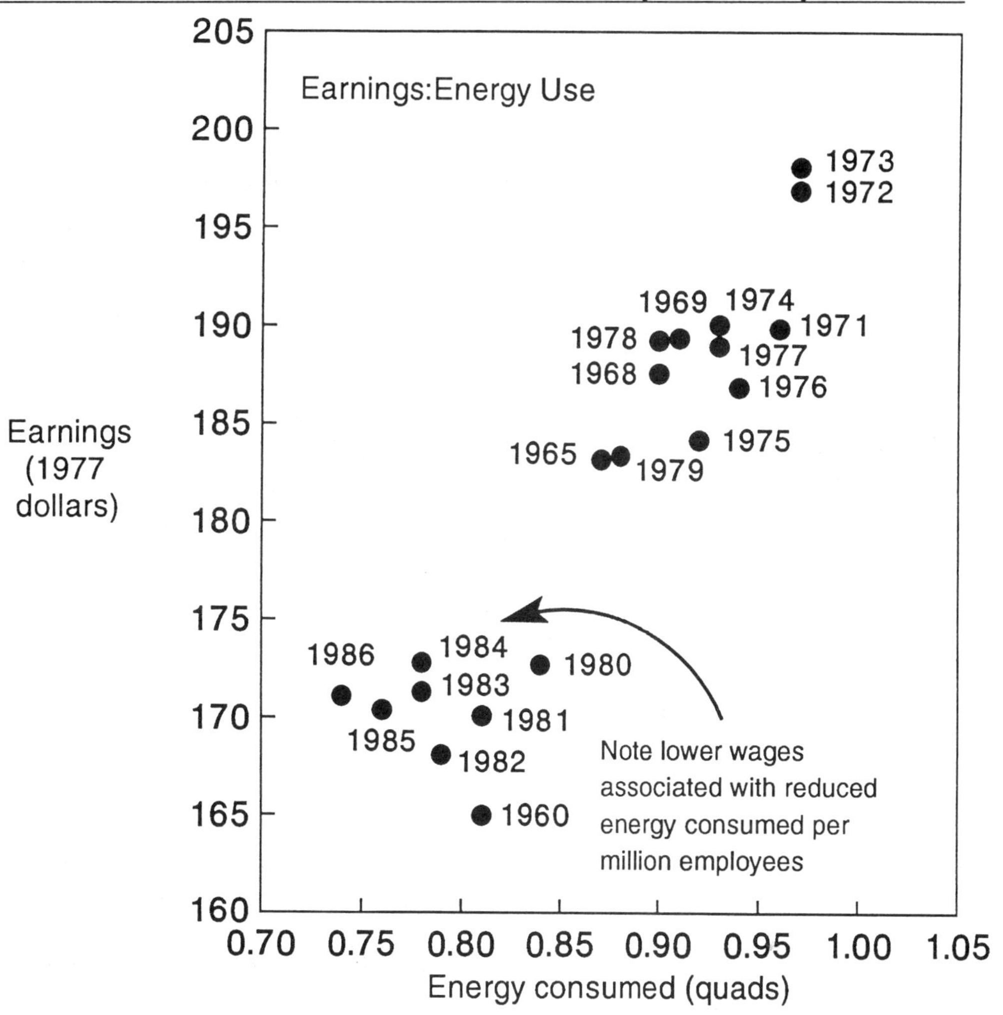

Figure 4-10. The relation between average weekly earnings and energy consumption per million employees in non-agricultural industries. Use of an energy measure allows us to aggregate statistics on all forms of coal, natural gas and petroleum on an equivalent basis. (SA 1987, Wages from Table 648 column 3, energy consumption from Table 904 column 7, labor force size from Table 640 column 2)

When energy becomes more expensive, all economic processes use fewer units of energy per unit of labor, which decreases labor productivity (Hall et al, 1986). Labor productivity, in turn, determines wages. Therefore the number of units of energy used with a unit of labor determines average wages (fig. 4-10). U.S. average wages marched steadily upward from 1750 to 1973, as progressively more energy was used per average unit of labor. Since then the process has been reversed as the energy used per unit of labor gradually declined in response to increased average price of energy. Wages increased slightly again after 1982, as energy again became cheaper.

If costs of land, labor, capital, energy, minerals or technology change relative to each other, managers substitute the cheapest for the more expensive.

This scenario illustrates a general phenomenon: relative amounts of various inputs used in any economic activity are dependent on their prices. Managers of all activities from farming to manufacturing to transportation seek to maximize profit by minimizing overhead. Overhead is minimized by constantly seeking the cheapest input that will get the job done. This means that if costs of land, labor, capital, energy, minerals or technology change relative to each other, managers will substitute the cheapest of the series for the more expensive.

Further, the same phenomenon occurs within a category of inputs. Thus among materials that do comparable jobs, there will be substitutions between alloys, ceramics, plastics and glasses in response to changes in their relative costs. As a resource becomes scarcer relative to other resources, it is used progressively more frugally and efficiently. This is achieved by using more and more units of less costly resources with it so as to maximize its productivity. Thus for about two centuries, to 1973, the value of labor grew more rapidly than the value of metals and mineral fuels, so wages and consumer purchasing power grew. After 1973, resources could no longer be substituted for labor so as to drive up wages, and the standard of living has dropped. The increase in use of consumer debt has masked this phenomenon. An opposite process is the increased demand for professionals with specialized expertise on maximizing efficiency of resource use, as resources become scarcer.

> *After 1973, resources could no longer be substituted for labor and so drive up wages, and the standard of living has dropped—masked by increase in consumer debt.*

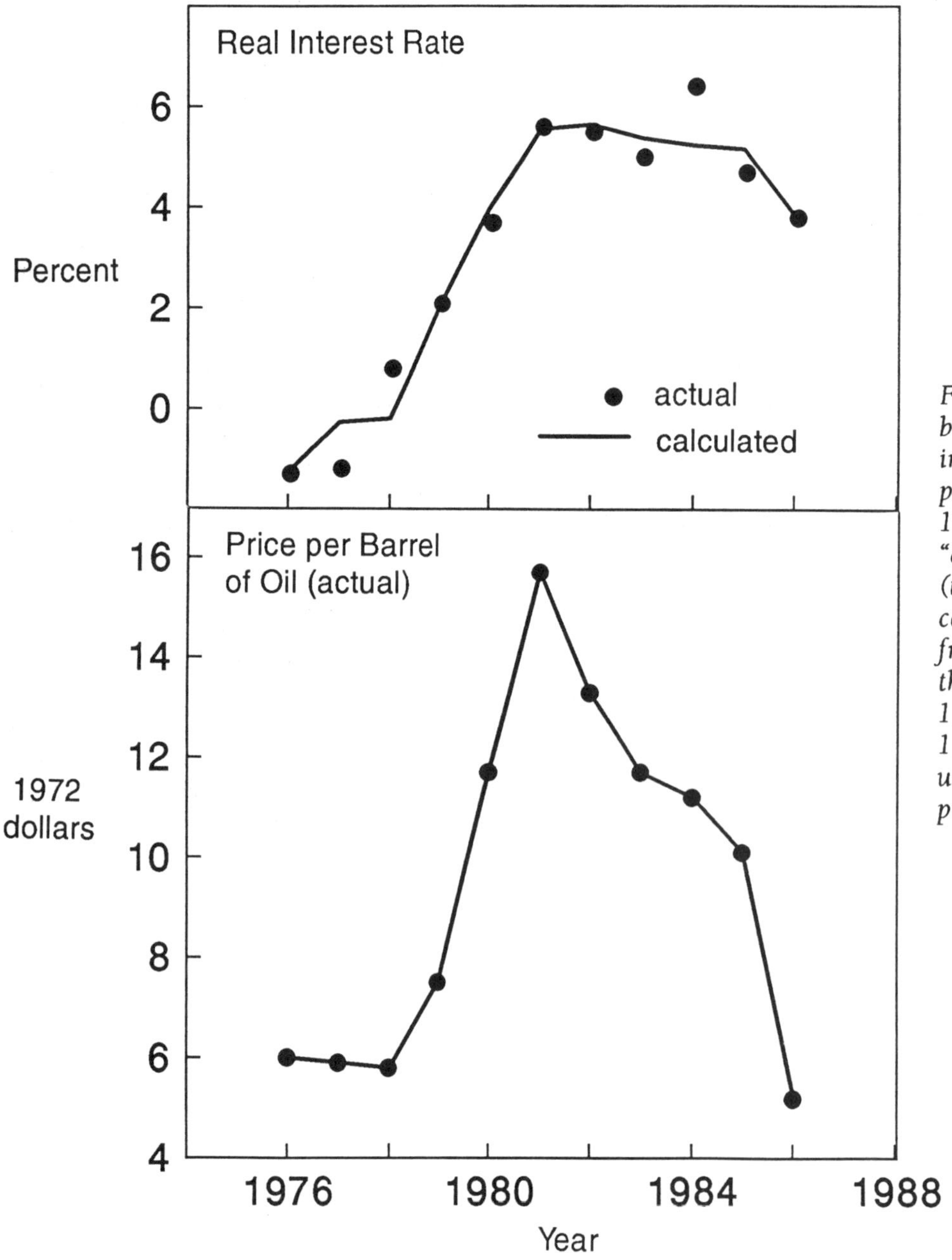

Figure 4-11. The relation between federal funds' interest rate and average price per barrel of oil in 1967 dollars. The "calculated" interest rates (top panel) were computed by the model from oil prices shown in the bottom panel (SA 1987, Tables 803 and 1176, price adjusted using Table 729 producer price index)

④ Energy and interest rates

Another argument for the pervasive effects of cumulative fossil energy use as the force driving various long-term trends concerns the impact on interest rates and hence the volume of investment.

The cumulative amount of energy already used determines the risk ratio for people investing in further exploration. As more of the safe, readily-accessible sites are depleted of fossil fuels, discovery and production from the remaining sites, such as the high arctic or deep outer continental shelf oceans implies a higher risk for investors. When banks or venture capitalists lend money, the interest rate they charge increases with the riskiness of the proposed investment. Riskier oil exploration drives up interest rates throughout lending markets. Then other borrowers must pay higher interest rates to compete in the capital market with borrowers of energy exploration loans. Therefore, as energy reserves becomes scarcer (measured by the constant-dollar price per barrel of crude oil), the long-term trend in interest rates should increase (e.g. fig. 4-11).

⑤ Energy as a leading economic indicator

Another argument pointing to fossil energy as a force driving all types of trends in society is based on the order in which different system measures change at important turning points in history. We argue that causes ought to precede effects, so we investigate the order in which events occurred prior to depressions, for example.

The drop in money supply was an effect, not a cause of the Great Depression.

Fig. 4-12 (next page) depicts the trend in various system variables prior to the Great Depression of the 1930s. In the first panel we find that the M2 measure of the money supply rose from 1926 to 1929. Since it did not begin to drop until 1930, it was a coincident, rather than a leading indicator. This suggests that the drop in money supply was an effect, not a cause of the depression, the same conclusion reached by Temin (1976). The second panel shows that the wholesale fuel price index dropped sharply in 1927 and continued to drop until 1932. Energy, therefore, does seem a likely candidate to be the force governing trends of a diversity of other system variables in society.

Further, the drop in energy price prior to a depression suggests overinvestment in a storage—energy production capacity—and a resultant excess energy supply relative to demand. (This aspect will be developed fully in Chapter 7.) The next two panels depict trends in the wholesale price indices for metals and farm products, respectively. They were both higher in 1929 than in 1927, so it appears that prior to the Great Depression, causality flowed from energy to other variables, not in the reverse direction.

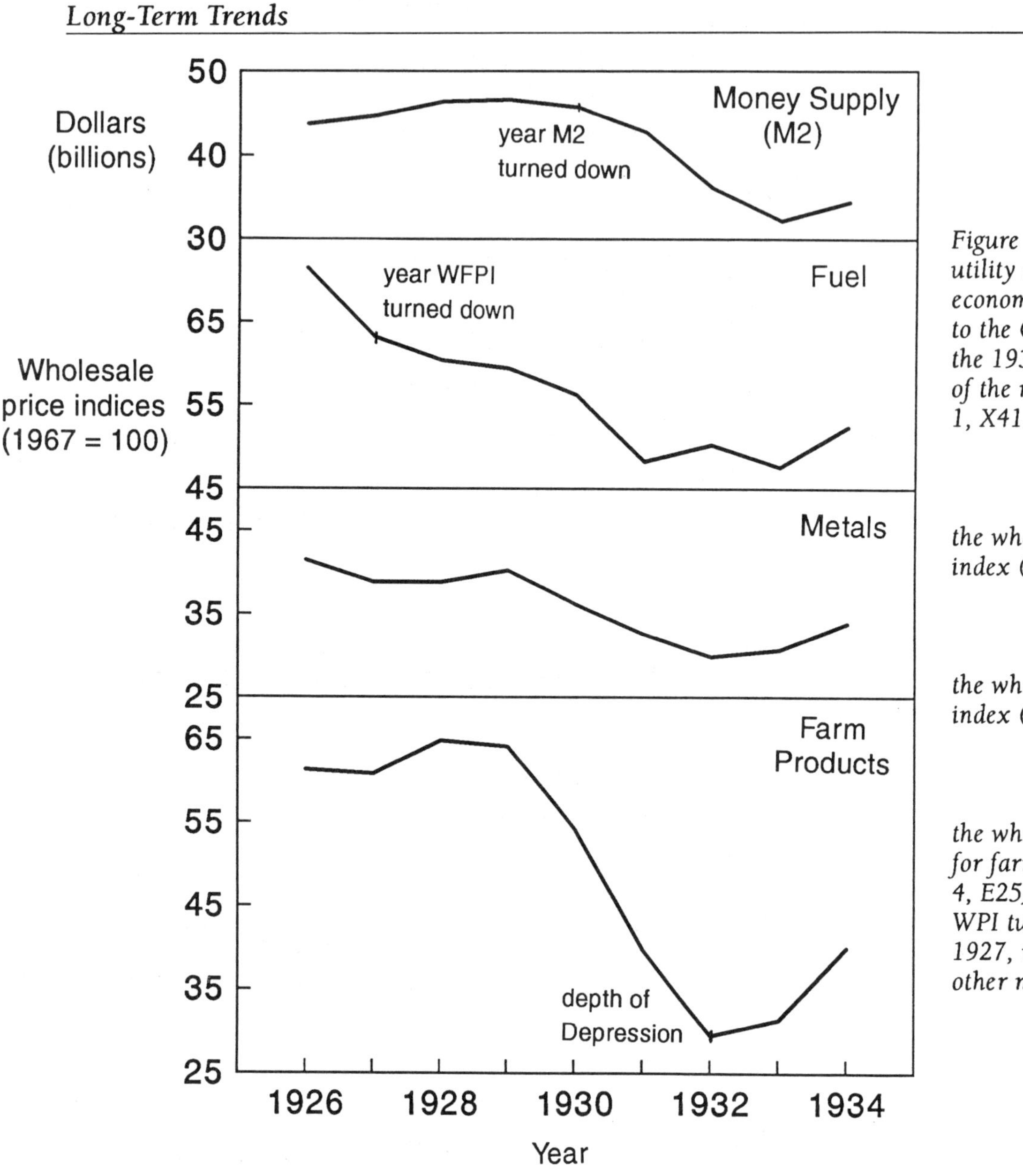

Figure 4-12. The relative utility of different leading economic indicators prior to the Great Depression of the 1930's: M2 measure of the money stock (panel 1, X415);

the wholesale fuel price index (panel 2, E29);

the wholesale metals price index (panel 3, E34) and

the wholesale price index for farm products (panel 4, E25). Note that fuel WPI turned downward in 1927, well before the other measures.

Fig. 4-13 depicts trends in price indices prior to depressions in the 1840s (top panel) and 1890s (bottom panel). In both cases, sustained drops showed up in energy prices prior to other wholesale markets. Further, the data for the depression that bottomed out in 1843 show that the price dropped for fuels first, then for commodities for which fuel costs were an input (metals and metal products), and last in commodities for which fuel cost was not an important input to the final wholesale price (hides, leather products, and building materials). This sequence of wholesale price changes prior to depressions argues that the energy cost of obtaining energy is the force regulating trends in other systems variables in modern industrial societies.

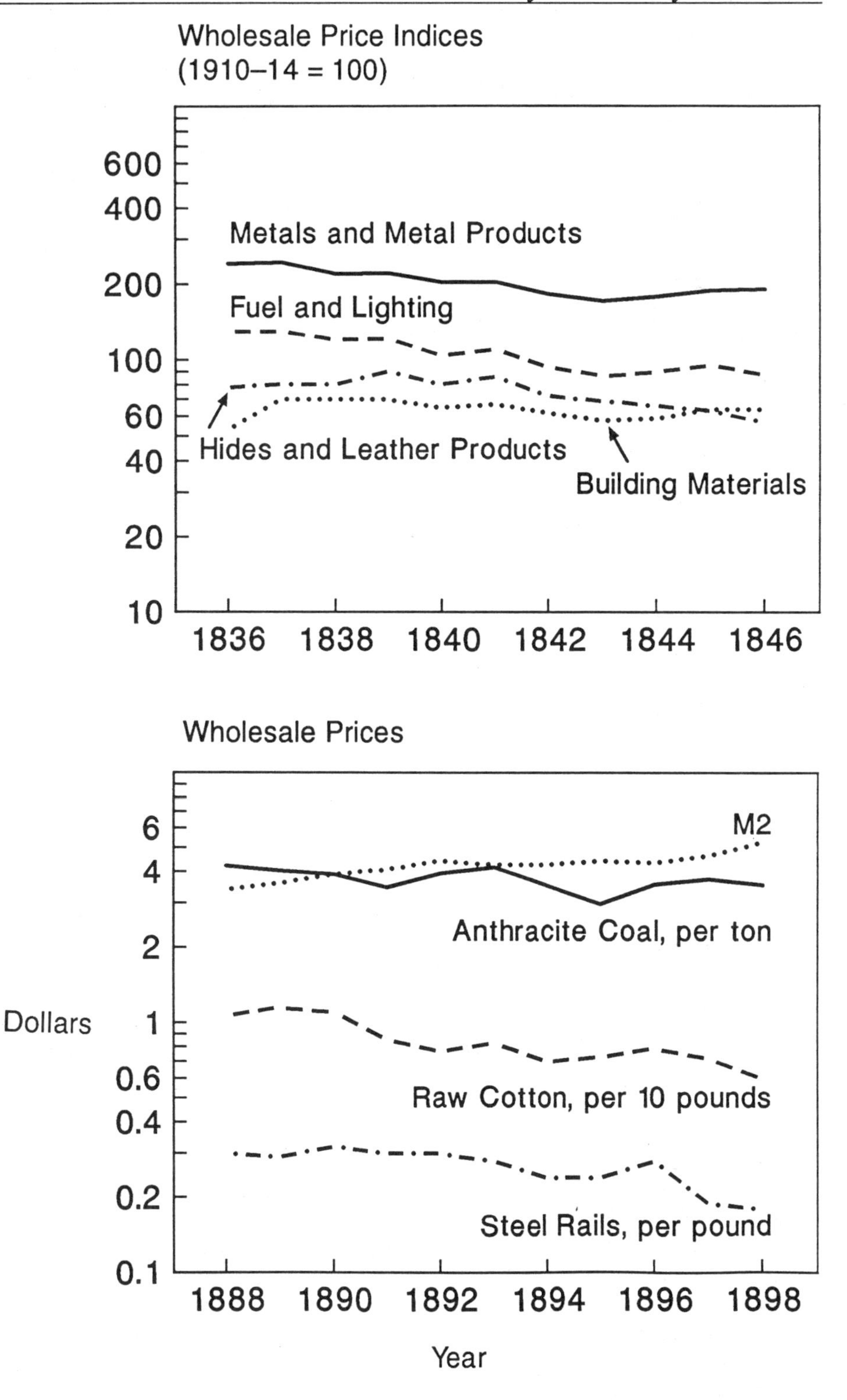

Figure 4-13. Relative utility of various leading economic indicators prior to the depressions of 1843 (top panel) and 1894 (bottom panel). Small arrows mark years when the earliest indicator turned downward. Note lag time until nadir of each depression. (E52-63.)

Fig. 4-14 supports the contention that oil price is the force driving inflation by showing how the effects of oil price increases radiate outwards to other system measures. The top panel shows that an oil price increase is followed shortly by a coal price increase. Price increases in competing forms of energy occur because oil price increases either

- increase competing forms' wage and profit potential, or
- become an input to solar or nuclear power costs, as increased costs to produce the raw materials (e.g. metals) and manufacture their equipment.

Therefore, an oil price increase is reflected quickly in the producer price index for energy generally. After a lag, this price increase shows up as an increase in overall consumer prices. One argument for the existence of a lag is that the consumer price index was still increasing in 1986, whereas the oil price had been dropping since 1982.

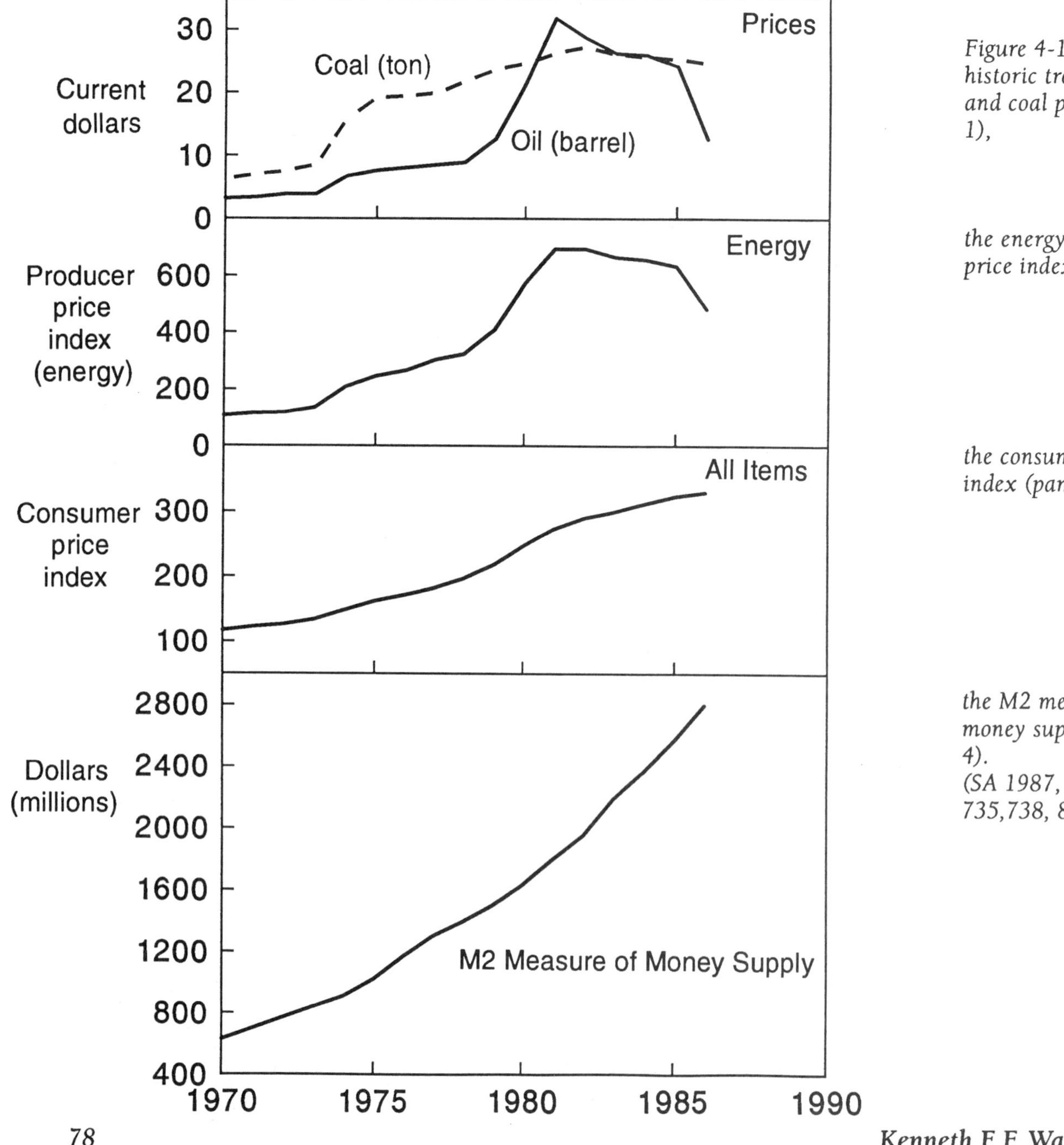

Figure 4-14. Recent historic trends in oil and coal prices (panel 1), the energy producer price index (panel 2), the consumer price index (panel 3), and the M2 measure of the money supply (panel 4). (SA 1987, Tables 1159, 735,738, 800.)

Finally, the oil price increase appears in the M2 measure of the money supply. The rate of increase in M2 provides the technically accurate measure of the inflation rate. In contrast, an increase in the general level of prices is a consequence of an increase in money supply. Note that there is a smoothing effect as the effect of an oil price increase radiates outwards in the system, which tends to veil the identity of the ultimate cause as we move outward from it.

Some people might argue that M2 increase causes increase in energy prices: increase in rate of growth of the money supply makes more money available with which to drive up energy prices. Oil exploration companies would have more money available to explore risky, expensive sites such as the outer continental shelf. Further, managers of central banks would increase the money stock faster after periods of very expensive exploratory drilling at large losses. These losses are magnified as they pass through the economy, with the result being heavy strain on venture capital markets and increasing interest rates.

The counterargument to this sequence of logic is that M2 was still rising rapidly from 1982 to 1985, even though the oil price had been dropping since 1981. Either exploratory drilling costs have minimal impact on venture capital markets, which violates common sense, or the causality runs (with a lag) from oil price increases to M2 increases, not the other direction.

Increase in resource availability is the real root of a nation's wealth, not increases in the money stock.

In addition, an increase in the rate of growth in M2 simply results in an increased general level of prices but produces no growth in real wealth. On the other hand, production of energy from major new fossil fuel discoveries produces a corresponding increase in the money supply. Reexamination of fig. 4-8 adds to the argument that increase in resource availability—and not in money supply—is the real root of a nation's wealth. Increasing the money stock simply decreases the value of money.

Analyzing *the order* in which producer price indices *top or bottom out* is another way to test the role of energy in determining the shape of long-term trends in other variables. If energy prices are regulating all other prices, then we should find evidence that wholesale energy price indices initiate waves that radiate outwards throughout all price indices. The order in which prices change should be:

① Energy prices, then

② Raw materials made from energy and other inputs, and finally

③ Highly processed materials, several steps in the causal sequence away from raw energy prices.

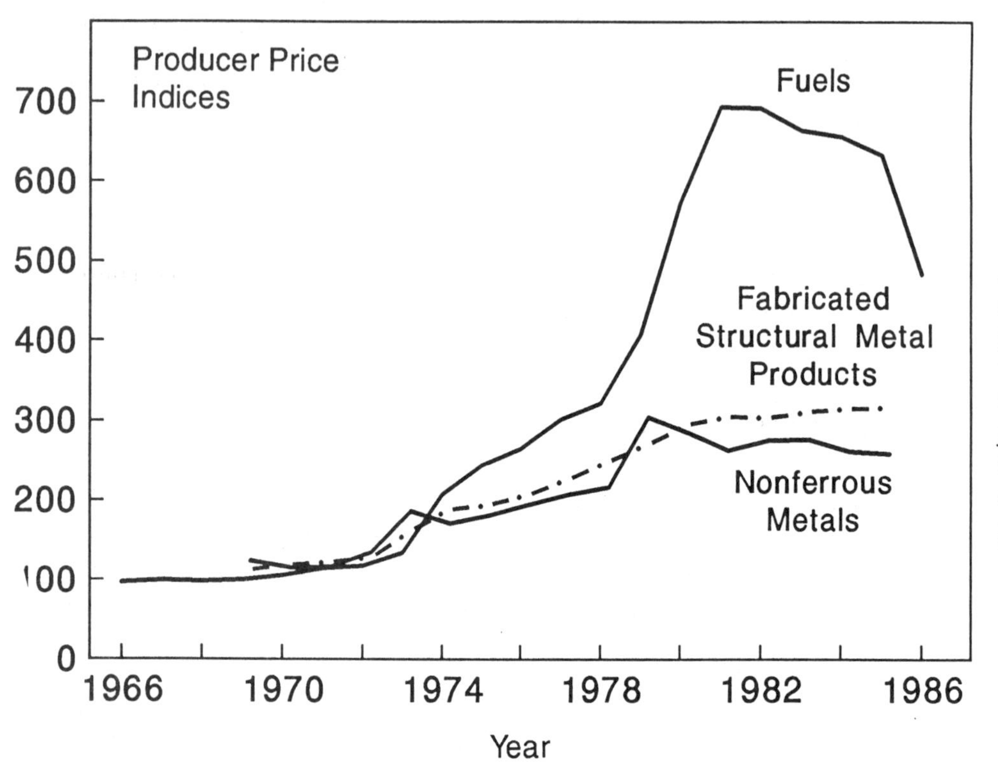

Figure 4-15. The outward radiation of price increases in energy. Producer price indices plotted are for fuels, nonferrous metals, and fabricated structural metal products. (SA 1987, Table 736)

In fact, we see that very pattern extending back into the mid-18th century. The pattern is very clear in accurate modern data (fig. 4-15) in which sharp price increases and decreases show up first in wholesale price indices for fuels, then nonferrous metals, and finally fabricated structural metal products (SA,1987, Tables 735,736). There was a sustained downward trend in the fuel price index from 1982 to at least 1986, whereas the nonferrous metal price was essentially flat from 1982 to 1986. The price for fabricated structural metal products actually continued to increase from 1980 to at least 1986.

Subsequent chapters will demonstrate that energy has remarkably pervasive effects, operating through national strategic decisions about choice of transportation systems, agriculture, wages and prices, and the international trade and monetary systems.

Summary of the argument that fossil fuel is the system driver

Long-term trends in the development of nations or civilizations are regulated by the size of critically important resource storages. The equations accounting for changes in these trends through time express the extent to which some stock or storage is depleted or supersaturated (Chapter 7), not the rate of some flow. This distinction between storages and flows has a significant effect on the mathematical formulation of the laws regulating trends (Appendix A).

Depletion of a nation's fossil fuel reserves increases prices, the monetary stock, the cumulative capital investment, and technological development of a society. Increased technological development implies that all activities will require less labor and more knowledge. These two factors operating in combination decrease the demand for children and increase their unit cost. Therefore, as fossil fuel storages are depleted, the birth rate trend drops. For a long time, however, these lower birth rates are multiplied by increased numbers of young women entering their reproductive years. Therefore, trends for number of births and number of people in each age group rise even though birth rates are falling.

As domestic resources are depleted, relatively expensive foreign resources are increasingly substituted for the more expensive domestic resources, and production of the latter declines. This is the pattern already showing up for a variety of metallic minerals in the United States (i.e. pig iron).

Need for long data series

In order to discover the precise form of the mathematical equation describing a long-term trend, it is critically important to examine data series for very long periods, preferably at least one–two centuries. Unless we have the perspective that comes from examining very long runs of data, it is impossible to understand the significance of the trend in the last 15 years.

To illustrate, unless we have a long run of data, we don't know if a downturn in the last three years is caused by

① A downturn in the long-term trend itself,

② A downturn in a wavelike oscillation about that trend, or

③ A downturn in a (short-term) high-frequency fluctuation about a wave.

To distinguish these effects, we need long runs of data. For example, we might have a case in which one variable is tugging a long-term trend strongly downward, but another variable is tugging a wavelike oscillation about the trend strongly upwards. In that case, the two forces would tend to cancel each other's effects, and the resultant appearance of stability would be quite misleading. Accurate forecasting would be impossible unless we understood the magnitude of the effect due to each of the three sets of forces operating on the trend in the variable of interest.

Long data series are also important for testing hypotheses about the causes of rare events such as depressions or major wars. A data series for only the last 90 years only includes one major economic downturn—so far—in the 1930s. We need a much longer series to test hypotheses about the cause of depressions. Otherwise, by chance alone, we may have an entirely coincidental correlation between a depression and some other variable that did not, in fact, cause the depression. By extending our data series backward in time to, say, 1750, we now have four serious economic downturns in the series. If all four are statistically associated with the same prior sequence of events, however, it is far less likely that the association is accidental.

Very long runs of data also allow us to conduct tests on the structural stability of the system.

- Is the system evolving through time, with new types of structural relationships between system components or new system vulnerabilities appearing?
- Have depressions always occurred for the same reason?
- Have the parameter values in the equations remained constant?
- Or, has evolution of a nation caused it to alter into a new character, with gradual development of vulnerability to depression from new sources of instability?

Long runs of data also allow us to detect very slight long-term changes in trends that would not be statistically detectable with time series extending over only a few decades.

Removing the effect of the trend

Having identified the force regulating a long-term trend, how do we remove the effect of that force from a data series so that we can isolate the effects of the forces that produce fluctuations around the trend?

To illustrate the process, when the wholesale fuel price index (WFPI) is plotted against cumulative domestic production of fossil fuel (fig. 4-16), we discover that the relationship is rectilinear—the trend is a straight line. The irregular line, however, represents the actual data. To ensure that the equation selected to describe the trend is realistic, we conduct a simple test. The actual values for the variable for each year are divided by the corresponding values computed from the trend equation. When the resultant ratio of actual to calculated values is plotted against year number, the graph obtained should show only fluctuations about a perfectly flat trend line, as in fig. 4-17.

Such patterns are typically startlingly different than those apparent in the raw data from which they are derived. Note that these ratios show pronounced, similar spikes in association with the Civil War, World War I, and the O.P.E.C. oil embargo of 1979–1981. The low periods in between these peaks are surprisingly long, and in each case show two low periods.

On use of different scales

Standard usage allows data to be plotted on various scales on the *y* axis. For example, a semilogarithmic scale may be used (e.g., fig. 4-16) so that very large values at one end of the scale don't prevent us from seeing changes in much smaller values at the other end.

Also, a semilogarithmic scale is required for the Y-axis when a variable is growing exponentially (as in compound interest on bank deposits).

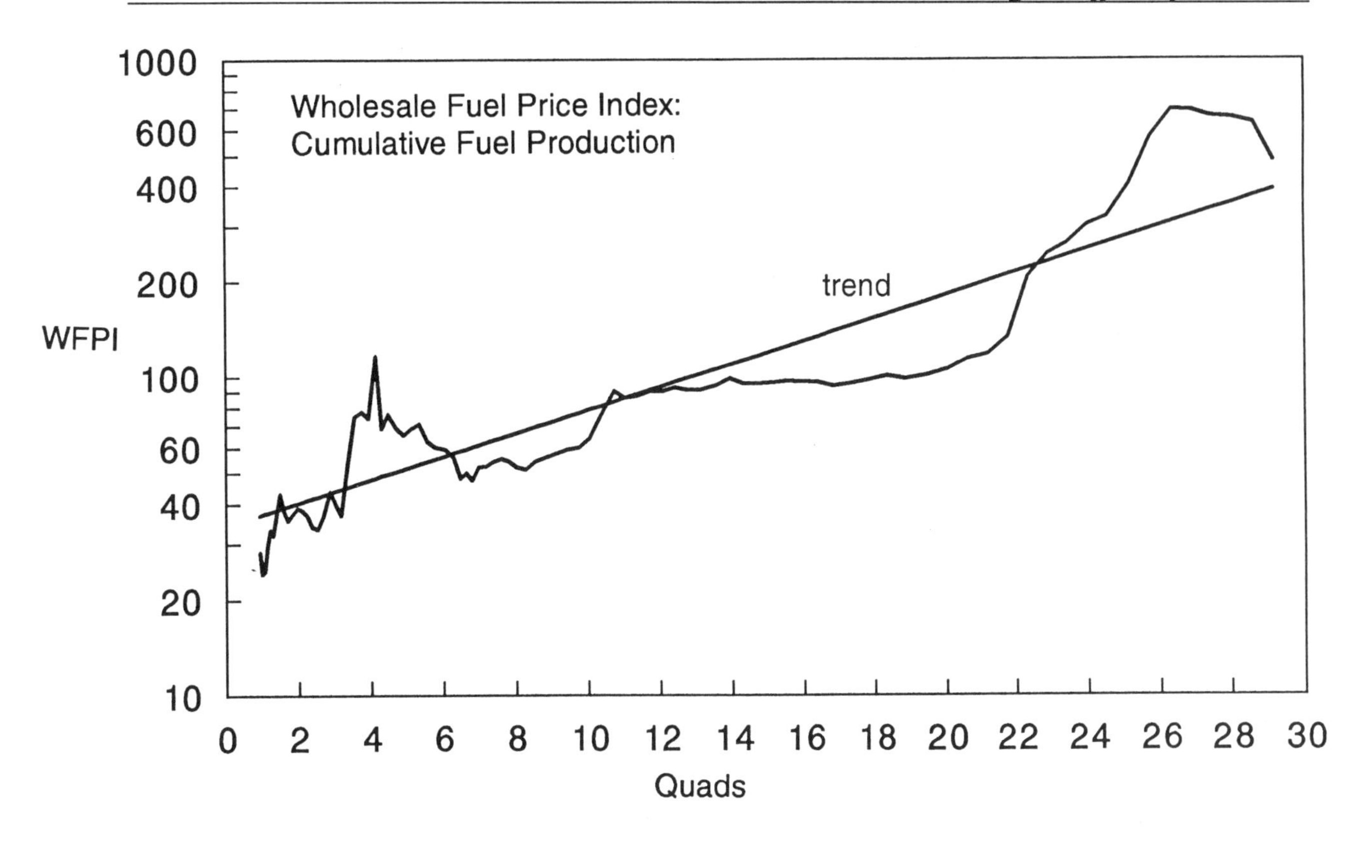

Figure 4-16. The relation between the wholesale fuel price index and cumulative U.S. production of fossil fuel. The straight line is the long-term trend. (E29 and M76 cumulated, updated using various SA.)

Fig. 4-17 absolutely refutes the notion that long wave cycles have been eliminated from the economy by clever management. Indeed, this graph is simply one example of a very large number of graphs from every aspect of society that exposes these cycles. To illustrate, we see the same long wave pattern in graphs of the ratio of loans outstanding to cash on hand in all insured commercial banks.

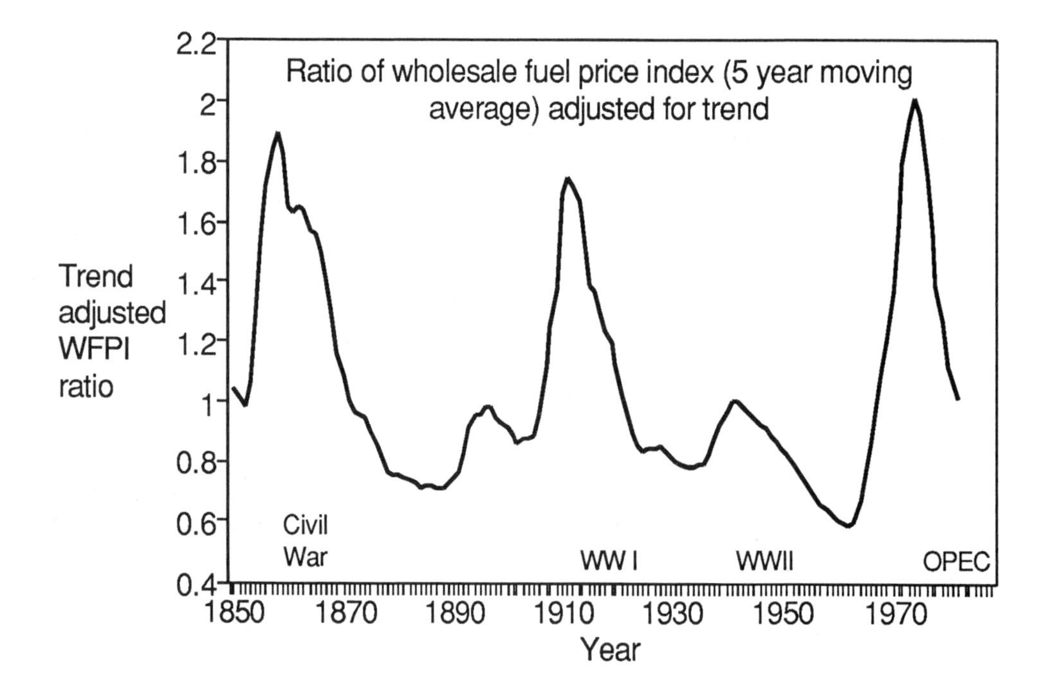

Figure 4-17. The trend in the ratio of wholesale fuel price indices, as computed from the trend equation (the straight line in fig. 4-16). Note that by eliminating the effect of the long-term trend, a startling pattern emerges of sharp peaks around a basically straight line.

In the next and subsequent chapters, we will be interested in accounting for patterns of change through time in system variables in both their trends and this kind of fluctuation about those trends.

Chapter 5

The Mechanisms That Produce Fluctuations

There is a reliable method for forecasting major downturns and inflationary blowoffs.

After establishing in Chapter 4 that fluctuations occur in long-term trends, I explain in this chapter how those fluctuations are produced. Then that knowledge of mechanisms is used to build a model for forecasting changes in the U.S. wholesale price index (WPI). After testing that model against data since 1832, the chapter concludes with a projection of the WPI to the year 2029. The goal is to show policy makers and investors that there is a reliable method for forecasting major downturns and inflationary blowoffs. Readers who wish to try out the method on their own computers or explore the structure of the forecasting model will find a program in Appendix A.

Theory about the forces that produce fluctuations in systems has been developed in several different fields, particularly engineering, economics, and ecology. To simplify explanation, I will illustrate this theory with an example where the data are complete, and we understand the causal mechanisms—fur bearers in northern forests. Because there are fundamental similarities between forces generating fur-bearer cycles and those operating on economic systems, we can apply the same theory to fluctuations in other variables such as the wholesale price index.

Cycles in furbearer populations

It has been known for a long time that populations of fur-bearing mammals fluctuated rhythmically in northern Canada (e.g. Elton and Nicholson, 1942; Keith, 1963; Finerty, 1976). Two puzzles are associated with the phenomenon.

- Why has the wavelength of the fluctuations remained at about 10 years for centuries?
- Why are the waves approximately synchronized over the northern hemisphere for periods of at least 11 decades?

Note that similarly puzzling wavelength constancy and synchronization in remote parts of the world also appear in the economy.

The Hudson's Bay Company ran a large fur business in Canada, buying furs at their many outposts from trappers who worked throughout the northern forests. From 1736 on, the Company kept complete, accurate records on the numbers of these furs—by species and region of capture.

By the 20th century, scholars wondered why snowshoe hares and several of their predators, such as lynx, fluctuated in such a remarkably regular fashion, with a 10-year wavelength, over very long periods and in synchrony over thousands of miles (e.g. Butler, 1953; Keith, 1963). The historical records have been subjected to diverse mathematical and statistical analyses. In addition, Keith and his students conducted comprehensive field research on important factors involved in snowshoe hare population fluctuations: birth and survival in hares and in various predatory species, particularly the lynx; population sizes of all relevant species; and quantitative measurements on type and amount of food vegetation available for the hares each year (Cary and Keith, 1979; Keith and Windberg, 1978; Pease, Vowles and Keith, 1979; Vaughan and Keith, 1981; Keith et al, 1984).

Useful Definitions

- Wavelength = the number of years between two consecutive peaks (zeniths) or troughs (nadirs) in a data series.
- Time lag = **T**, the number of years between the time that a variable deviates from the trend or equilibrium until the time when that deviation produces its effect.
- Oscillation = wave-like variation (movement) of a variable away from the trend or equilibrium.
- Amplitude = how far a variable departs from its equilibrium or trend.

Several hypotheses could account for the apparent regularity of these fluctuations.

- As in economics, some theories invoke exogenous causal mechanisms such as rhythmic fluctuations in climate, emissions of energy by the sun or the frequency of volcanic eruptions (which decrease global planetary temperature by partially blocking incoming solar radiation. These external forces would impose fluctuations on animal populations.)
- Other theories postulate forces endogenous to a single population and generating fluctuations in only one of: hare populations; predator populations; or availability of plant food for the hares.
- Two-factor interactions might cause the furbearer population fluctuations: hares–vegetation or hares–predators.
- The system control mechanism might involve interaction of three factors: vegetation–hares–predators.
- The final possibility is that system control resides in the interaction between one or more endogenous mechanisms and one or more exogenous mechanisms.

Keith and his students studied populations of hares, their food vegetation, and their predators for many years in central Alberta. The data they collected, combined with the long series of fur-return data on all furbearers, make this perhaps the best single body of data available for studying cycle-generating mechanisms in ecological or economic systems.

They discovered an approximately 10-year cycle in hare populations, fluctuating around an average April density of about 129 hares per 100 hectares (Cary and Keith, 1979; Keith et al, 1984). This equilibrium density occurs because the particular study plots could support exactly 129 hares indefinitely. The critical determinant was not space itself, but the amount of plant food that grew in 100 hectares. When hare populations exceed 129 per 100 hectares, they eat so much of their preferred plant food (fine twigs) that its abundance declines. That causes a decline in the nutritional condition of female hares, which reduces their reproductive rates and the proportion of their offspring that survive the first year of life.

We can explore the implications of these results for the dynamical properties of hare populations by using a simple forecasting model (Appendix A). This model assumes that change in number of hares from one year to the next is affected by only three variables:

- Intrinsic growth rate of the hare population, assuming a limitless environment.
- How far the hare population deviates in any year from the equilibrium value, 129.
- Time lag—the number of years that elapse from the year of that deviation to the year in which the deviation affects the rate of population change.

Keith and his students found the time lag to be two years. In the study plots, there was vigorous growth two years later if hare populations were far below 129, and rapid population decline if they were far above 129.

Figure 5-1. How time lags in control mechanisms produce oscillations in systems. Starting at point **B**, *a time lag takes time* (**T**) *to move the variable* **N** *(heavy line) away from equilibrium (line* **K**) *to a new point,* **A**.

Panel 2 shows that if the time lag were twice as long, the wave would shift to the right to reach from **B** *to the curve and would not begin to return to equilibrium until* **N** *had reached point* **A'**. *That is, a* ***longer time lag produces longer wavelengths with wider oscillations*** *away from equilibrium.*

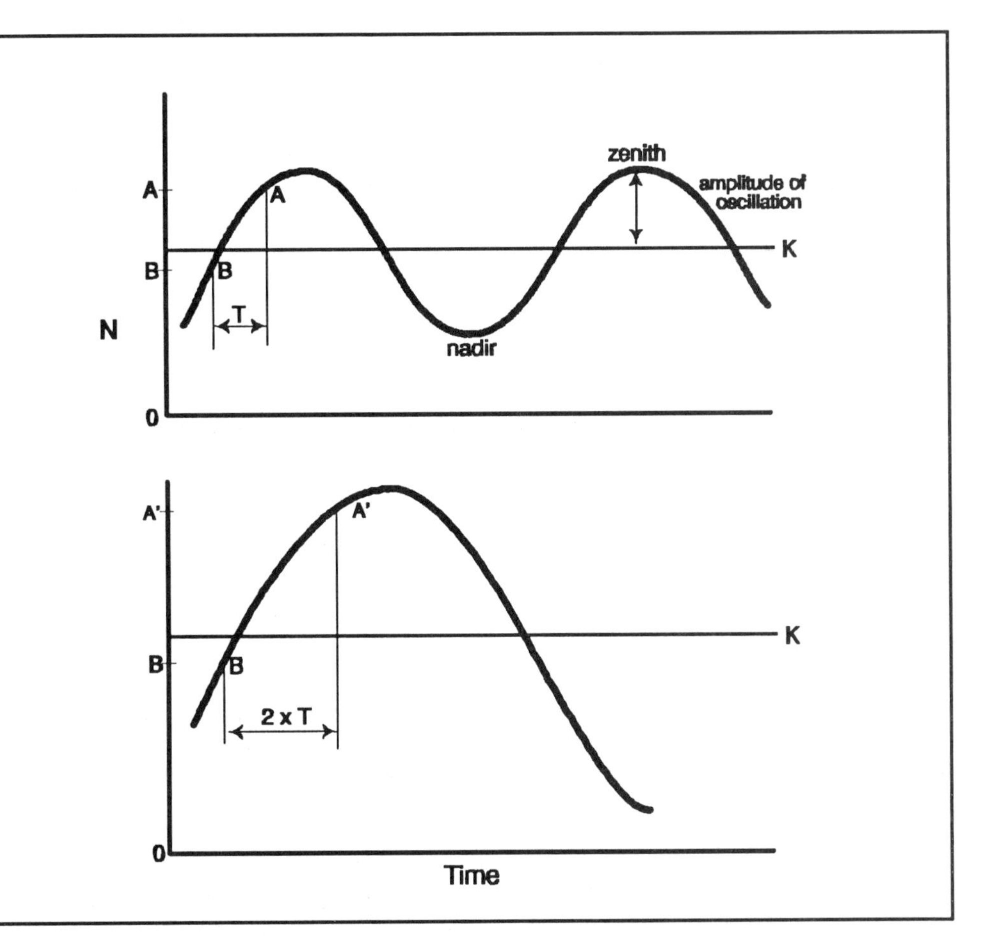

Fig. 5-1 shows how the length of time lags in control mechanisms regulates the wavelength in fluctuating systems. We can use the hare population to illustrate how the control mechanism works. Suppose the population size were controlled by some mechanism that requires *no* time lag to return population size to its equilibrium whenever it deviates from it. What would happen when some sudden environmental perturbation, such as a year of weather extraordinarily favorable for vegetation growth, raises the hare population to point **A**? The population would immediately decrease from **A** to equilibrium **K**.

Suppose, now, that the population is regulated by a mechanism that has a time lag of length **T** years, as shown in fig. 5-1. In effect, when the population level is at **A**, the control mechanism "senses" that the population is still at **B**. Therefore, instead of forcing the population to decline rapidly to **K**, the equilibrium density, it forces it to continue growing, as if it were still *below* **K**, and not where it actually is—*above* it. The control mechanism doesn't kick in until the actual population size is at point **A** on the higher swing of the cycle; then the control mechanism "realizes" that the population is above **K** and therefore must be forced to decrease.

Clearly, time lags in control mechanisms allow systems to grow far above their equilibria or drop far below them. Further, the greater the time lag **T**, the greater the magnitude of departure from **K**. Thus both wavelength and amplitude of oscillation increase with time lag. They also increase with the inherent growth rate of any system. The greater the growth rate, the more likely the system is to "overshoot" equilibrium when either dropping or rising toward it. In fact, any time we see a fluctuating system with large-amplitude fluctuations and wavelengths of many years or decades, we know we are looking at the consequences of a system control mechanism with very long time lags, or a high inherent growth rate, or both.

Any time we see a fluctuating system with large-amplitude fluctuations and long wavelengths, we are looking at a system control mechanism with very long time lags, a high inherent growth rate, or both.

Testing the effects of time lags and growth rates

Effects of time lag

Computer simulation was used to explore the sensitivity of hare population stability after perturbation to variation of population growth rate and length of time lag. Results of this simulation are depicted in fig. 5-2. In each panel, the part of the graph left of the arrow is the actual data trend; the remaining part of the graph was obtained by simulating the response to a perturbation. Readers may use their own computers to experiment with the effects of altering time lag and growth rate; the program is in Appendix A.

When the simulation started with the first 15 years of actual population data and with intrinsic population growth rate set at 1.271, three very different outcomes resulted, depending on how long the time lag was:

- **Time lag = 1 year**: the simulated population immediately returned to the equilibrium population of 129 and stayed there (first panel, fig. 5-2).
- **Time lag = 2 years**: the simulation exercise produced a regular, 9-year cycle (second panel).
- **Time lag = 3 years**: the simulation produced violent oscillation over the first 20 years, and extinction of the simulated rabbit population by the 23rd year (third panel).

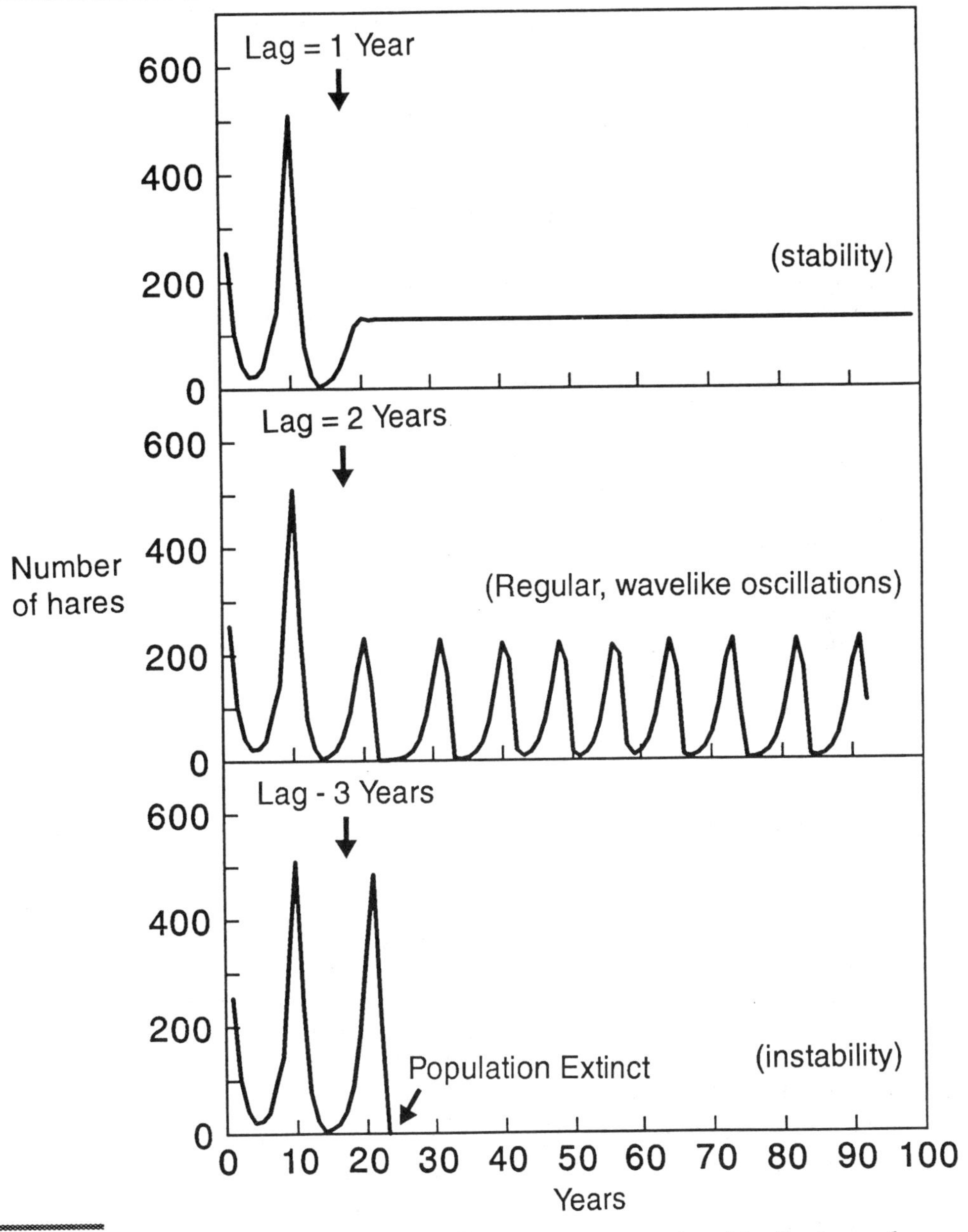

Figure 5-2. Simulated hare population numbers per 100 hectares. The assumed lag length in the population self-regulatory mechanism was 1 year (top panel), 2 years (second panel), and 3 years (third panel).

The three panels illustrate, respectively, stability, regular wavelike oscillations, and instability. Actual data are used for the years prior to the arrow in each graph and were obtained from field studies by Keith and his associates (e.g. Keith et al, 1984).

Economic cycles are astonishingly sensitive to very slight changes in length of time lag.

Thus the stability of the fluctuating system is critically dependent on the length of the time lag in the system control mechanism. This same phenomenon has shown up in statistical analyses of economic cycles: they are astonishingly sensitive to very slight changes in the length of the time lag.

Effects of growth rate

The pattern of population fluctuations was also very sensitive to variation of the intrinsic population growth rate. If that rate was decreased from 1.271 to 1.1, for a lag of 2, there was a pronounced decrease in the amplitude of fluctuation, and the wavelength decreased from 9 to 6 years. Very slight increases in the growth rate above 1.271 caused the population to go extinct by about the 22nd year. That is, **decreasing the growth rate dampened the wave oscillation; increasing the growth rate exaggerated wave oscillation.**

Implications for economic processes

These results fit the theory that has been developed in several fields. They have two extremely important implications for decision-making in human societies and specifically, for economic decisions.

- Because long time lags are a principal reason why systems undergo wavelike oscillations of large amplitude, **we must shorten time lags if we wish to minimize the amplitude of the waves.**

We must shorten time lags if we wish to minimize the amplitude of the waves

We saw in Chapter 4 that large excursions above long-term wholesale commodity price trends imply war and large excursions below those trends imply depressions; this gives us a huge motivation to modify the way we make decisions. For example, suppose we had a 20-year time lag that we wished to shorten. We could do this by making decisions, not on the basis of the present state of the system, but on realistic forecasts of the way it would be in 20 years in response to various alternate decisions we might make now.

- A second reason for large amplitude wavelike fluctuations is that **decision-making is too sensitive to departures from trend**. That is, it is too pessimistic in bad times and excessively optimistic in good times.

Decision-making is too pessimistic in bad times and too optimistic in good times.

If the responses to good news or bad news could be made less vigorous, the magnitude of the overshooting of the trend line could be decreased. There is a purely selfish reason for doing this also: "contrarians" are people who get rich by always doing the opposite of everyone else. They know that bad times are temporary, so they buy when others are selling. They also know that good times are temporary, so they sell when others are buying.

A puzzle: Why are animal population fluctuations so sensitive to small changes in parameter values?

This sensitivity would suggest that population control mechanisms have evolved with both time lags and intrinsic growth rates so precisely tuned to the environmental food supply that the slightest alteration will lead to extinction of the population. That's hard to believe. It seems implausible that long-term survival of entire populations would depend on population control mechanisms that had to have very precise parameter values—that must remain constant indefinitely. Logic suggests that population regulation mechanisms are more complex than that. That is, rather regular-appearing wavelike patterns of oscillation through time may not be purely the product of some regulatory mechanism operating within the system of hare food, hares and their enemies. Some outside force may be interacting with this system to produce the observed, rather regular-appearing pattern.This issue is worthy of careful exploration, because whatever the phenomenon is, it may well be common to economic and ecological systems.

Some outside force—common to economic and ecological systems—may produce the observed, regular patterns.

In order to test more elaborate hypotheses, we turn to the much longer lynx data series collected by the fur company, as reported by Elton and Nicholson (1942). The longest running data set, from the Mackenzie River District, is plotted in the top panel of fig. 5-3. Two features are evident:

① The pattern of fluctuation is irregular with respect to wavelength and amplitude (how far apart the peaks/valleys are and how far they vary from the trend or equilibrium, see earlier side bar).

② The two measures seem correlated:

- A very low nadir in 1842 falls between peaks 10 years apart;
- A very high nadir in 1908 separates peaks only 9 years apart.
- Smaller than average amplitude seems to coincide with smaller than average wavelength.

During some cycles, some factor operating over great areas synchronizes fluctuations in all areas, while in other cycles, fluctuations gradually drift apart. This suggests that some external shocks are lengthening the wavelength and amplifying amplitude of oscillation.

This suggests that some force reenergizes both amplitude and wavelength simultaneously. Further, data series from widely separated regions reveal variation through time in the degree of synchronization of nadirs over vast stretches (2500 miles). In seven areas, six nadirs were in 1842 and one in 1841. Three nadirs later, one nadir was in 1869, four in 1871, and one in 1872. This suggests that during some cycles, some factor operating over great areas synchronizes fluctuations in all areas, while in other cycles, fluctuations gradually drift apart. This type of observation suggests that the control mechanism is unlikely to be purely endogenous; some external shocks, analogous to war and oil price shocks economists have noted, are both lengthening the wavelength and amplifying the amplitude of oscillation in these furbearer systems. Whatever that factor is, however, it only operates rarely. It also operates globally.

External causal mechanisms

A combination of statistical time series analysis and computer simulation shows how much of the causal mechanism was endogenous, how much was exogenous, and the exact role of each (see Appendix A).

In the second panel of fig. 5-3, we see the simulated trend in lynx fur catches when data for each year are projected using a model along with data from actual catches in the two previous years. The hypothesis being tested is that fluctuations result only from operation of an endogenous density-controlling mechanism. The match to actual data is impressive.

This isn't a very rigorous test of the hypothesis, however. Because the data for each year are computed from actual data for the two previous years, this test procedure would conceal any drifting apart over long periods of the model results and real world data.

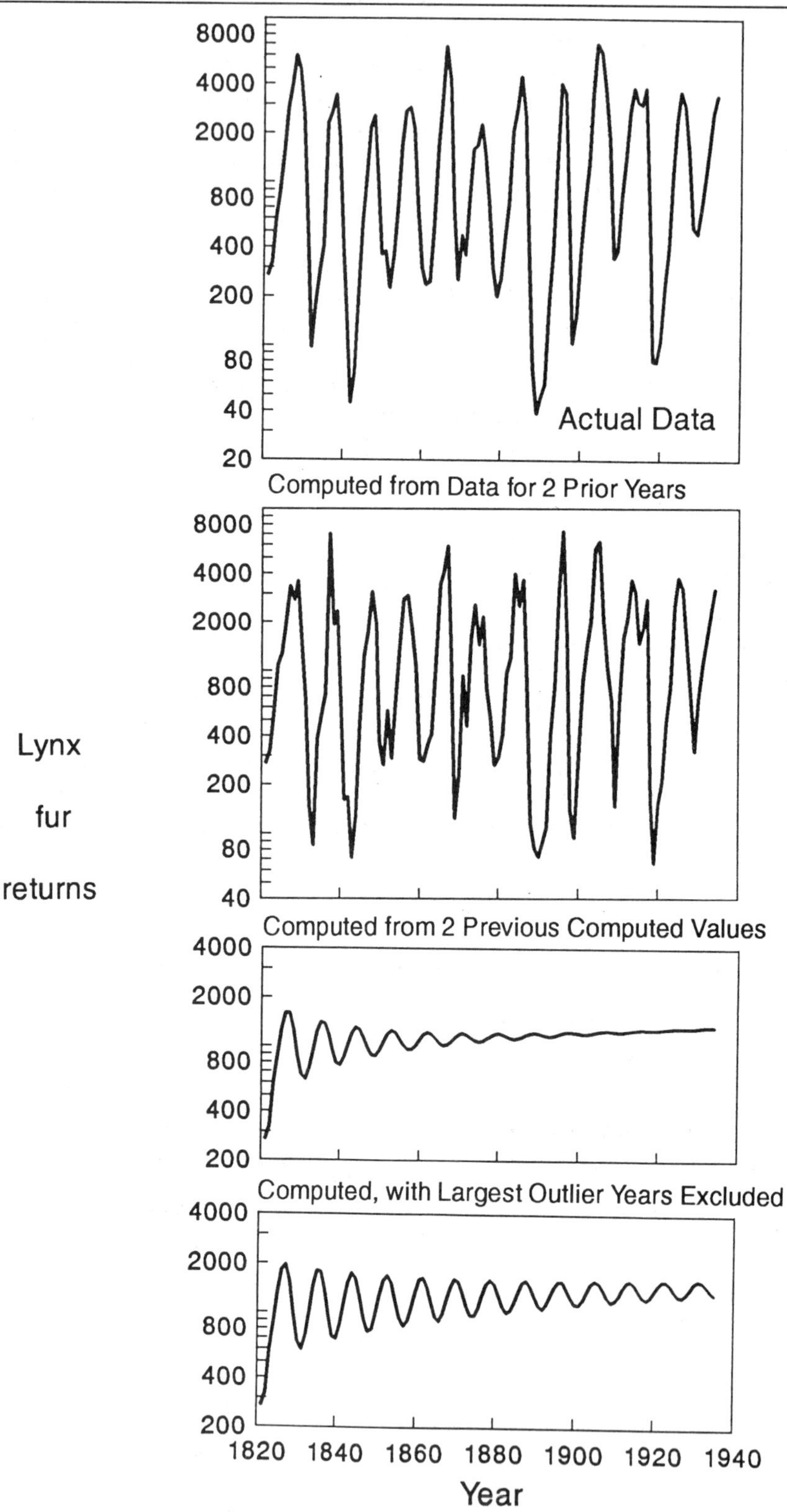

Figure 5-3. The number of lynx fur returns from the Mackenzie River District. Top panel: actual data from Elton and Nicholson (1942).

Second panel: computed from model, with each datum computed from the actual data for the two previous years.

Third panel: simulated sequence of fur returns, with each value after the first two being computed from the two previous computed values—that is, from endogenous values. The fluctuations have become almost totally dampened within 110 years.

Fourth panel: same as for third panel, only the model used to simulate the sequence of fur returns was computed from a data set from which the eight largest outliers had been excluded.

Accordingly, the third panel of fig. 5-3 depicts the results when the first simulated datum for a computer scenario—that for the third year—is computed from the actual data for the first two years. Then the simulated datum for the fourth year is computed from the real world datum for the second year plus the simulated datum for the third year, and so on, with points for the remaining years computed strictly from simulated data points. (Appendix A).

The results are a revelation, typical of those obtained with all biological and social sciences data: under this far more rigorous test of the hypothesis, the endogenous component of the wave-producing mechanism now appears far less important relative to the exogenous component. The amplitude of oscillation is far less than in the real world data, and the fluctuations have almost totally dampened out in 110 years.

Amplitude, constancy of year-to-year variation, and perhaps also wavelength magnitude are strongly reinforced by some occasional exogenous influence.

We have now discovered that the appearance of an entirely self-regulatory mechanism controlling the size of the storage (the number of lynx) and generating the data in the top panel of fig. 5-3 is an illusion. Magnitude of the amplitude, constancy of the year-to-year variation through time and perhaps also the magnitude of the wavelength are being strongly reinforced by some occasional exogenous influence. We hypothesize that the endogenous component of the system control mechanism is being obscured by a random shock mechanism—the counterpart of wars intermittently shocking economic systems.

Very large discrepancies between observed and calculated values are associated with years of large volcanic eruptions.

We can test that hypothesis by examining a table of differences between observed fur returns and those calculated from the model. A provocative pattern appears: very large discrepancies between observed and calculated values are associated with years of large volcanic eruptions. To aid in interpretating years of outlier data, I used a table listing for the period since 1680 those volcanic eruptions that injected very large volumes of extremely fine dust particles into the atmosphere and giving estimates by geophysicists and historical climatologists of the dust veil created by each (Table 10.3, Lamb, 1972).

It has been the conventional wisdom of geophysics since Humphreys (1913) that the greater the dust in the atmosphere from volcanic eruptions, the lower the mean global temperature will be in the next few years. The dust decreases the transparency of the atmosphere to incoming solar radiation that warms the earth's surface.

Table 5-1. Major weather-related events, years of low lynx fur returns, and time lags between them Locations shown are sites of volcanic eruptions that produced the greatest dust veil indices after 1821.

Event	Year	Years of lowest lynx catches	Time lag
Coseguina (Nicaragua)	1835	1842	7
Armagora (South Pacific)	1846	1852	6
Very cold weather	1866–7	1871	4–5
Ghaie (New Ireland, Bismark Archipelago)	1878	(effect slight)	—
Krakatau (Indonesia)	1883	1889	6
Very cold weather	1893	1897	4
Katmai (Alaska—a smaller eruption)	1912	1917	6

There were eight years when lynx fur returns deviated most from those we'd expect if the population dynamics in the vegetation–hare–lynx system were controlled by an internal mechanism. Four of these years were 6–7 years following a volcanic eruption (Table

5-1). Of the remaining four years of data deviating markedly from expected results, fur returns were too low in 1871 and in 1897. The years 1866 and 1867 were two of the three coldest since 1820 for St. Paul, Minnesota; 1893 was also very cold(HS, J-266).

Thus we have a consistent pattern of lynx fur returns being unexpectedly low 4, 5, 6 or 7 years after years of unusually low temperature or light intensity or both. A reasonable explanation is that either condition depresses vegetation growth, lowering availability of food for hares. After a lag, that decreases reproductive rate in adult female hares and survival of their offspring. That, then, decreases availability of young hares, the principal food for lynx. After a further lag that depresses reproductive rate in adult female lynx and then survival of their offspring. After a lag, that decreases the rate of lynx catches by fur trappers. The sum of these various lags accounts for the delay of 4 to 7 years from dates of unusually low light intensity or temperature to years of low lynx fur catches.

These observations suggest a hypothesis: the reason for the discrepancy between the first and third panels of fig. 5-3 is that random shocks from volcanic eruptions obscure the strength of the underlying endogenous cycle-generating mechanism. To test that hypothesis, the parameters in the forecasting model (Appendix A) were reestimated with the data sets for the eight outlier years removed from the computation. The simulation of fur returns resulting from using these new parameters is in the fourth panel of fig. 5-3.

Clearly, random shocks do veil or mask the cycle-generating strength of mechanisms that are purely endogenous to the cycling system. When we remove years of unusually extreme variation from the trend are removed from the data, the underlying cycle shows clearly. The fluctuating pattern in the fourth panel has larger amplitude than that in the third panel, and it would take about twice as long to dampen completely.

Random shocks mask the cycle-generating strength of mechanisms that are purely endogenous to the system.

Conclusions about random shocks

By comparing the first and fourth panels in fig. 5-3, we can gain more insight into the role of random shocks in determining the pattern of fluctuation in biological or socio-political-economic systems. The random shocks elongate the wavelength slightly: there are 12 nadirs and zeniths in the top panel, 14 nadirs and 13 zeniths in the bottom panel (that is, shorter wavelengths with no random shocks). The two deepest nadirs in the top panel occurred in 1842, 6 years after Coseguina, and in 1889, six years after Krakatau, two of the three largest volcanic eruptions in the 110 years covered by the data set.

According to the simulated time series, lynx returns should have been increasing in 1842, and the next zenith should have been reached by 1844. In the actual data set, lynx returns decreased from 1841 to 1842, and the next zenith was not reached until 1848.

Summary: cycle-generating mechanisms

The volcano-vegetation-hare-lynx system has been discussed at this length because it is a model for processes that occur throughout biological and social systems. Table 5-2 compares events in furbearer cycles with those in economic cycles

Table 5-2. Comparison of cycle generating mechanisms in a biological and economic system

	Exogenous shocks	Ultimate resource	Resource consumer	System output
Northern furbearer system	cold weather; low light	vegetation	snowshoe hares	lynx fur pelts
Industrial economies	fuel price shocks (e.g., from wars)	fossil fuel reserves	production industries	retail sales/ prices

In economic systems, the exogenous shocks that intermittently reenergize the oscillating system—increasing wavelength and amplitude of oscillations—come not from volcanoes, but the extraordinary fuel price shocks resulting from wars or other incidents creating sudden fuel shortages, as with crude oil between 1979 and 1982.

Note there are differences in detail between the systems:

- The ultimate resources for advanced human societies as they are presently organized are fossil fuels, not vegetation.
- The scale of the systems components utilizing ultimate resources are determined by investment in resource production industries, not prey population sizes.
- The system output is retail sales and prices for retail goods, not lynx fur pelts.

There are striking similarities, however. In both cases:

- Fluctuation occurs about a long-term trend line for which the pattern of change through time is determined by the status of a storage: critical limiting nutrients (or fossil energy reserves).
- There is a self-regulatory control mechanism: the supply-demand-price system in social systems and the effects of population density on resource availability in biological systems.
- Amplitude and wavelength are increased by random shocks that prevent dampening of the oscillation.

In biological systems, information is communicated directly by resource availability and in socio-economic systems, information is communicated by price, which measures resource availability.

Developing forecasting models

Statistical analysis and simulation modeling can be combined to analyze fluctuations in systems at any level of complexity, by adding various refinements and complications as more and more complex phenomena and systems are considered.

① The first step is always to **eliminate the effect of the long-term trend line**. This is done by identifying a fundamental force regulating the long-term trend line for the variable of interest. Then we figure out the equation and find the parameters for the relationship expressing the impact of the force on the system. If we don't know the identity of the force or don't have a complete set of measurements for the period for which we have system measurements, we use year number or month number as a surrogate measure of the force for all years or months (so you don't have to "splice" two different time series—one for energy and one for time).

Often, in systems where growth has occurred over decades or centuries, measurements of the system will range very widely. In such cases, we transform the measurements to logarithms before analysis, so that the larger measurements don't swamp the variation in the smaller ones.

② The second step is to **account for fluctuations about the trend in terms of endogenous or exogenous regulatory mechanisms** or a combination of both. In all cases, the appropriate measures of the controlling variables will be from

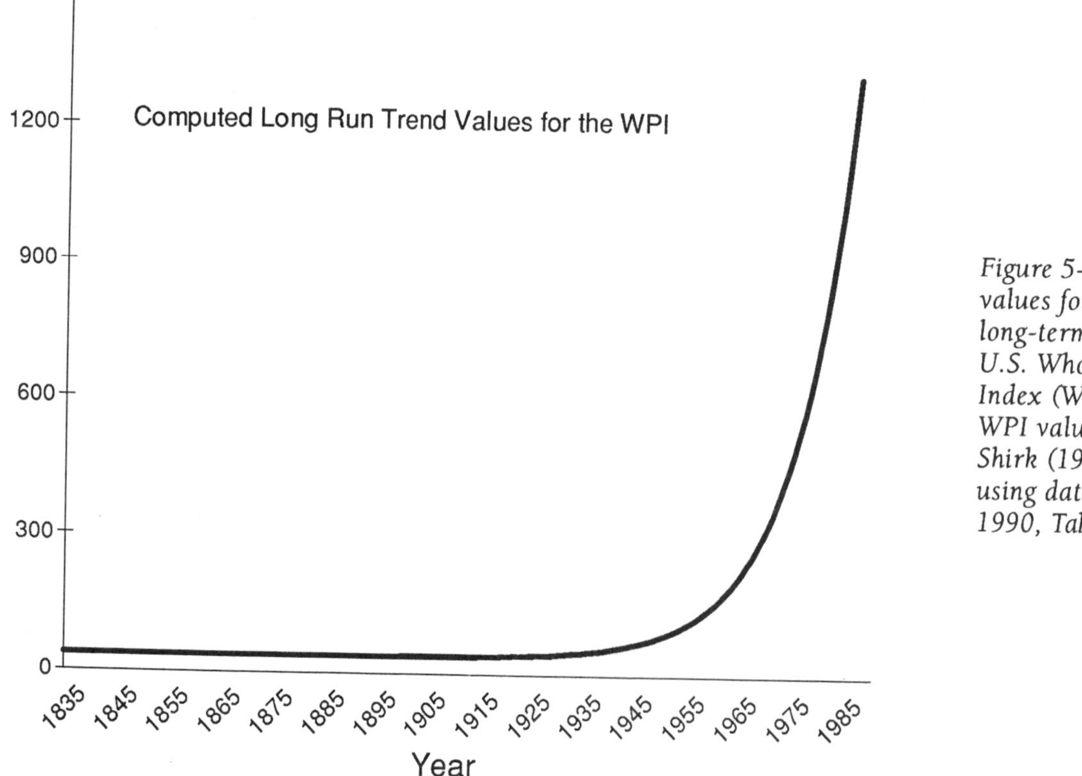

Figure 5-4. Computed values for the long-term trend in the U.S. Wholesale Price Index (WPI). Raw WPI values were from Shirk (1985), updated using data in SA 1990, Table 772.

A more complex example: The U.S. Wholesale Price Index

I use a consistent strategy in this book to develop forecasting models for socioeconomic systems. All these models share a basic structure. The value of any variable, **V**, in year **Y** is expressed as the product of a number of terms. The first of these terms expresses the value of **V** as given by the long run trend line for **V**, **TREND(Y).** This is a mathematical expression describing the effect of the fundamental system driver governing **TREND**. In most cases, **TREND** is governed by the status of fossil fuel reserves in a country. That status is measured by the cumulative consumption of domestic fossil fuel reserves, for each year since consumption began, to and including the present year. Where we need to compute **TREND** values far back in time, very old, highly accurate statistics are not available for fossil fuel consumption, so year number is used as a surrogate variable for the status of fossil fuel reserves.

Departures about that trend are expressed as **MULTIPLIERS**, which are proportions or multiples of the value given by the **TREND** for each year. To illustrate, if the **TREND** value for 1960 is 120, a **MULTIPLIER** of 1.5 means that the expected value is 180. A **MULTIPLIER** of .5 means that the expected value is 60. The **MULTIPLIERS**, in turn are mathematical expressions describing the impact of one or more independent variables that produced deviations about **TREND** for the variable of interest.

What we observe about a trend line is ***deviations***. However, we do not have any way of knowing which factor or group of factors have have caused a deviation until we have done a statistical analysis. This analysis attempts to account for the magnitude of deviations about a long run trend in terms of one or more **MULTIPLIERS**, each of which is caused by one or more fundamental system drivers (independent variables to statisticians). Thus the multipliers are computed, not observed quantities. The difficulty in relating multipliers to deviations is particularly problematical when there are two or more multipliers causing deviations. This complication absolutely necessitates nonlinear regression analysis, a type of statistical analysis used on nonlinear equations.

There may be several multipliers. The forces producing fluctuations about **TREND** for any variable are split into groups on the basis of the time delay from the time the force operated until the time its effect shows up. Each multiplier expresses the effect of one such group of forces. To illustrate for the wholesale price index (WPI), we need separate multiplier terms to express the effect of forces that produce fluctuations about the trend in WPI, about 15 years later, and those that produce deviations about 35 years later. The typical form for a computer model to forecast the value of **V** in year **Y** therefore is

V(Y) =[TREND(Y)]
[MULTIPLIER 1(Y)]
[MULTIPLIER 2(Y)]
[MULTIPLIER 3(Y)],
etc.

The quantities in square brackets are all multiplied by each other to yield the forecast value of the variable in year **Y**.

Figure 5.4 gives the value of **TREND** for the U.S. WPI since 1833. There was no growth in **TREND** until about 1915; since then it has been increasing at an ever-increasing rate. The underlying trend for the WPI is clearly hyperinflationary, when the obscuring influence of wavelike oscillations about the trend is removed.

Both actual historical values of WPI and the values computed from the forecasting model were divided by **TREND** to expose the long run pattern of fluctuations about the trend. The light line in Figure 5.5 depicts the actual pattern of fluctuations; the heavy line depicts the pattern of fluctuations computed from the forecasting model. The curve is the product of the computed multiplier terms in the forecasting model. This product is typically in the range .7–1.3. The startling feature of this graph is that the computed WPI values for each year were calculated from data 10 to 40 years prior to that year. Evidently, a rather clear picture of the long run future is available far in advance of actual events. Major wars typically occur near the peak of an inflationary cycle following a depression. Another curious feature is common to major wars: they follow a period when actual prices fell far below prices as projected from the model. The wavelike oscillations about the long run trend have taken an unprecedented steep drop below the trend since about 1950. This has worked against widespread recognition of the fact that we are in a hyperinflationary period. It is also noteworthy in the actual data (light line) that depressions occurred around 1846 and 1896 (50 years apart), and 1932 (36 years from the last depression). The wavelength is shortening, and this provided a major clue as to the nature of the forces controlling the economy. At least two different mechanisms have been controlling economic waves for the last two centuries, and one with a shorter wavelength has come to replace one with a longer wavelength.

one or more time steps in the past. (Remember, there would be no departures from the trend if control mechanisms operated instantaneously.) The variables that best account for present departures may not be measures of the controlling variable or variables for a particular time step in the past, but may be a sum or some function of the values for a sequence of past time steps. In general, models accounting for fluctuations in systems variables about their trends will be developed in terms of past fluctuations of regulatory variables about their trends.

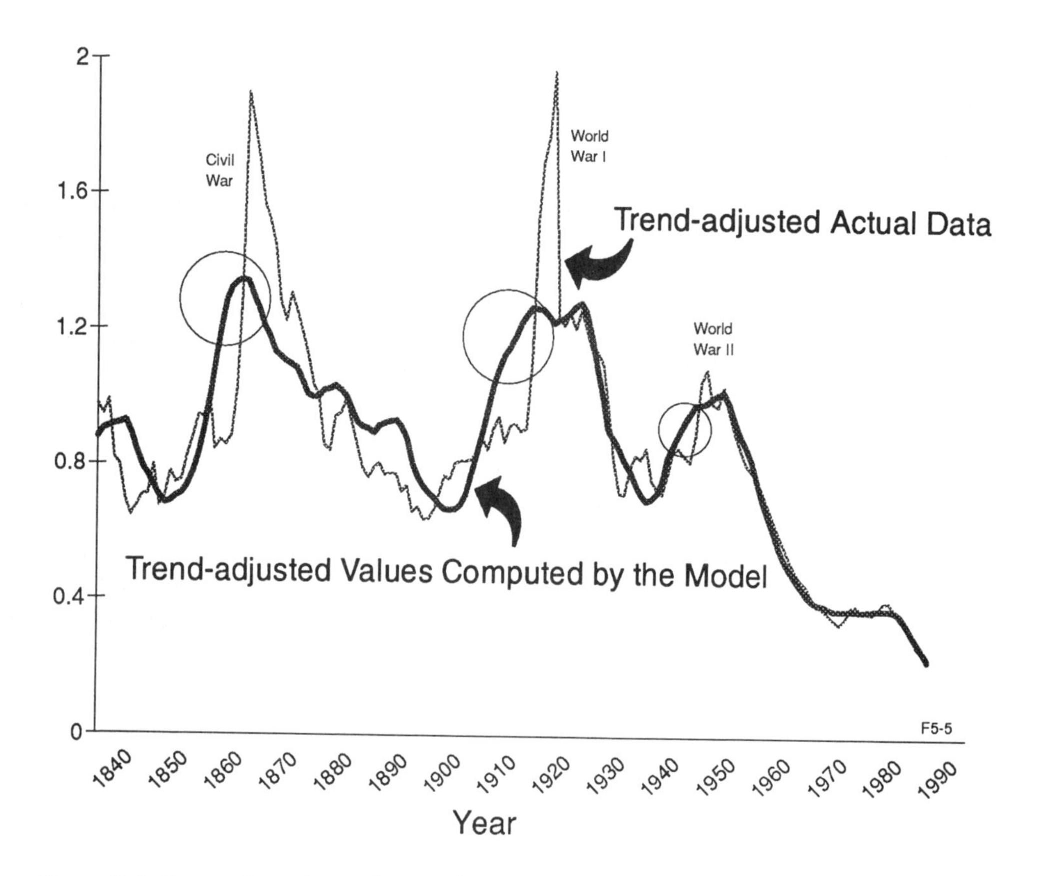

Figure 5-5. Comparison of actual WPI values with those computed from the model. Both series have been divided by the computed values for the long-term trend in WPI in fig. 5-4 to reveal the match between actual and calculated patterns of fluctuations around the trend. Circled areas indicate atypical behavior of the system due to wars (see text). (See figs. 4-16 and 4-17 if you need refreshing as to why the series is divided by the values for the trend.)

How useful is this model as a forecasting tool?

We answer that by seeing how close the correspondence is between model and reality. The computer model accounts for 98.83 per cent of the year-to-year variability in WPI from 1833, inclusive, to 1988 (see side bar and fig. 5-5). Why not 100.000 per cent? Most of the unaccounted-for variation is due to 6 years in the Civil War period (1864–1869), and 4 years in the World War I period (1917–1920) when prices increase to an extent not explained by the model. Putting it differently, price behavior in those 10 years was atypical of the socio-economic system in the remaining years. When those years are excluded from the data set, the model accounts for 99.315 per cent of the year-to-year variation in the WPI.

Also, correspondence between model and reality improves through time. If we look at only 1921 and the years since, the model accounts for 99.5 per cent of year-to-year variation. Remember, this is using a forecasting model that draws only on data from 10 or more years before the fact.

Volcanic eruptions deal random shocks to the economic system as well as to the hare-lynx ecosystem. Ejecting masses of fine material into the upper atmosphere blocks incoming sunlight, decreases crop production, and thus raises food prices. That phenomenon had particularly striking effects between 1816 and 1820 and between 1837 and 1839. The lack of major volcanic eruptions since 1921 is one reason for the very close agreement between model and reality in that period.

The model would not call market turns within a year, but it would suffice for planning major capital investments or "buy and hold" stock or bond purchase strategy, rather than a rapid turn-over trading strategy.

Of more importance for investors and planners is the utility of this model in calling market turns a decade in advance. The depression of the 1840s had a rather flat bottom, from 1842 to 1849; the model puts the exact nadir at 1849. The year of peak prices in the Civil War period was 1864; the model put it at 1863. The exact bottom year for prices in the 1890s was 1896; the model put it at 1901. The peak year for prices in World War I was 1920; the model put it at 1925. In terms of deviations about the trend, two years were almost equally low bottoms: 1933 and 1940; the model put the actual bottom at 1937. The next peak above the trend line was 1948; the model put it at 1951. The next clear bottom was in 1972; the model put it at 1971 or 1974. The next peak was 1981 for reality, 1980 for the model.

The model would be no use for calling market turns within a year, but it would suffice for planning major capital investments or fundamental analysis for a "buy and hold" stock or bond purchase strategy, rather than a rapid turn-over trading strategy.

The forecasting model that generated the heavy line in fig. 5-5 uses two multiplier terms calculated from actual data. These two multipliers (a birth rate–labor market mechanism and a mechanism for allocating capital allocation among sectors) are shown in fig. 5-6.

Nature of mechanisms producing fluctuations

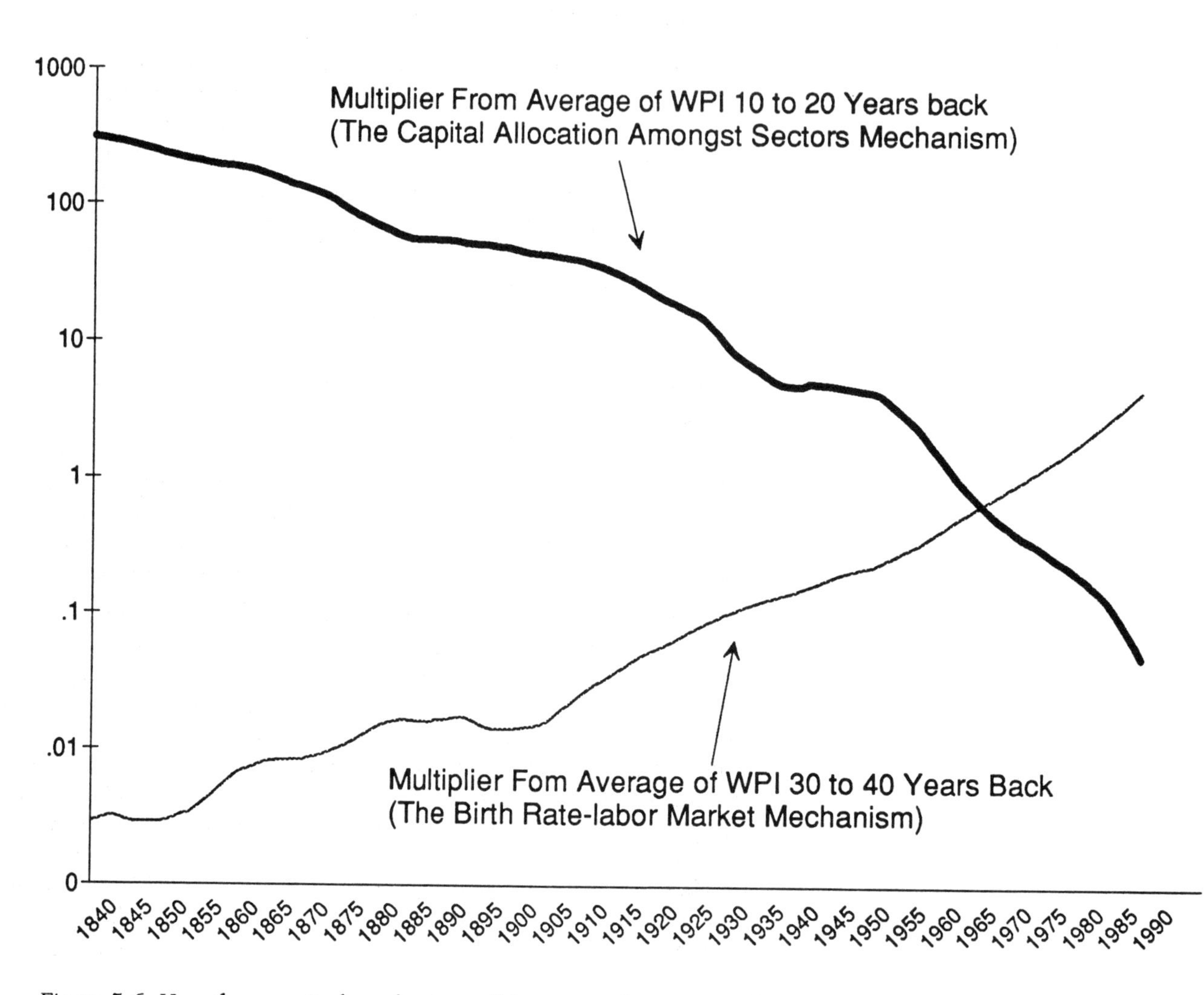

Figure 5-6. How the magnitude and nature of the two mechanisms regulating fluctuations of WPI values about their trends change as society develops. Note that after 1965 the demographic mechanism (birth rate/labor market) has a greater effect than the capital allocation mechanism—a fundamental turning point in the evolution of our society.

① The birth rate–labor market mechanism

The birth rate–labor market mechanism expresses **the effect on present WPI of the actual average WPI values 30–40 years back.** This mechanism operates through the effect of prices on the dynamics of the labor market about 30 to 40 years later. There are two different causal pathways through which this effect moves.

- In the first, the general economic environment affects the sense of prosperity of young couples and hence the number of children they decide to have. High prices produce high birth rates; low prices produce low birth rates. High birth rates in a particular year mean that about 34 years later, there will be an unusually large number of 34-year-olds competing for jobs. This depresses average wages at what should be a particularly productive period of life, and wages regulate prices. (Depressed wages mean depressed prices relative to those we would otherwise expect, and elevated wages mean elevated prices.)

- The second mechanism involves the rate of migration of laborers from primary sectors of the economy, (producing basic industrial commodities such as wheat, corn, lumber, fish, iron, coal and steel) to secondary and tertiary sectors. When prices are low, they are most depressed in these primary sectors. This increases the subsequent rate of outmigration of young men. About 35 years later when their fathers retire, there are no sons to replace them in the labor force producing basic commodities. The result is a decrease in the labor force and a decrease in supply relative to demand, producing an increase in prices.

For most of U.S. history, these mechanisms operating through the labor market have tended to affect prices relative to their long-term trend, 30-40 years later. The thin line in fig. 5-6 depicts the long-term trend in the value of this multiplier. Only since about 1975 has this mechanism had much effect in raising prices.

Note that the preceding discussion was not a hypothesis; it described historical fact. Each step in the argument is supported by all available data. For example, prior to this century, economic boom times have raised birth rates, producing a surplus supply of 29–39-year-old laborers 30–40 years later, which then suppressed wages and hence prices. Series A126 and A127 can be added to give the U.S. male population 30-39 each census year. From this we can compute the ratio of the male population 30–39 in a census year to the corresponding number 10 years back. That ratio was only 1.15 in 1870 (stimulating the economy), had risen to 1.37 by 1890, which helped produce the depression of the 1890s, had dropped to 1.23 by 1900 and was 1.27 in 1910, ensuring the relatively good times of 1900 to 1914.

② We turn now to the capital allocation mechanism. The causal pathway depicted by the heavy line in fig. 5-6 is the long-term trend in the value of the multiplier for capital allocation—**based on the average of the actual WPI 10–20 years back.** This multiplier raised prices above their long-term trend through most of history and only depressed them in the 1970s and 1980s.

Table 5-3. Fuel and food WPI peaks and pits. Notice 1) that the fuel index fluctuates more widely than the food index—characteristic of a system driver; 2) the fuel index is higher than the food index just after wars, which use up a lot of fuel and cause bottlenecks. (Wholesale prices for fuels and foods are given as proportions or multiples of the corresponding WPI for the highest or lowest prices in the preceding economic long wave.)

Year	Relevant historical event	Position on economic long wave	Fuels WPI	Food WPI
1982	OPEC price increases	top	6.53	2.24
1932	Great Depression	bottom	.41	.44
1920	World War I	top	4.83	3.12
1896	Depression	bottom	.30	.36
1864	Civil War	top	2.67	2.12
1843	Depression	bottom	.166	.385
1814	War of 1812	top	5.53	1.99

This mechanism operates through the effect of the WPI on patterns of capital allocation in society. Whenever the composite WPI for all commodities was extremely high, the prices of fuels was even higher than other components of the composite WPI, such as food. Whenever the composite WPI was extremely low, fuel prices were even more depressed than prices for other commodities (Table 5-3). In other words, fuel prices were the driver forcing wide-amplitude swings of the composite WPI about its long-term trend.

Fuel price explosions, typically caused by a war, then cause a massive diversion of capital away from other sectors, such as manufacturing, towards investment in discovery, production, transportation and refining of fuel. In the 19th century, the average effect of this mechanism has been to produce a subsequent increase in the rate of growth in prices, about 10 to 20 years later. (This causal pathway will be discussed thoroughly in Chapter 7.)

Fig. 5-6 shows clearly how control over the timing of major societal perturbations has shifted through history from the mechanism with the 30–40 year delay (thin line), to that with the 10–20 year delay (thick line). The thin line has very pronounced downward dips coincident with the depressions of 1843–1849 and 1893–1900, but not for the depression of the 1930s. The thick line lacks the distinct downward dips for the two depressions of the nineteenth century, but has a very distinct downward dip for the depression of the 1930s. Putting this differently, the depressions of the 1840s and 1890s were produced by a mechanism with a 30–40 year time delay, whereas the depression of the 1930s was produced by a mechanism with a 10–20 year time delay.

Depressions of the 1840s and 1890s were produced by a mechanism with a 30–40 year time delay, whereas the depression of the 1930s was produced by a mechanism with a 10–20 year time delay.

The meaning of this switch in system control mechanism

Early in the Industrial Revolution, the 30–40 year mechanism operating through prices, then birth rates, and then the labor force market acted to restrict economic growth rates. Labor was typically superabundant; shortage of capital and energy limited economic growth. Energy prices rose, which stimulated investment in energy production that removed a bottleneck to economic growth (see also Chapter 7). Excess labor would mean depressed prices about 35 years later.

More recently, the economy is not so much supply-limited as demand-driven, and excess population is responded to by increasing the rate of increase in the money supply, to stimulate demand. We are super-saturated with energy, even though we rapidly approach a worldwide geological shortage of petroleum. A worldwide energy glut, which has dropped energy prices, stems from massive overinvestment in energy production infrastructure in response to energy price surges in 1973–82.

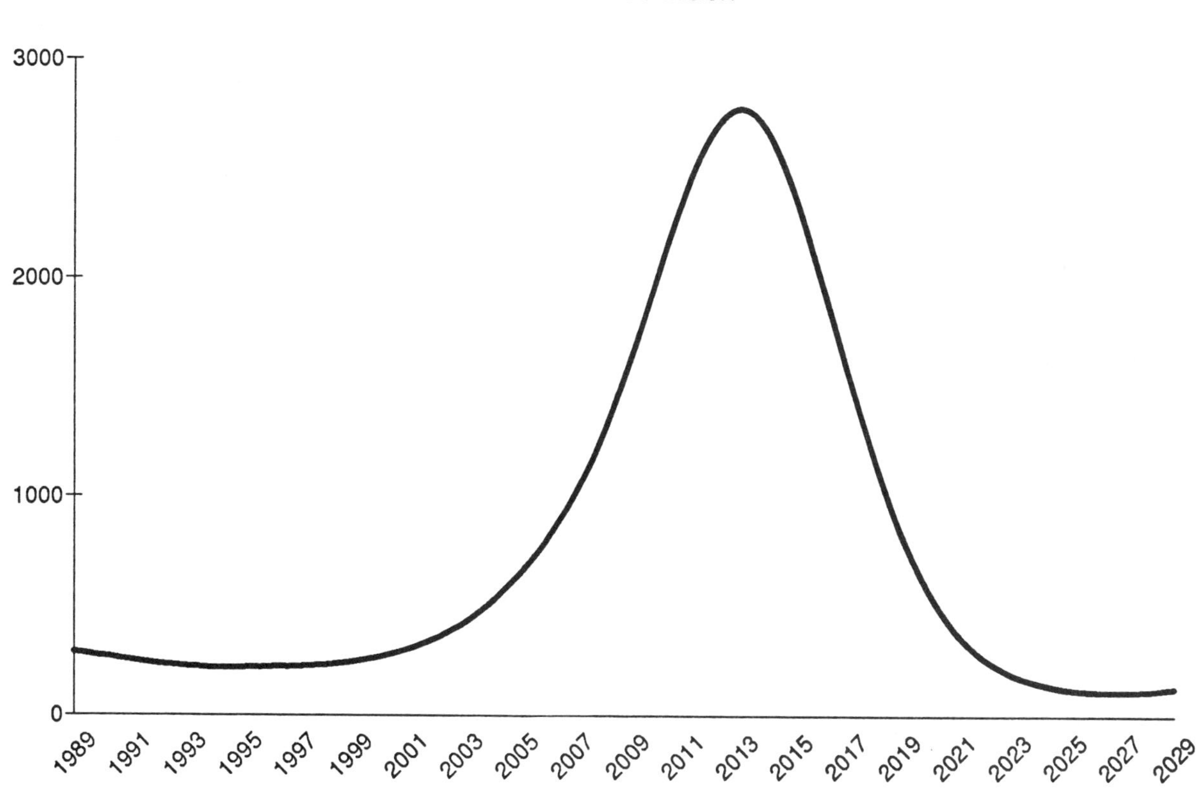

Figure 5-7. Future Wholesale Price Index (WPI) values projected by computer simulation model. 1967 WPI = 100.0.

Applying the model

The model whose fit to past data was depicted in fig. 5-5 can also be used to project the future, as in fig. 5-7. This projection warns of a gradually deepening economic crisis that does not bottom out until 1995. Then it projects a huge hyperinflationary price explosion that worsens to about 2013, then gives way to economic collapse to about 2027, after which this wide-amplitude oscillation is repeated. It is important to note that such predictions assume that government and corporate decision-making will continue as at present, with no highly realistic forecasting or planning and continuing the tendency to over-shoot or undershoot realistic investment targets.

If the forecasting and planning activities were to become more realistic, these wide-amplitude excursions could be avoided. Under the present system of no realistic forecasting or planning, liquid fossil fuel prices could stay depressed until shortly before they run out, worldwide.

Conclusion

Chapters 4 and 5 have outlined a procedure for determining long-term trends, then adjusting variables to remove the effect of the trends, and identifying the mechanisms that produce fluctuations in the resulting trend-adjusted system variables. This procedure holds promise as a first step in developing computer forecasting models of dynamic systems. In subsequent chapters we begin from that starting point and go on to explore the extensions of this method required when we consider progressively more complex systems.

Chapter 6

Fluctuations in Human Populations

This chapter brings together all the main themes of the book and shows how forecasting models can be developed by splitting variation through time into three components:

- Long-term trends,
- Waves about those trends, and
- High-frequency fluctuations about the waves.

It also demonstrates that it is literally impossible to develop accurate models unless we make that separation.

Building on what we showed in Chapter 5, demographic variables in particular

- Follow long-term trends that represent transformation of social systems as national storages are depleted (forests and fossil fuels) and other storages are increased (capital investment in high technology.)
- Wavelike oscillations about those trajectories reflect self-regulation of storages (numbers of people in particular age groups).
- High-speed fluctuations are superimposed on those two patterns by wars.

Causal pathways flow toward demographic variables from resource, political, and economic variables.

Historical pattern of American birth rates

The historical pattern of fluctuation in American women's birth rates is a particularly clear example demonstrating the logic underlying my mode of analysis. The following discussion takes us through this example step by step.

Accounting for long-range trend

Fig. 6-1, panel 1 plots the observed birth rate in American women. Note the general decline. We use the computer model to generate an equation for the long-range trend (panel 3, and see explanation accompanying the figure).

Figure 6-1. Why it is necessary to separate out variables that produce change by the wavelength of the fluctuations they generate.

1: Birth rates for American women 15–44 years old, **raw data** (B-8).

1. Raw Data: Observed Birth Rates

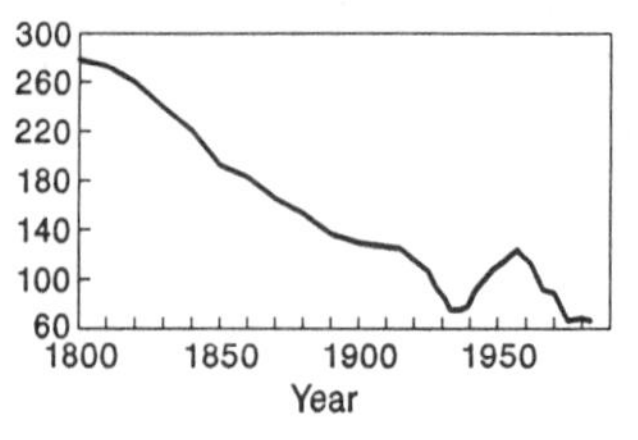

2: Here we **plot birth rates against average birth rates 16–24 years earlier**. From the hypothesis, we would expect to find that when we plot birth rates for each year against the average of birth rates 16–24 years ago, we obtain a curve from the upper left to the lower right corner of the graph. In fact, we get the opposite, a rising curve. The **long-term trend has completely obscured the effect of the force producing fluctuations** about it.

2. Preliminary Test of Hypothesis

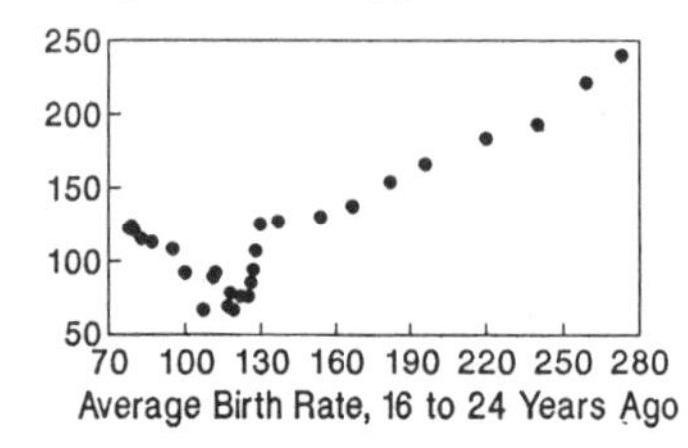

3: To remove this trend effect, we **obtain and plot an equation to describe the long-term trend for birth rates** (Appendix A).

3. Computed Long-term Trend

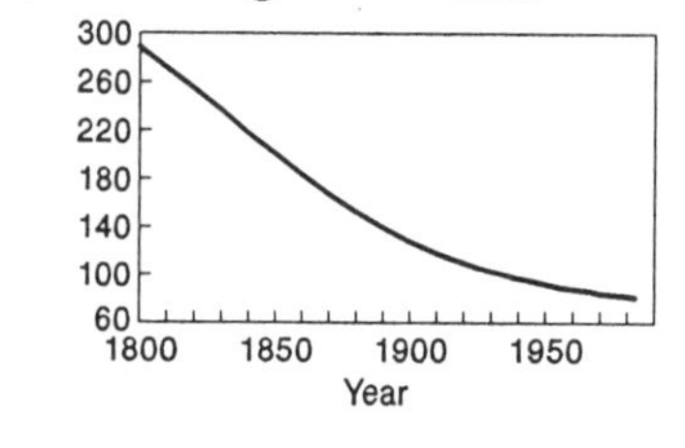

4: Now we **divide the birth rate for each year by the birth rate expected from the long-term trend**. The resulting ratios are then plotted here against year number, **to ensure that there is no trend remaining in the ratios**. We should have **fluctuations about an imaginary flat line** parallel to the x-axis. If we have, this **means the equation was a realistic descriptor of the long-term trend** in birth rates.

4. Trend-adjusted Birth Rate

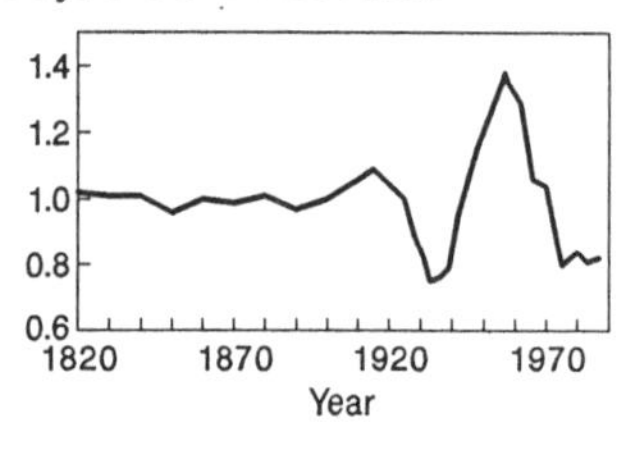

5: Now we're ready to do what we started out to do—**test the hypothesis that wavelike fluctuations in birth rates about their trend are caused by birth rates 16–24 years ago**. Here we plot trend-adjusted birth rates for each year against trend-adjusted average birth rates 16–24 years ago. **Now we have the expected downward-sloping relationship**. There is evidently a marked average tendency for high birth rates about 20 years ago to result in low birth rates a generation later, and conversely, for low birth rates to result in high rates about 20 years later. We spot two complications: a cluster of points in the bottom center of the graph and considerable scatter about the trend line.

5. Test of Hypothesis

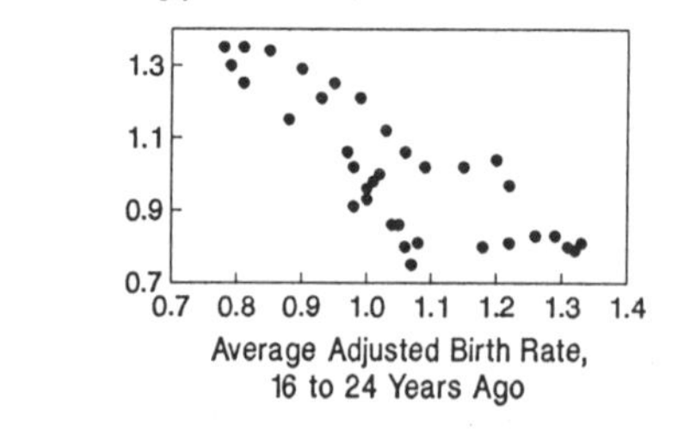

6: We can seek explanations by plotting the data points, labelled by year number. Here we plot sample points, including outliers. Through most of U.S. history, birth rates departed very little from the long-term trend line. (Technical jargon for points around the trend is "global equilibrium region.") There is a small such region indicated by the circle; **the system still oscillates about that set-point**, as illustrated by the point for 1943.

6. Sample Trend-adjusted Years Including Outliers

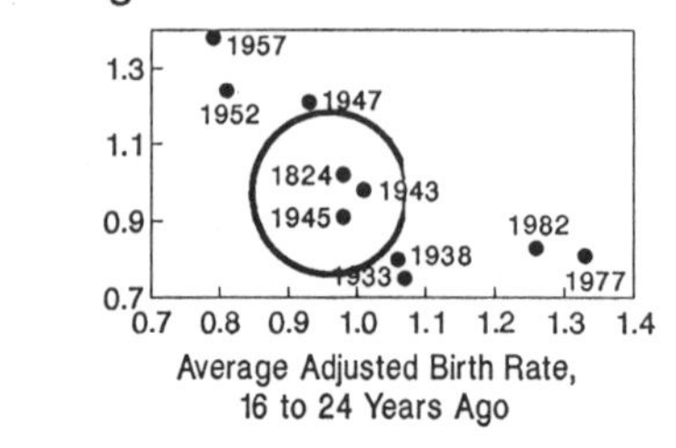

Identifying wave-like oscillations

In the last few decades, birth rate in each year seems to be regulated by average birth rates 16–24 years ago, higher birth rates resulting in lower birth rates 16–24 years later. A plausible hypothesis accounts for this correlation. Low birth rates occur because 16–24 years ago a large number of children were born, and their survivors were too numerous to be absorbed by the labor market when they were old enough to seek permanent employment for the first time. Therefore, these 20-year olds had an unusually high unemployment rate and poor long-range economic prospects. Therefore they had low birth rates. In the opposite situation, unusually low birth rates produce high birth rates 16–24 years later. (See fig. 6-1, panels 1–4.)

Identifying high frequency fluctuations

In the 1930s, however, birth rates were shoved violently downward below their trend line. This happened to many system variables, and it reminds us of the effect of volcanic eruptions on furbearers. As with the furbearers, this initiated an increase in the amplitude of oscillation of birth rates, to six times greater than it had been previously.

The cluster of data points at the bottom center of panel 6 (for years 1933–1938) represent the state of the system when birth rates were shoved far below the trend line. This happened in part because of earlier high birth rates about 1915, but mostly because of a huge perturbation external to the birth rate subsystem—the Great Depression. That functioned like a volcanic eruption in nature and initiated the rather violent, wavelike oscillation in birth rates that has been operating ever since—without further stimulation by the economic system. If it seems circular to you that the Depression can be both an external shock causing high frequency fluctuation and is itself a result of endogenous high birth rates earlier, you are exactly right. A circular causal feedback loop is in operation.

Another source of external shock is a war. In the typical sequence, birth rates are elevated the year after large numbers of servicemen go abroad, are depressed while they are away, surge in the two years after they return. Panel 6, fig. 6-1, shows birth rates far below the expected line in 1945, a year after many men had been fighting abroad, and high above it in 1947, more than nine months after they had returned.

Conclusions

This example illustrates the fundamental nature of change through time in all subsystems in modern societies. In this case, a higher technological level of society was achieved at the expense of depleting a storage—domestic coal, gas, and crude oil reserves. (Chapter 4 proved that depletion of energy storages caused various trend lines to increase; logically enough, more energy use per year results in greater energy intensity in a number of areas, including labor costs.) Because of its greater use of energy per unit of labor, high technology raises labor costs and so reduces demand for labor. This has produced a gradually decline in the value to a family of one extra child compared with the added cost of raising that child; the result has been a drop in birth rates.

This point becomes clear if we consider an example. U.S. farming shifted from labor-intensive to energy-intensive over the last century, so there has been a decrease in the need for farmers to have large numbers of children. Thus, the long-term trend line for birth rates is ultimately controlled by the status of a nation's fossil fuel reserves.

Two subsystems—demographics and the economy—are closely coupled in this example. Endogenous to these subsystems are two self-dampening mechanisms. One with a time lag of about 20 years produces waves, and one with a lag of about two years produces a surge in births after a birth deficit caused by a foreign war or some other perturbation. Either of these self-dampening mechanisms would produce cycles of gradually declining amplitude, as we saw with the lynx or hares. Just as in furbearer cycles, amplitude and wavelength will be maintained indefinitely so long as there are sporadic shocks that re-energize the cycle-generating mechanism.

Fitting lines to data points

A "fitted" equation refers to the statistical procedure called regression analysis. An equation to describe the trend in a data series is obtained by computing the parameter values that minimize scatter of the actual data points about a computed trend line and equation.

Developing a forecasting model for American birth rates

Our starting point is actual data points for the U.S. live birth rate (a flow) per 1000 women aged 15–44 (a storage regulating that flow). The dots in fig. 6-2 depict these raw data, and the line represents an equation fitted to the data (Appendix A). The model will forecast year-to-year variation in birth rates by dealing separately with the variation we've identified due to the long-term trend and that due to the wavelike oscillation around the trend.

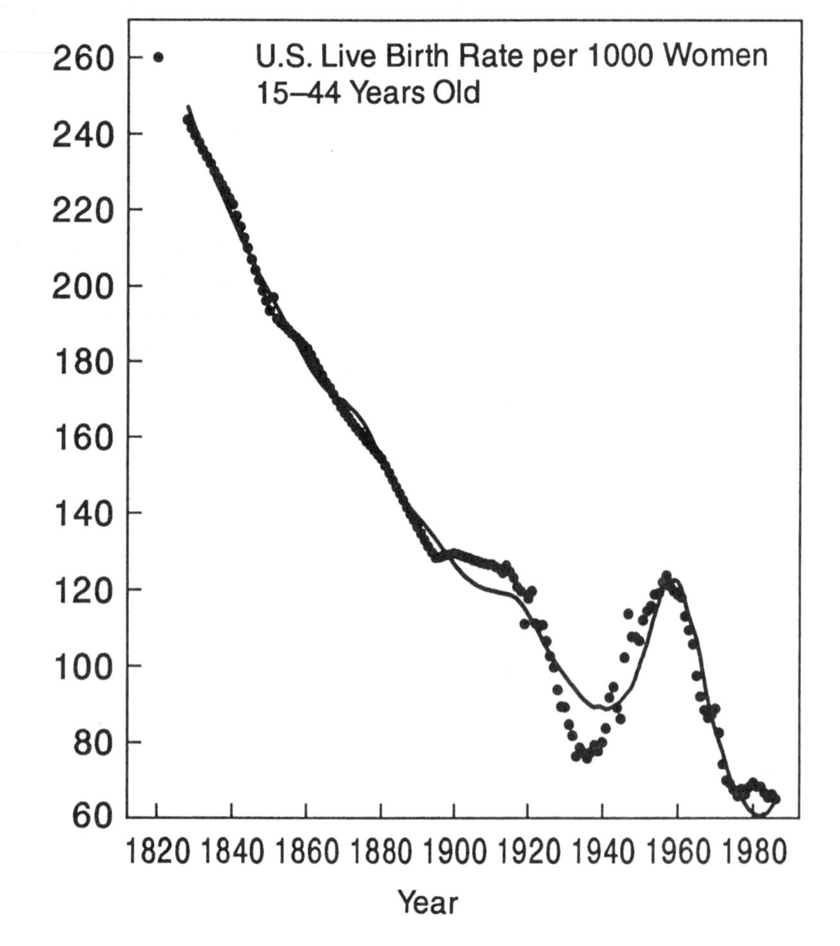

Figure 6-2. U.S. live birth rates (dots) (taken from B9 up to 1909; after, B8). The line is computed from the fitted equation in Appendix A.

Finding the birth-rate mulitplier

In the final version of the model, the variable used to forecast wavelike oscillations about the trend was the average birth rate over the period 20–28 years ago. The magnitude of the departure from the trend line is called the *birth-rate multiplier* and is expressed as a number between 1 and 7.

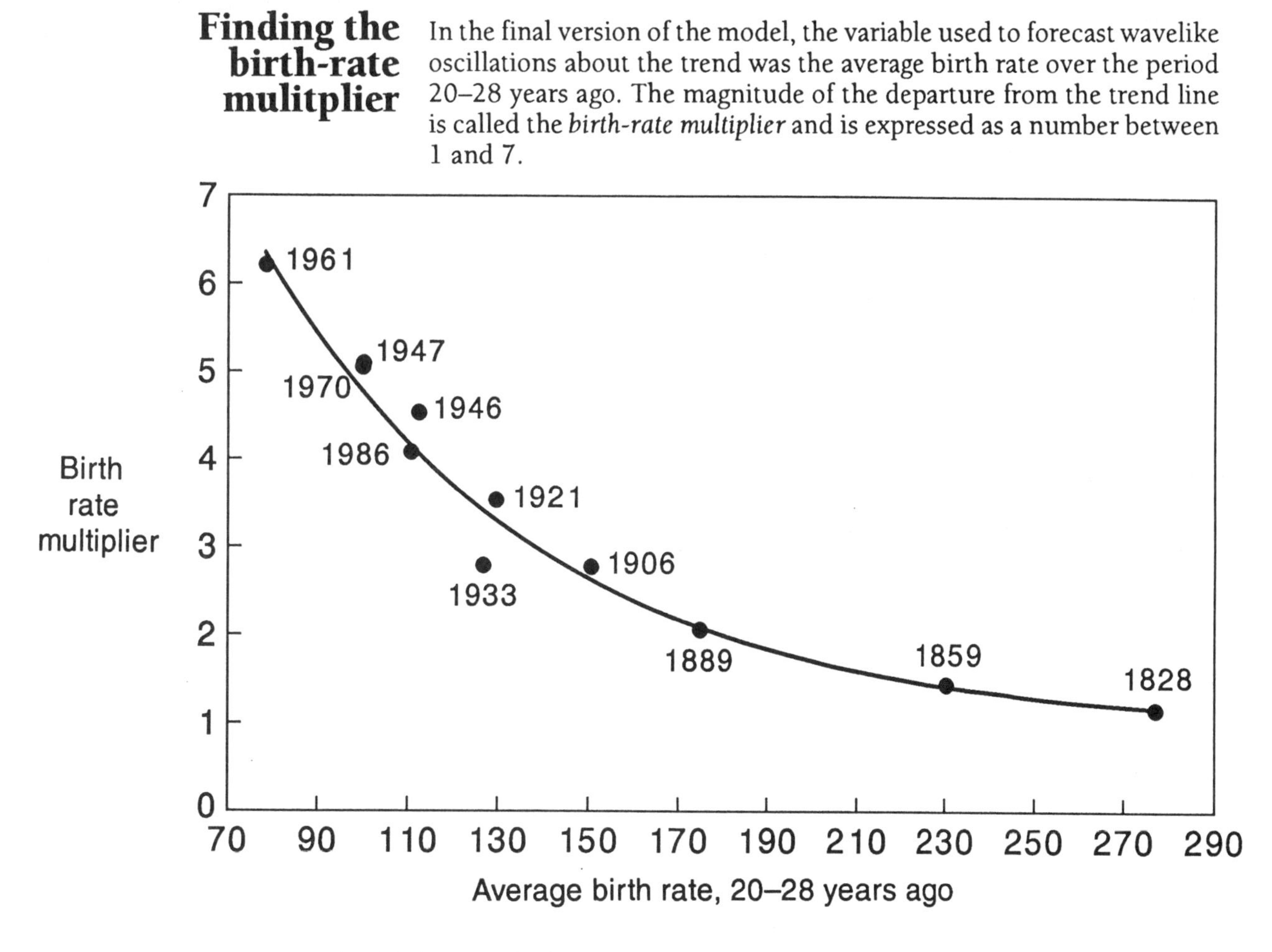

Figure 6-3. Birth rate multiplier as a function of birth rates 20–28 years earlier. The multiplier was computed from the equation in Appendix A.

Fig. 6-3 illustrates how perturbations associated with wars account for most of the residual variation (high-frequency oscillations). The curve is the fitted multiplier term, which was computed from past birth rates. Points above the curve—1946–47 and 1921—indicate higher birth rates following the ends of wars. Birth rates in Depression year 1933, however, are below the fitted multiplier term.

The fitted multiplier term in fig. 6-3 provides a good description over a very wide range of years: example, points plotted for 1961, 1986, 1906, 1889, 1859 and 1828 fit closely to the line.

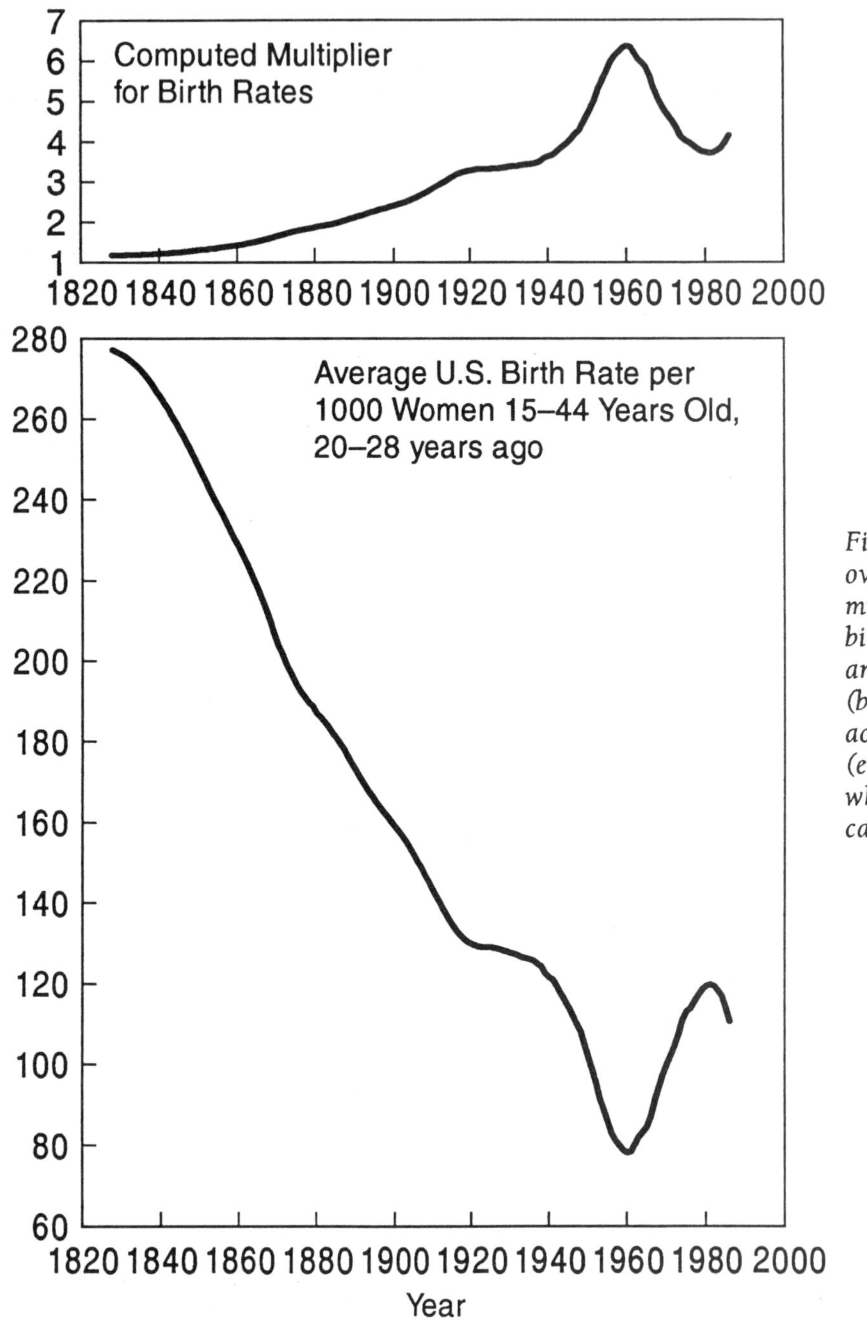

Figure 6-4. The trend over time in the empirical multiplier for U.S. live birth rates (top panel) and its determinant (bottom panel)—the actual, observed (empirical) data from which the multiplier was calculated.

Adjusting for trend

To trend-adjust the data, actual birth rates for particular years were divided by the values computed for the long-term trend (as you've seen here several times thus far). The result (fig. 6-4, top panel) is a measure of the birth rate multiplier for that year. Fig. 6-4 shows how the computed multiplier for birth rates (top panel) changes through time in response to change in the average birth rate 20–28 years previously (bottom panel).

Developing a forecasting model for U.S. number of live births

This method of adjusting for trend and splitting the components of change into categories by wavelength can also be applied to another variable—live births in the U.S. (Note that this variable is a storage—the number of people born in a year.) The data are of high quality, and only three independent variables account for virtually all of the year-to-year variation in this century. Fig. 6-5 presents the data on number of births each year (dots) and output from the forecasting model (smooth, oscillating line). The number of live births rose to a peak between 1915–1924, declined dramatically in the depression, rose to another peak in 1957, declined again, then rose again in the 1980s.

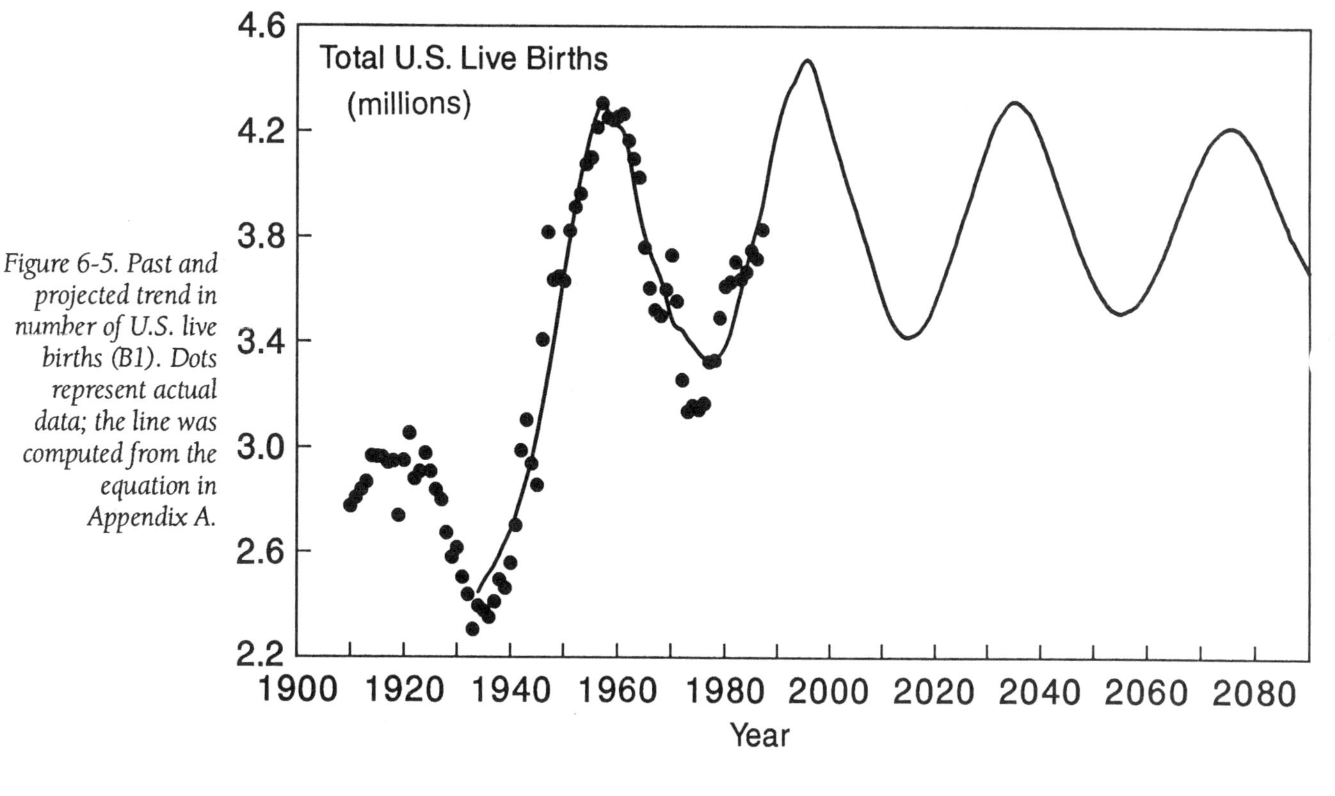

Figure 6-5. Past and projected trend in number of U.S. live births (B1). Dots represent actual data; the line was computed from the equation in Appendix A.

There are apparently three sets of forces affecting this variable (Appendix A).

① The first of these produces a long-term trend line, expressing the effect of the cumulative production of U.S. domestic fossil fuel on the level of technological development of society, and hence the ratio of benefits to costs for one new child (fig. 6-6).

② The second is the average number of births 16–24 years ago.

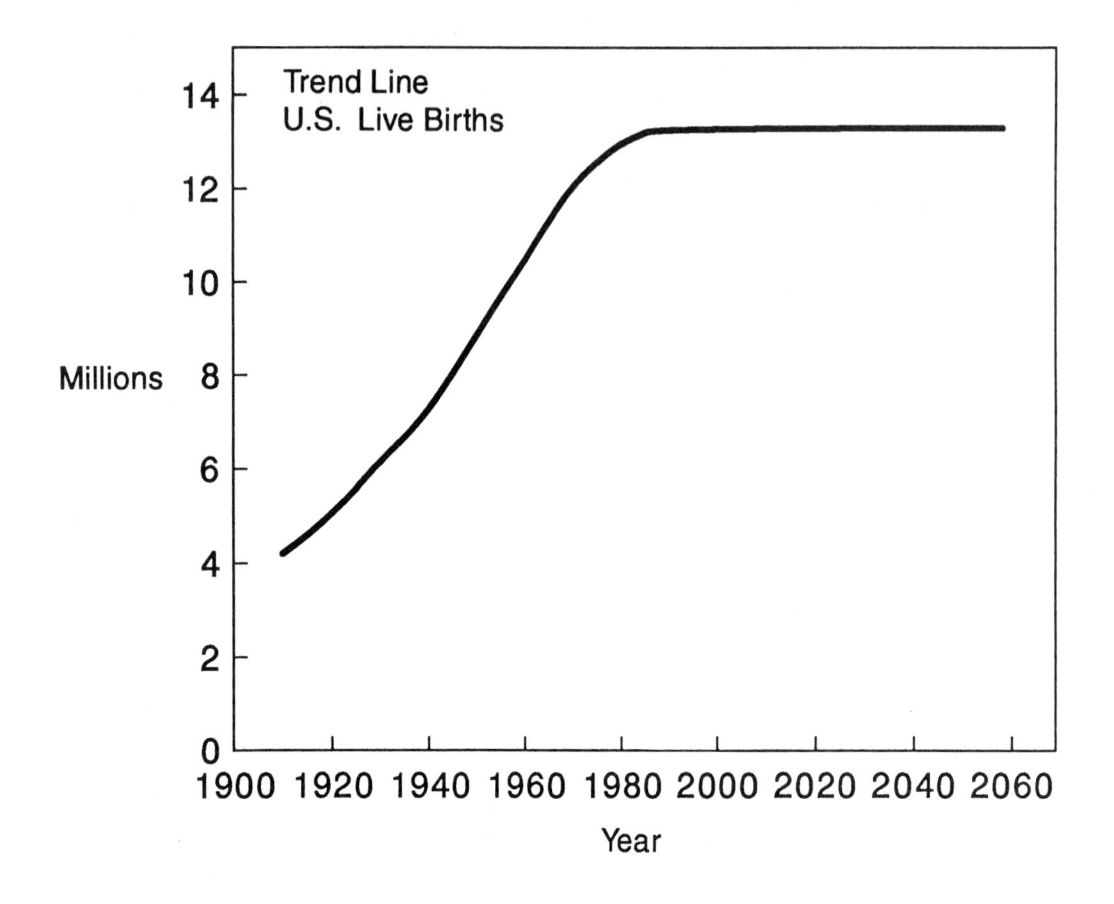

Figure 6-6. The trend line for live births in the U.S., computed from the equation in Appendix A.

The following hypothesis is proposed to account for this relation. Unexpectedly high birth numbers are followed 16–24 years later by supersaturation of the labor market by an unexpectedly large number of new labor force entrants. This depresses wages relative to the long-term trend line for wages, reduces standards of living below its trend, and therefore lowers the desire to have children to below its trend line. On the other hand, low birth numbers produce a generation of prospective labor force entrants 16–24 years later, in *undersupply* relative to demand, who therefore have wages elevated above the wage trajectory and who produce a number of offspring elevated above the live birth numbers trajectory.

Some readers will be curious as to why lag lengths are 16–24 years for the number of live births, but 20–28 years for live birth rates. We don't yet know for certain why this is so.

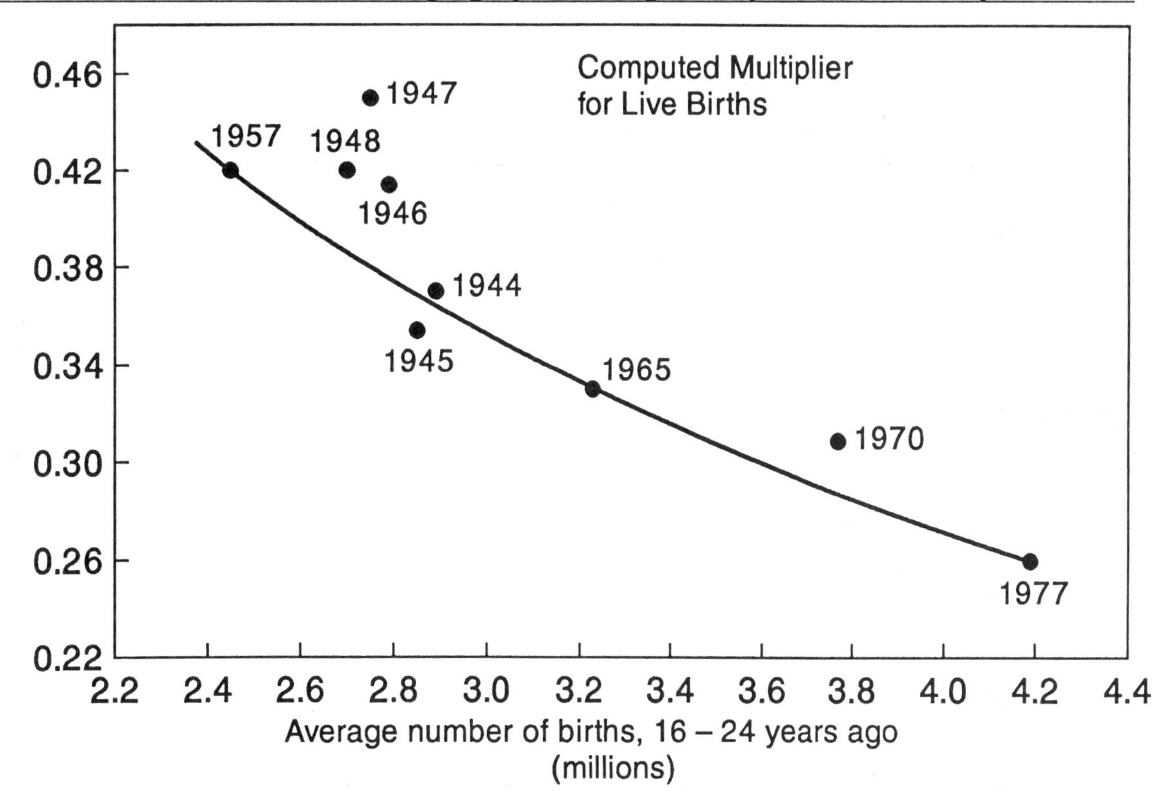

Figure 6-7. Number of live births multiplier as a function of birth rates 16–24 years earlier. The line was computed from the equation in Appendix A.

The effect on birth numbers each year of the average number of births 16–24 years ago is depicted by the curve in fig. 6-7. During years free of perturbations associated with wars, the line describes the data well, as illustrated by the points for 1957, 1965 and 1977. Wars, however,produce a characteristic and historically repeating pattern of deviations about this line.

③ The third force affecting the variable (number of births) is war.

We can study the pattern of deviations by adjusting for trend (dividing actual birth numbers for each year by the value projected by the trajectory equation). This gives us an empirical measure of the birth multiplier that can be compared with the value expected from the statistically fitted term for the birth multiplier.

To illustrate, the point for 1944, representing births produced by conceptions in 1943 is right on the line. By 1944, large numbers of American males were fighting abroad, so there were few conceptions in that year, and the data point for birth numbers in 1945 is far below the line. By late 1945, large number of servicemen were back home and by 1946, almost all were home. The result is the data point for births in 1946 is well above the line, that for 1947 is even further above the line, and that for 1948 is still well above the line. Similarly, 1970—a year after large numbers of Vietnam veterans had returned home—is far above the line. Thus the effect of war-induced perturbations, as measured by the number of U.S. servicemen stationed abroad is revealed as the determinant of high-speed fluctuation about the birth number long-term trend line.

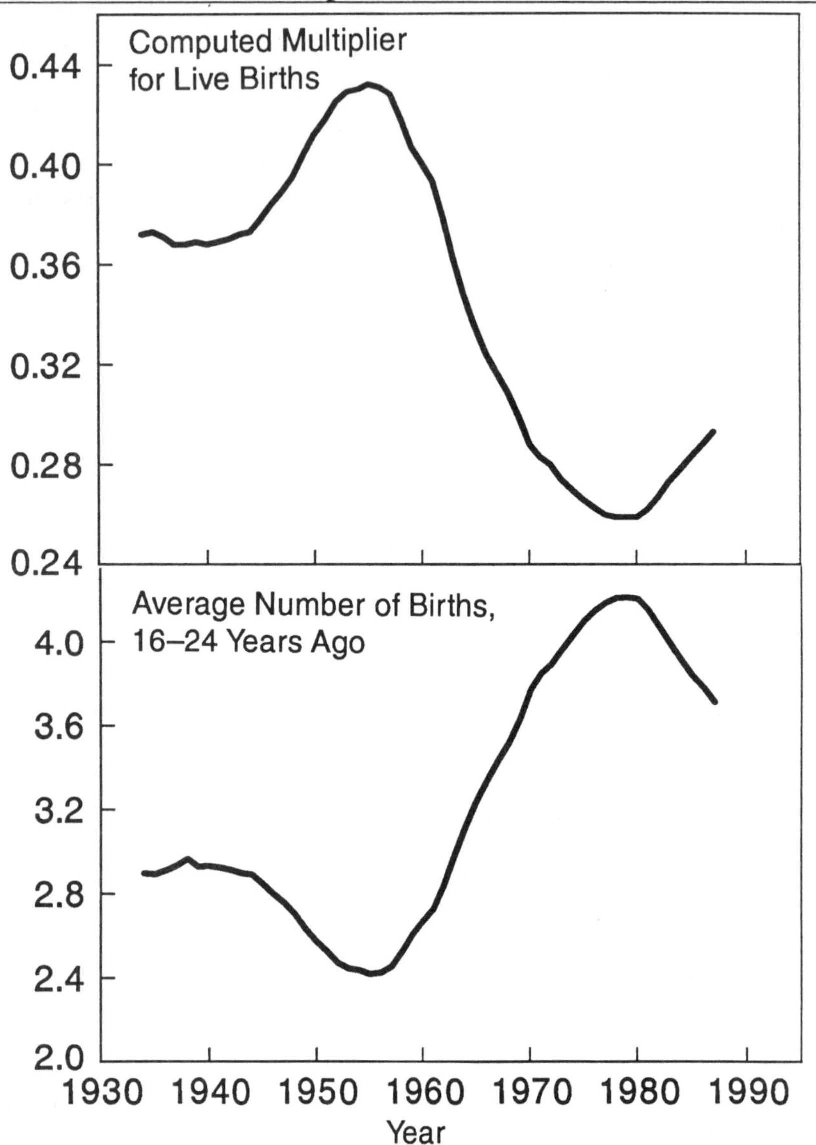

Figure 6-8. The trend through time for the U.S. live birth multiplier (top panel) and its determinant (bottom panel).

Fig. 6-8 presents another way of understanding wavelike oscillation in birth numbers. The bottom panel depicts the trend in the average number of births 16–24 years ago. The figure clearly shows there is an inverse relation between high birth number in the previous generation, about 20 years ago and high birth numbers in this generation.

Putting what we've found out into a theory

We can now formulate a theory to account for year-to-year variation in live birth numbers.

① The trajectory in live birth numbers is regulated by cumulative domestic fossil fuel production, a measure of the depletion of a storage, national fossil fuel reserves.

② Wavelike oscillations about that trend are regulated by the average number of births 16–24 years ago.

③ Deviations about these waves are accounted for largely by a third factor, perturbations associated with wars.

From 1940 to the present, wavelike oscillations in birth numbers have been almost totally under endogenous control. Since it has been possible to account for variation in birth numbers as if they were largely unaffected by their "environment", this variable qualifies as a state variable, rather than a state dependent variable, which is computed at each time step from the values of other variables in its "environment". It is characteristic of state variables, in that it has a high degree of inertia, being regulated by its own past variables many years ago.

Implications of these findings

These results have thought-provoking implications. The high proportion of the variance in both birth numbers and birth rates accounted for by such simple models is surprising. Common sense would suggest that a realistic model of either birth numbers or birth rates would be obtained by developing a set of models for women of each age group separately, then adding the numbers for all ages or averaging the rates for all ages, to obtain a composite statistic for the entire population.

I have discovered that even in these highly aggregated, high-quality social science data, the random error in the data is so high (because of the perturbations associated with war) that I had to use either 3-year or 5-year moving averages for the dependent variables, to allow for operation of the computer procedure that obtained the parameter values for the equations. In other words, improvements in accuracy come about by increasing the degree of aggregation (lumping) of statistics, not the degree of disaggregation (splitting). This type of finding argues for the simple models used throughout this book, rather than the much more complex models that have been the standard tool in large-scale forecasting models. Putting it differently, it has proved more important to seek the robustness of statistics that comes from pooling, rather than the precision that comes from splitting data into subcategories. The latter "precision" has proved largely illusory.

Wars are not "sideshows" in modern civilization; they are the main show.

These results make a point that emerges from all our studies of data sets over long periods of time: wars are not "sideshows" in modern civilization; they are the main show. Wars not only introduce major perturbations into every process in modern society at the time they occur, they also have huge lagged effects long afterward. Thus, the strongly elevated birth numbers around 1947 associated with the end of World War II contributed to the surprisingly depressed birth numbers around 1971–1975 (fig. 6-5). As we shall see later, this only hints at the magnitude of the long-delayed and enormous impacts of war on modern societies, long after the cessation of hostilities.

Some of the 1930s drop in birth rates occurred because birth rates stopped declining so fast in the 1910s—without having to invoke an effect of economics on demographics.

Another provocative finding is that some of the great drop in birth rates in the 1930s occurred because birth rates stopped declining so fast in the 1910s. That is, one of the most startling phenomena of the Great Depression—the collapse in birth rates in the 1930s—can be partly explained without having to invoke an effect of the economic system on the demographic system. This raises a most important issue. Could it be that the **causality flows the opposite direction, with the excessive number of young people in the 1930s that collapsed**

birth rates also contributing importantly to the economic collapse? As we shall see later, the answer is "yes, *with the causal pathway working along a chain from excessive numbers of prospective labor force entrants, to depressed wages, then depressed consumer purchasing power, depressed prices, and layoffs."*

Theory from systems analysis and economic historians: long waves are due to causal pathways with surprisingly long time lags.

The findings here support a theory coming from both systems analysis and some economic historians: there are long waves in modern society and due to causal pathways operating with surprisingly long time lags. Short lags such as 3–5 years do not produce patterns such as those depicted in figures 6-2 and 6-5.

Figures 6-3 and 6-7 demonstrate that growth rates in modern societies are under strong self-regulatory (homeostatic) negative feedback control. High growth rates simply result in lower growth rates subsequently.

The results to this point help clarify the distinction between state variables and state-dependent variables. Birth numbers (a storage) and birth rates (a flow regulated by a storage) are typical of variables whose present behavior can be rationalized almost entirely on the basis of their own past history and the behavior of one or a small number of other state variables. The depression of the 1930s had a major role in initiating oscillatory behavior in birth numbers and birth rates, but subsequently, that behavior can be rationalized statistically without appeal to any "environmental" factor.

If this view of complex systems is correct, it allows for enormous simplification in building simulation models for forecasting.

This also suggests that there may be some small number of variables, the state variables for any system, complete knowledge of which is adequate to account for almost all the dynamic behavior of a system. The current behavior of the rest of the variables in the system—the state *dependent* variables—can then be computed simply as algebraic functions of the current values for the state variables. If this view of the nature of system dynamics for complex systems is correct, it allows for an enormous simplification in the task of building simulation models for forecasting.

Another example: population numbers in any age group

The U.S. total population 22 years of age will be used to illustrate the procedure for modeling the trend in size of a group of a particular age. The trend in size of this group from 1931–1983 is depicted in fig. 6-9. The number had risen fairly steadily throughout this century, except for a clear decrease in growth rate between about 1910–1920. That was likely due to the after-effects of the depression of the 1890s, when birth rates and birth numbers were probably depressed below their trajectories.

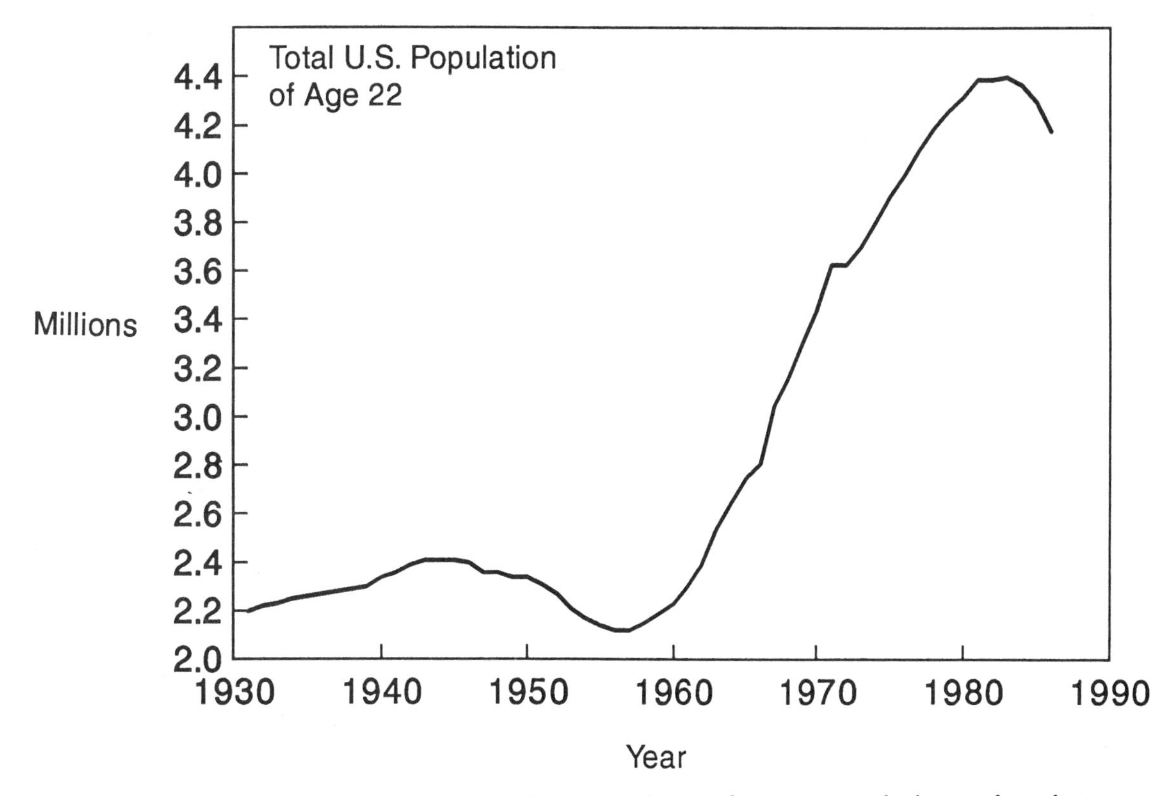

Figure 6-9. Trend in the total U.S. population of age 22, smoothed as explained in the text. (Raw data from series A-32 and documents used to construct this series by U.S. Bureau of the Census. See discussion of relevant Current Population Reports in HS.)

To model the trend in numbers of people of a particular age, we assume that number is the number of births in the year the group was born times a proportion that measures probability of survival from year of birth until the age in question. Again, we assume the state variable regulating probability of survival to that age is cumulative production of domestic fossil fuel.

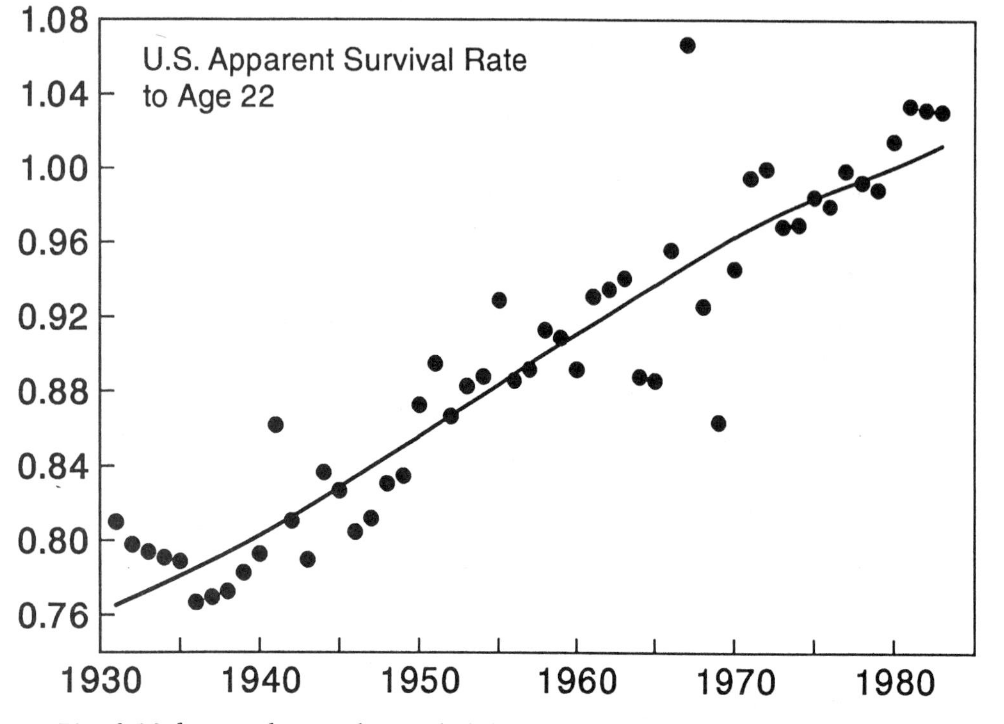

Figure 6-10. Apparent U.S. survival rate to age 22. See text's discussion of scatter.

Fig. 6-10 depicts the trend in probability of survival. Dots are apparent survival rates for each year, and the curve was determined by the equation in Appendix A. The points are widely scattered about the line. Astonishingly, this occurs even after the data have been subjected to considerable smoothing. The numerator for the "apparent survival rate to age 22" was the average U.S. total population in each of the ages 20–24, inclusive. That numerator was divided by the total number of U.S. live births 22 years previously. Then a 5-year moving average was taken of the resultant ratio. Given this amount of data massaging, the degree of scatter depicted in fig. 6-10 is surprising. Further, it reinforces the point made previously that "splitting" instead of "lumping" or "pooling" social sciences data has less value than usually imagined. Given that these national totals or averages are some of the cleanest data originating in the social or biological sciences, the implications for other disciplines is provocative.

Empirical estimates of proportion surviving in fig. 6-10 are biased upwards because of immigration between birth of the age group until the time they are 22 years old. Because there is an unknown amount of undocumented immigration, it is not possible to separate out the effects of domestic births and immigration on number of people 22 years old in any year. Therefore, instead of designating the multiplier term as "probability of survival" we call it "apparent survival rate to age 22".

The line in fig. 6-10 has the shape of a stretched-out letter S, with growth starting from a flat base, then rising to an upper limit. The underlying theory holds that as cumulative production of domestic fossil fuel increases, it provides capital for improved diet, standard of living, and health care delivery. Survival was clearly low in preindustrial times, but probably oscillated about a constant for a long time. As industrialization progressed, powered by fossil fuel use, survival improved at a gradually increasing rate, then stopped growing so fast as an upper limit was approached. The upper limit was imposed by human biological characteristics and by characteristics of the social environment, including smoking, alcohol, drugs, inappropriate diet, and environmental pollutants.

Death rates—and AIDS

Death rate is simply 1.00 less survival rate. To forecast population numbers, all we need is birth numbers and survival rates, as already indicated. Recently, however, forecasts of survival rates need to be modified to include the impact of AIDS (acquired immune deficiency syndrome). AIDS has the potential to cause surprising demographic changes in third-world countries (e.g. Anderson, May and McLean, 1988). The most recent, authoritative research suggests that it will have a much larger impact in the U.S. than generally recognized, as well (Johnston and Hopkins, 1990). This is presumably true for all developed countries.

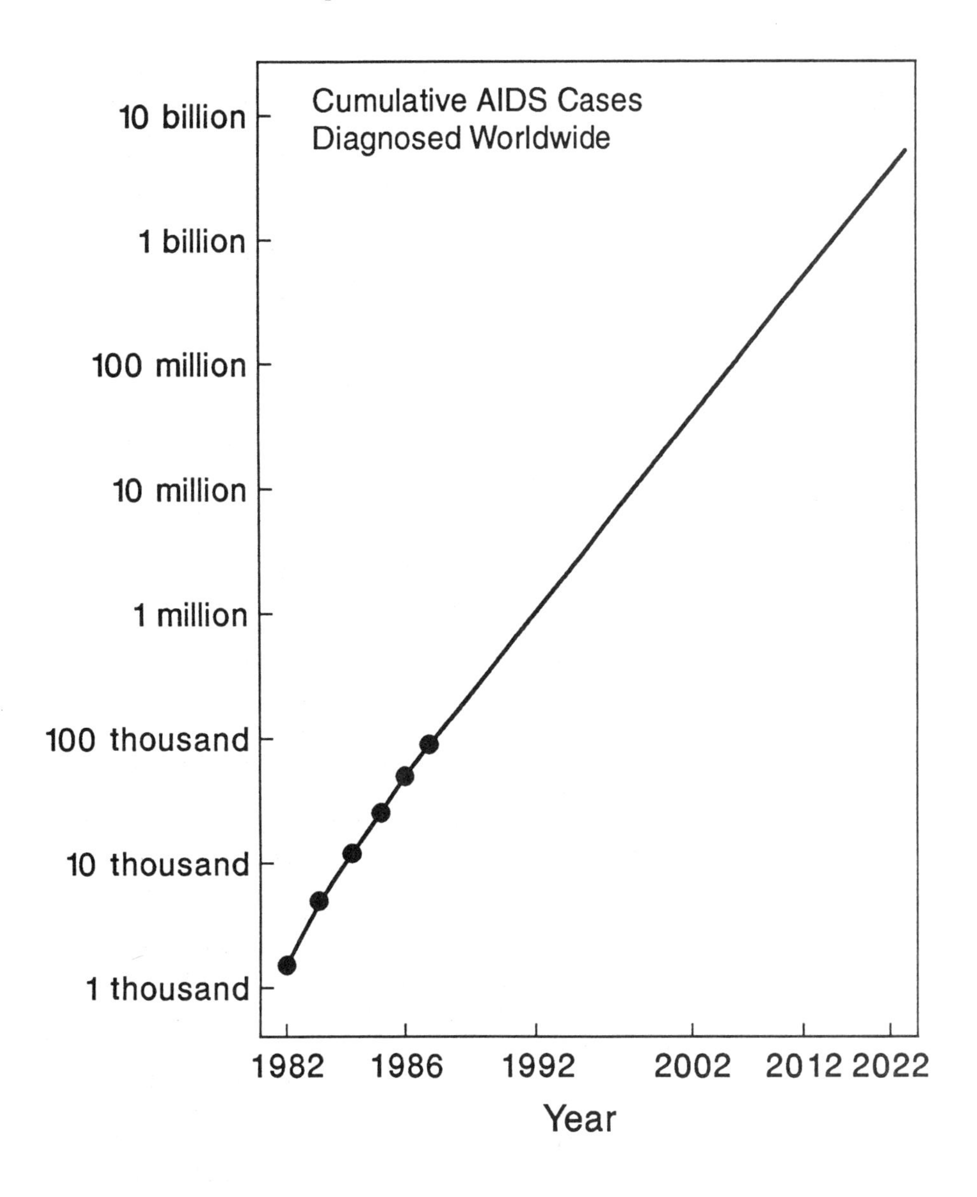

Figure 6-11. Cumulative number of newly diagnosed AIDS cases worldwide. The dots prior to 1988 represent actual data (WHO, 1988). (As work on this book was being completed, it appeared that the slight bend to the right in this graph was entirely an artifact of underreporting.) For years after 1988, the fitted line was computed from the equation in Appendix A.

Probably their most important finding is that people only alter their sexual behavior to avoid risk of AIDS long after they realize how serious a threat it is. Specifically, in the one population group most carefully studied, sexual behavior to avoid AIDS was only adopted after 60 percent of the group was already infected (HIV-seropositive). The authors above present a great many data to demonstrate how difficult it is to change sexual habits of large populations.

Sexual behavior to avoid AIDS was only adopted after 60 percent of a carefully studied group was already infected.

The World Health Organization has estimated cumulative number of people diagnosed as having AIDS, worldwide, each year beginning in 1979 (Programme for AIDS Prevention, 1988). The round dots in Figure 6-11 represent data through 1987. The curve was computed from a simple model projecting the future trend in cumulative worldwide number of diagnosed AIDS cases. Several studies indicate that if this trend continues during 1982–1992, that number will increase by a factor of 875.

I believe that at some point there will be a worldwide shift towards safer average sexual behavior; about ten years later the epidemic will begin to end. After that, the line projected in fig. 6-11 will bend sharply to the right. The problem is, we don't know for sure when that behavioral shift will occur. The shift could occur when cumulative cases has reached 10 million—or as late as when cumulative cases is a billion or more.

A mathematical theory of epidemics of long standing (Kermack and McKendrick, 1927) has proved useful and realistic in understanding other major epidemics. This theory concludes that ultimate severity of an epidemic is proportional to infectivity rate **I** and inversely proportional to **R**, the rate at which infected individuals are removed from the population by recovery, quarantine, or death.

*AIDS—in contrast to all previous infectious diseases—has extremely low values of **R** (removal of infected individuals from the population).*

Most important epidemics came to a halt after days, weeks, or months because of high **R** values. High recovery rates (e.g., influenza) or high death rates (e.g., plague, smallpox or syphilis in the middle ages) ensured high rates of removal from the infected pool and termination of the epidemic. In contrast to all previous infectious diseases, AIDS has extremely low **R** values. People may spread the epidemic for years before they are diagnosed as carrying it. The most recent estimates on AIDS' "incubation period"—the time from contracting the disease to the time it is detected—average 7 years (Anderson and May, 1988). As this book goes to press, new estimates increase this to 10 years. **This guarantees that the epidemic will be very severe and involve a large proportion of the population**, barring a massive, major change in sex habits.

Demographic implications of AIDS

The demographic implications of AIDS become clear when we compare two frequency distributions: those for distribution of sexual behavior in the population, and those for distribution of reproductive rates in the population.

Table 6-1 presents the implications of survey findings among U.S. white wives on how many children they expect to bear. As the table shows, the difference between population growth and population decline is created by that 9 percent who expect to bear 4 or more children each.

Similarly, most adult people have a small number of sexual partners in any two-year period. Only a tiny percentage of the population has an average of 50 sexual partners in that time. All other things being equal, it seems reasonable to expect that the most sexually active people would also have higher-than-average level of reproductive activity. (This follows because celibate people with zero sexual partners have a reproductive rate of zero.) If this is true, then AIDS has the most startling implications for average population growth rates: at least in some third-world countries, populations will be declining rapidly by about 2030. AIDS will have selectively eliminated much of that small proportion of the population that converts population decline into population growth. This suggests that demographic implications of AIDS in developed countries will be much larger than expected.

Table 6-1. The impact of most reproductively active wives on population growth rates.

Lifetime births by white U.S. women 18–34 years old in 1985	Percentage of all mothers	Cumulative number of children per mother	Cumulative average number of children
0	6.4	0.0	0.0
1	12.6	12.6	0.66
2	49.8	112.2	1.63
3	22.2	178.8	1.96
4 or more (assume 5)	9.0	223.8	2.24

From Table 97, SA (1986).

Population growth (resulting from bearing more children than the replacement value of 2) is created by only 9 percent of mothers (in this group).

There is another way to project the demographic implications of AIDS. If we project world population and population growth rates for several decades into the future, we can compute the projected number of people that are likely to be added to the population each year. In order for population growth to cease, AIDS has only to remove (by death) a number equal to the number added each year due to population growth. Any such calculation includes many imponderables. For example, perhaps those people who will die of AIDS are risk takers who would have a higher probability of death, anyway, due to some factor already operating.

A crude exercise reveals the following. From SA (1987) Table 1376 we obtain 7.192 billion as an estimate for world population in 2010 and 1.4 percent as an estimate of world population annual growth rate for 2005–2010. From these values we can project the estimated population for each year thereafter. We can also project for each year the number of additional deaths that would stabilize population, assuming the annual growth rate continues. If the AIDS epidemic continues on the present trend, world population will have ceased to grow by 2025. Shortly thereafter, it will decline precipitously. Not only will removals by deaths be increasing faster than additions due to births, but **births will have begun to drop precipitously due to selective elimination of the most reproductively active women.**

Some people may object that this scenario is excessively pessimistic. In fact, a number of steps were taken to make it excessively optimistic, if anything. For example, we used estimates of AIDS cases that are widely believed to be under reported by at least a factor of two. Also, estimates of the incubation period keep lengthening as we get more information; as we have seen, longer time lags (i.e., incubation time) lead to longer wavelengths and wider oscillations—greatly increased instability.

Chapter 7

The Mechanism Producing the Long Wave

The goal of this chapter is to reveal the root cause of the long wave behavior that has been discovered in:

- Modern economies (e.g. Kondratieff, 1925), war cycles (e.g. Dyer, 1985).
- The interaction between economic and war cycles (Goldstein, 1985, 1988).
- Long waves in a variety of other areas, such as culture (Namenwirth, 1973, Weber, 1981,1983).

This chapter shows how far we can go in understanding economic and cultural long waves in a modern nation by examining the interplay between just two system driving forces:

① The status of that nation's fossil fuel reserves, and

② A capital investment cycle that responds to fluctuations in fuel scarcity.

Searching for causes of long economic waves

Economists have observed for a long time that of all economic sectors, *primary* industries (such as pig iron production) showed the widest-amplitude fluctuations around their trend lines throughout cycles of depressions and inflations (e.g. McConnell, 1966, Fig. 11-4). The fluctuations in sales of nondurable goods and services were much less pronounced. Accordingly, in this chapter we use millions of tons of pig iron shipped as the most revealing available measure of wave-like fluctuations in a nation.

The search for an explanation for long waves leads quickly to the conclusion that lagged effects of wars are somehow implicated, and then to notions that the causal pathway for this effect works through supply-to-demand ratios for fuels, and then to capital investment cycles. We arrive at these conclusions from studying both historical data series and the writings of economists. Relevant observations are summarized in Table 7-1.

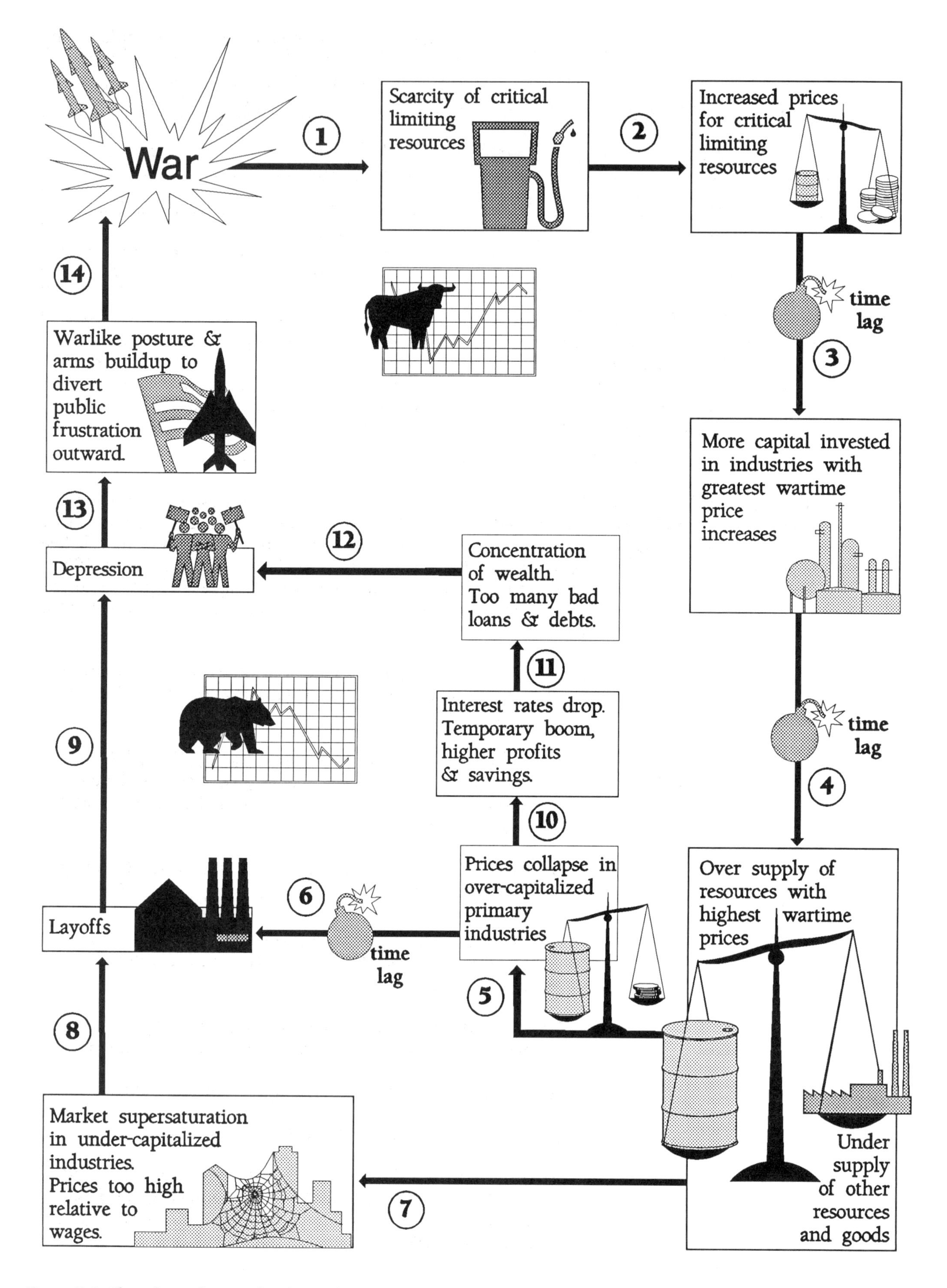

Figure 7-1. Flow chart of a postulated causal pathway generating long waves in modern industrial nations (after Watt, 1989).

*Table 7-1. Observations that point to a lagged effect of war-related high fuel prices on shipments of pig iron**. *Lag time is number of years between postwar zenith of WFPI and nadir year for pig iron shipment.*

Year war ended	WPI (fuel) peak year	Pig iron shipment low point year	Lag time
1865	1865	1876	11
1919	1920	1932	12
1945	1948	1058	10

* Data from HS, E29, E46, E57 and M217.

Note. The list of economists who have pointed out that depressions might be lagged effects of wars includes Clark (1931), Dickinson (1940), Director (1940), Thorp (1941) and Gaines (1962). Gaines (1962) leads one to speculate about how rapid retirement of war debt might affect unwise patterns of capital investment. Watt, Craig and Auburn (1988) tested the hypothesis that rate of war debt retirement is the key factor in producing economic waves. They found that variable highly correlated with some time series measuring postwar events, but not with all.

Tracing effects of critical limiting resource

From the argument in Chapter 4, we would expect the most critical limiting resource in the last century to have been fossil fuel. For other historical periods and nations it would have been different: salt-free agricultural soil in ancient Mesopotamia (Jacobsen & Adams, 1958), firewood in 16th century England (Watt, Craig & Auburn, 1988), or wheat and wood for shipbuilding in 16th century Spain (Braudel, 1972, 1973).

Fig. 7-1 presents the **hypothesis that long-wave economic cycles are driven by the interaction of fossil fuel resources with the capital investment cycle.**

① Beginning in the upper left corner (causal pathway ① in the flow chart), wars use and destroy massive amounts of fuels—or some other event such as actions of the O.P.E.C. cartel causes fossil fuel shortages.

② Price increases would be greater for the most critical limiting resource than for other resources (causal pathway ②).

③ After a time lag, capital investment would be shifted to those industries that had the greatest price increases during the time of shortage.

④ After a further lag of several years, excessive capital investment has resulted in excessive supply of those resources.

⑤ The result would be a price collapse in those resources.

⑥ After a further lag, layoffs result.

⑦ Meanwhile, in those industries that have been short on capital investment, supplies would now be inadequate. Prices would have become excessive relative to average wages, leading to market supersaturation.

⑧ Here, also, therefore, there would be layoffs because of high wages and not enough product to supply demand.

⑨ Layoffs from both ⑥ and ⑧ lead to a depression.

⑩ Price collapse in primary industries would lead to a decline in real interest rates and temporarily inflated profits.

⑪ This would lead to excessive concentration of wealth in the hands of investors, who would have more money than could be loaned out wisely. That would imply an excessive number of unwise loans and debts, which would be reflected in the banking system as an unusually high ratio of loans to cash on hand.

⑫ Instability in the banking and investment sectors generates another causal pathway leading to depression.

⑬ Nations that had the most severe internal problems with their citizenry, use an armaments buildup and subsequent mobilization to restimulate the economy and also to direct the hostility of the citizenry outwards.

⑭ Preparation for war sometimes leads to war quickly and in other cases after a considerable lag. The length of the lag may be affected by the intensity of the internal political-economic problems of the nation that initiates the war. Germany initiated the second world war 7 years after it had an unemployment rate of over 30 percent (Mitchell, 1975). Czarist Russia was the first nation to mobilize for World War I; 65 percent of its factory workers had been on strike in 1914 (Ferro, 1973). The latter situation, with far more intense intranational problems, produced the shorter time lag before war. Also, as we saw in Chapter 5, the wavelength on modern societies is contracting.

War creates fuel shortages

We can examine the trends before, during and after the two World Wars in two ratios:

- Year end coal stocks:coal production the following year, and
- Year end crude oil reserves:production the following year (HS M102:M93 and M142:M138, respectively).

These trends are plotted in fig. 7-2. There was a pronounced drop in the ratio of coal stocks to production from 1942–1948 (top panel), a precipitous drop in the ratio of petroleum reserves to production from 1914–1922, and a less precipitous drop from 1941–1947. It would appear that war does create a significant draw-down of fossil fuel stocks or reserves relative to rates of production.

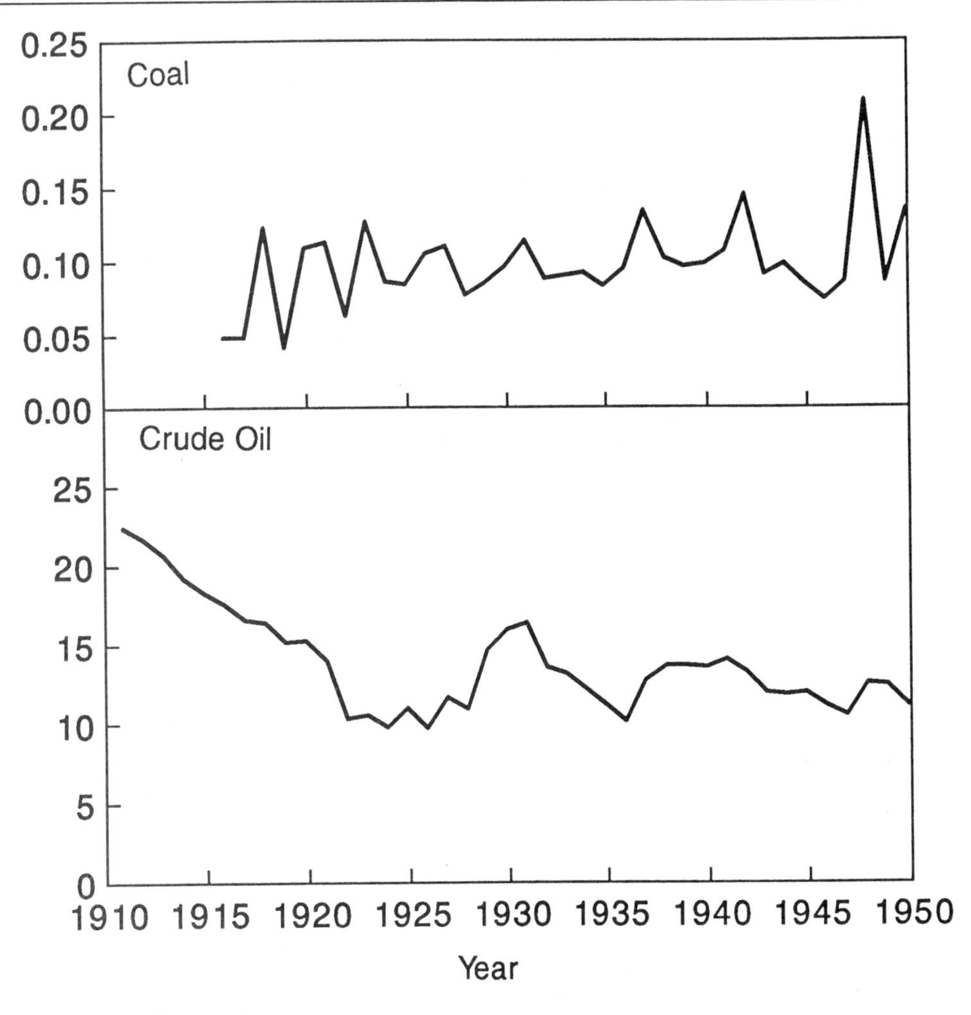

Figure 7-2. Indicators of the impact of wars on supply:demand ratios for fossil fuels. Top panel shows ratio of year-end coal stocks to coal production following year (HS M102/M93).

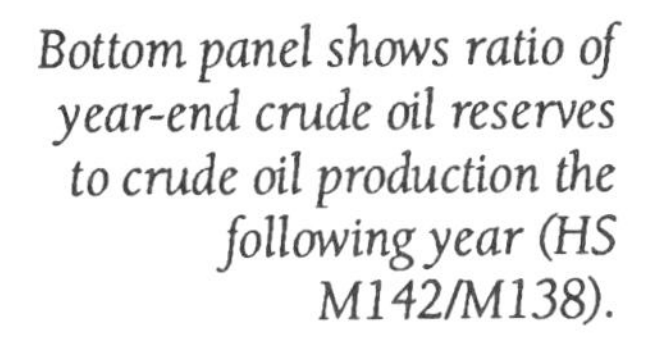

Bottom panel shows ratio of year-end crude oil reserves to crude oil production the following year (HS M142/M138).

Test of step ②

Do fuel prices increase in response to a war proportionally more than prices of other basic commodities? Table 7.2 shows that during the first world war there was a marked increase in the price per barrel of oil relative to the price per ton of iron (HS, M139/M218). During the civil war, energy prices increased 168 percent (HS E57); metal and metal product prices only increased 101 percent (E58).

Distribution of wealth

The wave-generating mechanism detailed here, interacting with the long-term trend imposed by cumulative production of fossil fuel, initiates causal pathways whose effects permeate every aspect of society, including politics, and all aspects of culture. Batra (1987) has discussed linkages between cultural and economic cycles. He noted the association between processes leading to depressions and concentration of wealth in a progressively smaller proportion of the population. Eventually, a few people have far more money than they need and most have far less. This increases pressure both to lend money and to borrow it. As the creditworthiness of the majority deteriorates, banks must become less and less choosy about prospective borrowers, and more and more banks hold relatively shaky loans. Batra's argument is supported by many other data sources.

Table 7.2. Trend in ratio of price per barrel of oil:price per ton of iron (M139/M218). Asterisks indicate years when oil prices were high compared with pig iron prices.

Year	Oil price:iron price
1915	.046
1916	.055
1917	.040
1918	.060
1919	.073*
1920	.073*
1921	.079*
1922	.067*
1923	.052

Time delays in major capital projects

The reader may have realized from the flow chart in fig. 7-1 that there are additional, disquieting consequences of the time lags in steps ③–④ . Many years elapse from the time a capital project is planned—counting on energy resources having a particular value—until the time when the money must actually be spent on equipment and structures. In fact, there are very surprising lags from the time major capital projects are planned until the time construction is well under way (e. g. Hirsch, 1987). The astonishing lags from planning initiation until project completion are well known and much discussed in the media for very large projects such as rapid rail transit systems to serve metropolitan regions.

One rather extreme group of cases in which these lags have been carefully studied concerns U.S. nuclear power plants. The delay from time of application for a construction permit to the time the permit is issued has ranged from about 5–60 months, with 30 months being typical. From issuance of the construction permit until issuance of the operating license (implying completion of the plant), the typical time has been 60 months, with a range from about 40 to about 120 months. After that, it took an additional 2–16 months before the plant was declared operational (e.g. Mooz, 1978).

Thus readers may be prepared to accept the notion that there is a 9–13 year lag from the time the wholesale price had a particular value, until the time expenditures on plant and equipment responded to that value.

Another explanation for the delay will be offered in the next chapter: delays occur because after a fuel price increase or decrease, it may not be economically rational to respond immediately by investing in new capital stock more appropriate for the new energy price environment, because of the large sunk cost of the capital plant already in existence.

A possible explanation is that wars consume and destroy massive amounts of fuels, while much of the metal in materiel such as tanks and airplanes can be and is recycled.

Test of step ③

Is there a shift of capital investment away from other basic resources and towards production of energy in response to war-related energy price increases? Table 7.3 shows that there was a shift of capital investment from production of iron and steel and products to petroleum refining, about 25 years after the Civil War and 10 years after World War I (P158/P160).

Table 7.3. Trend in ratio of capital investment in petroleum refining to capital investment in production of iron and steel and products (HS P158/P160). Asterisks indicate years when investment in petroleum refining was high compared with investment in iron and steel production.

Year	Investment in petroleum production:investment in iron and steel production
1879	.084
1889	.119*
1899	.109
1904	.088
1909	.075
1914	.115
1919	.206
1929	.923*
1937	.911

Pig iron

Pig iron refers to iron after it has left the blast furnace, been poured into molds and has cooled into large bars called ingots. The term "pig iron" refers to the arrangement of the molds around the trough through which molten iron flows (the "sow"), as piglets are gathered around the sow's teats. Pig iron is basic to primary industry, because it is the first step in the process of manufacturing steel alloys.

Test of steps ③–④

The shift continued for another 7–10 years afterward, well into depressed periods, evidence for the time lag in step ④. Table 7-4 shows availability of oil relative to availability of iron ore peaked in 1932.

Table 7.4. Trend in ratio of barrels of oil produced per ton of iron ore produced (HS M138/M205).

Year	Oil production:iron production
1929	13.79
1930	15.38
1931	27.36
1932	79.70
1933	51.42
1934	36.91
1935	32.69
1936	22.54
1937	17.74

Fuel prices as early warnings of depressions

Perhaps the most convincing argument that increases in fuel prices are very early warning indicators of depressions comes from history. There were major energy price increases resulting from the Civil War and World War I, and both those wars were followed by depressions. There was no major energy price increase following World War II, and that war was not followed by a depression.

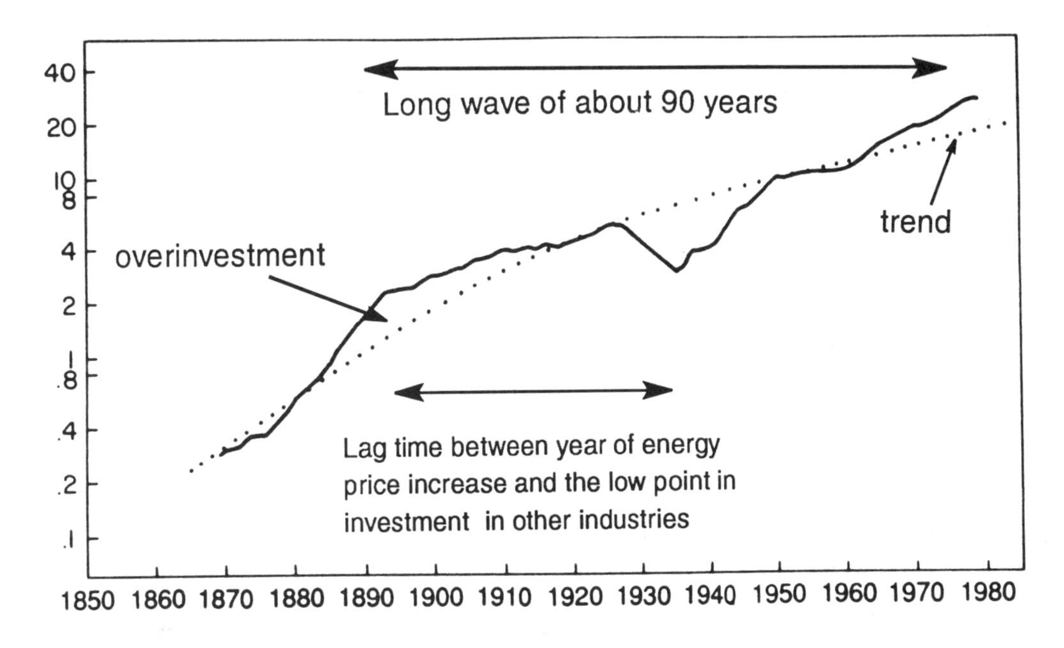

Figure 7-3. The trend in the 9-year moving average investment in equipment and structures in private manufacturing industries (solid line) superimposed on its computed trend (dotted line). (From HS P110; Watt, 1989). Notice the long-term wave of about 90 years.

Another test of ③

Another way of testing the realism of causal pathway 3 in fig. 7-1 (diversion of capital investment towards fuel production, away from other sectors) is to study the pattern of fluctuations in purchases of equipment and structures for privately owned manufacturing industries (HS P110) relative to their trends.

In fig. 7-3 we note a 90-year long oscillation in capital investment (solid line) about its trend (dotted line). A reasonable explanation is that capital investment in manufacturing was unusually low at 1878 and 1936, 11 and 17 years, respectively, following large energy price increases caused by wars. It appears that there is a lagged inverse relation between trend-adjusted wholesale fuel price indices and trend-adjusted investment in manufacturing. This is consistent with causal pathway ④ in fig. 7-1.

A critical test of the hypothesis

The discussion to this point suggests a critical test of the hypothesis shown in fig. 7-1. If that theory is correct, then it should be possible to demonstrate that **energy prices have a lagged effect on deviations of pig iron shipments about its trend.**

The measure of lagged WFPI values that best accounted for fluctuations in pig iron shipments was the sum of trend-adjusted values 9–13 years ago (Appendix A). The top panel of fig. 7-4 depicts the trend, since 1865, in the quantity of pig iron shipped in the U.S. The bottom panel depicts the corresponding trend computed from the equation explained in Appendix A.

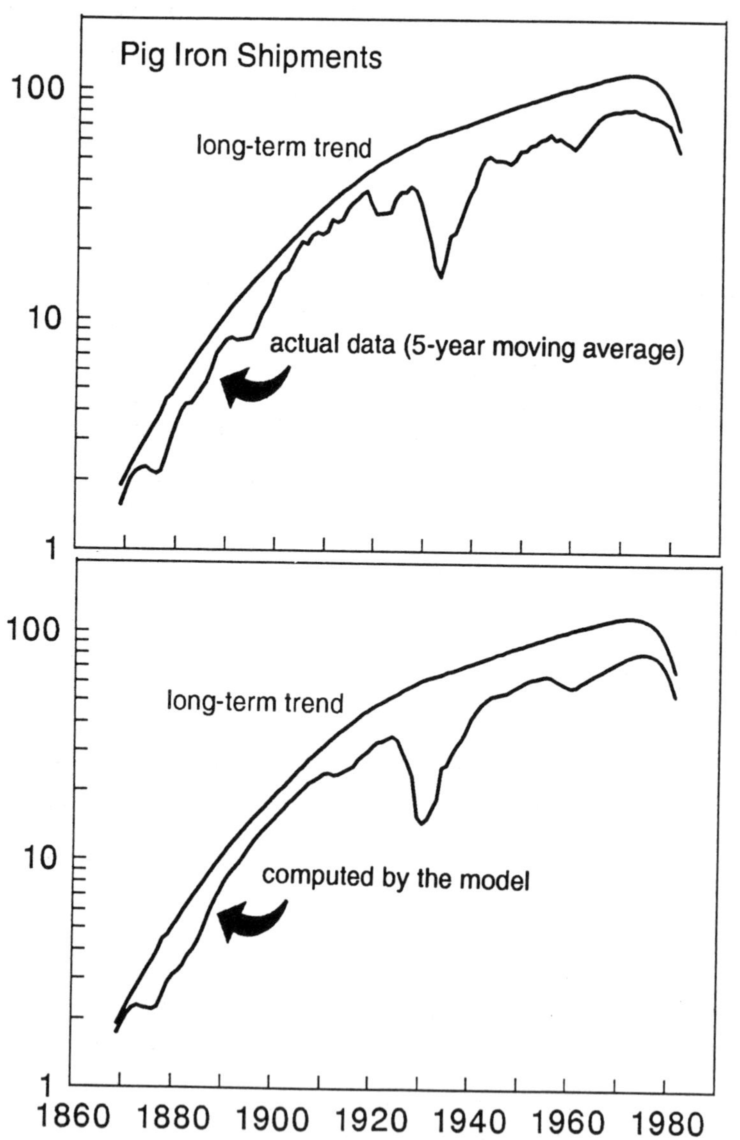

Figure 7-4. The trend in number of tons of pig iron shipped in the U.S. Top panel: actual data smoothed by taking 5-year moving averages (HS M217).

Bottom panel: values computed from equation derived in Appendix A.

In each panel the upper smooth line represents the computed long-term trend for the volume of pig iron shipments (Watt, 1989).

This equation assumes only two system driving forces: cumulative U.S. domestic fossil energy production (**C**), and deviations of wholesale fuel price from their trajectory, 9–13 years ago (**F**). To facilitate visual comparison of the actual and computed trends, the computed trend, calculated from (**C**), is plotted just above each. Note that the trend drops sharply after 1975.

Additional evidence

Two additional types of graphs provide more revealing tests of the hypothesis that time lags in WFPI account for deviations of pig iron shipments from its long-term trend line.

Use of the model to account for long wavelength oscillation about the trend

Chapter 5 explained that we could decompose the variation of a variable changing through time into a component due to the trend and a component due to wavelike oscillation about the trend. Fig. 7-5 plots the actual values divided by the values computed from the trend in the top panel, the computed multiplier producing the waves in the second panel, and the variable or variables allegedly driving the waves in third and subsequent panels. All are plotted against year.

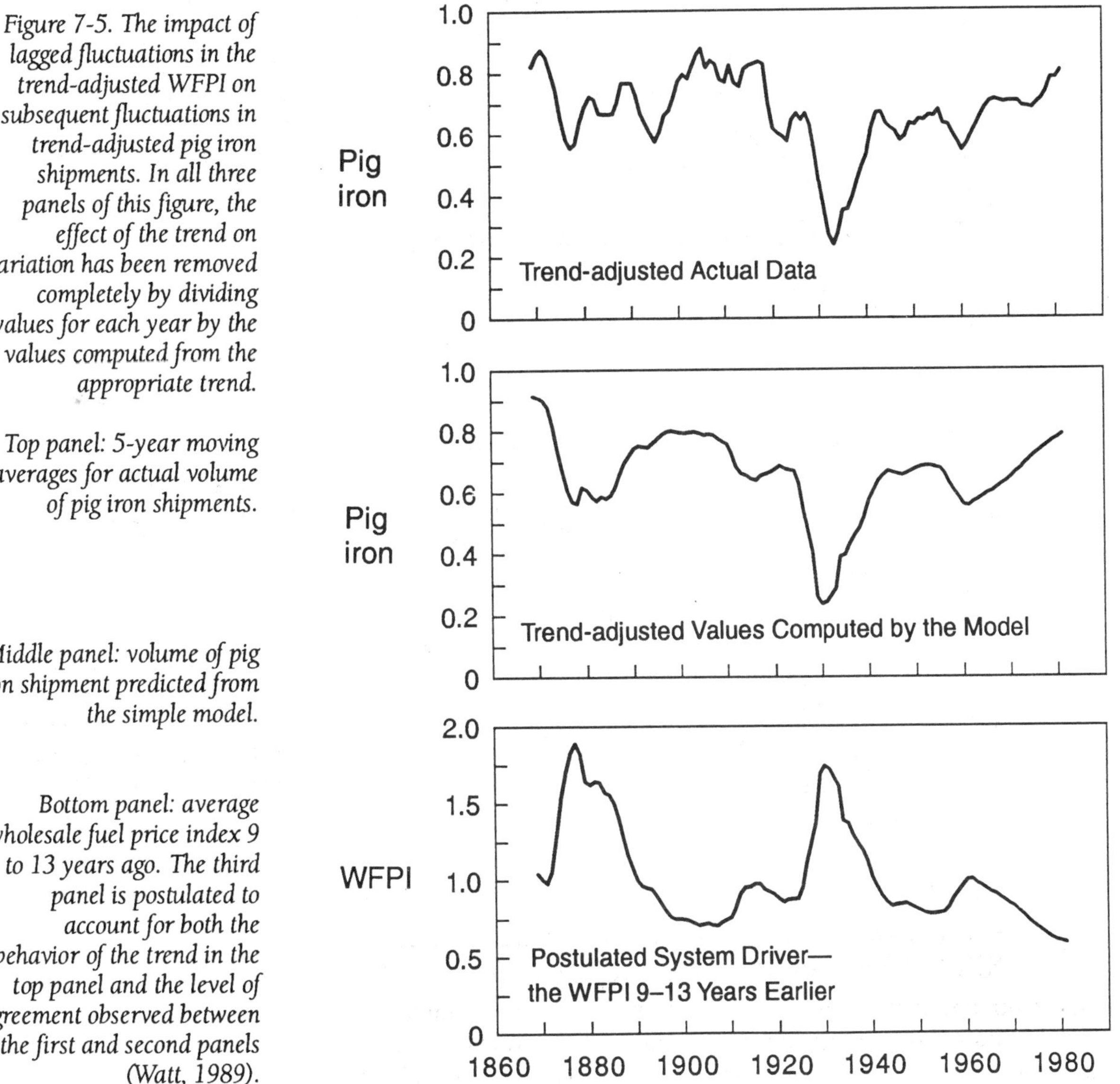

Figure 7-5. The impact of lagged fluctuations in the trend-adjusted WFPI on subsequent fluctuations in trend-adjusted pig iron shipments. In all three panels of this figure, the effect of the trend on variation has been removed completely by dividing values for each year by the values computed from the appropriate trend.

Top panel: 5-year moving averages for actual volume of pig iron shipments.

Middle panel: volume of pig iron shipment predicted from the simple model.

Bottom panel: average wholesale fuel price index 9 to 13 years ago. The third panel is postulated to account for both the behavior of the trend in the top panel and the level of agreement observed between the first and second panels (Watt, 1989).

Statistical analysis reveals that WFPI of 9–13 years earlier accounts for 62.5 percent of the variance in the ratio of actual to trend values for pig iron shipments. Detailed comparison of these two panels reveals why 37.5 percent of that variance is unexplained. In the first and second panels, the deepest nadir is in the 1930s, and there are minor nadirs at 1878 and 1960. Each curve is highest at 1870 and again at around 1905.

WFPI of 9–13 years earlier accounts for 62.5 percent of the variance in the ratio of actual to trend values.

There are important differences between actual data and the model's curve, accounted for by wars and changes in ease of borrowing (i.e., the ratio of loans to cash on hand in banks). In the series computed by the model, there was a mild recession and decline in pig iron shipments between 1913 and 1919; in reality at that time there was a surge in pig iron shipments due to World War I. The low point in computed pig iron shipments was 1930; in reality the nadir was delayed until 1933. The Great Depression may have been delayed by making credit very easy in the late 1920s, as measured by the ratio of loans to cash in banks. In 1928 and 1929 that ratio was at its highest levels since 1840, just prior to the previous most serious depression. Another revealing discrepancy is at 1965. The Vietnam War elevated pig iron shipments far above the level projected from the lagged effect of prior WFPI.

Conclusions

Detailed study of the similarities and differences between computed and actual volumes of pig iron shipments shows clearly how important are just these two process-regulating forces: lagged WFPI and wars. The discrepancies due to war convey an important message: **no computer model that overlooks the impacts of the international system on the internal dynamics of a nation can mimic events completely realistically**.

Granted that caveat, the model mimics major features of the actual history. On the face of it, this is rather astonishing, given the simplicity of the assumptions underlying the model.

Assumptions behind the model

Accordingly, we reexamine the character of the chain of reasoning that lead to the discovery of these assumptions, in the interest of pointing out a model for a chainlike type of logical process that will be followed repeatedly in this book. The process of explaining that chain is like peeling layers off an onion. Peeling off the first layer reveals only a proximate cause. We must peel off layer after layer to get at deeper and deeper levels of explanation until finally we discover the ultimate cause.

In this case, a reasonable place to look for the proximate explanation for most of the fluctuations about the pig iron trend is a long oscillation in capital investment about its trend, and that is what we found (fig. 7-3). We saw that purchases of equipment and structures for privately owned manufacturing industries were slightly below its trend around 1875, far above the trend from 1890–1910, far below the trend from 1930–1945, and far above it after 1965. There is a long-term wave in capital investment with a wavelength of about 90 years. When capital investment is either too far above or too far below its long-term trend value, supply and demand are out of balance, and there is a mild to severe depression (fig. 7-4). Capital investment has been much too high recently, relative to its long-term trend. In common experience, this situation is reflected in high vacancy rates for office space in big cities, excessive electrical generating capacity and overinvestment in oil well drilling equipment, etc.

Root causes of a capital investment cycle

Now we peel another layer off the onion, and ask why there should be a long-term capital investment cycle above and below its trend. Six arguments are helpful in seeking the root cause of a capital investment cycle.

① From economic theory we would expect to find that the amount of capital investment planned for any particular type of production facility is driven by estimates, at the time the investment was being planned, of profit to be made from the investment. **Profit projections** would be high if either:

- Costs of all inputs for the investment appeared to be very low at the time planning was being done, or
- If it appeared that there were going to be shortages, and therefore high prices in the future for the output from the investment.

② From Chapter 4 we have reason to suspect that **energy has an overridingly important impact on input costs**, because it is an input to the costs of everything else. Thus the wholesale fuel price index is identified as a variable that probably drives a composite input cost index (or composite overhead index).

③ We know that there is a lead time of **several years from the time major capital investments are planned until they are completed**. This subject has been studied by various national committees and research organizations, and they all conclude that there is a lag of many years from the time planning begins to the time projects are completely operational (e.g. Hirsch, 1987). Also, common sense tells us that after a period of high output, it would take a number of years before the economy became supersaturated with that output. This argues that the level of capital investment in a particular year is probably inversely proportional to the average of the wholesale fuel price indices, relative to their trend, over some series of previous years.

④ The theory of systems stability in modern applied mathematics and engineering shows that length of time lag in systems control mechanisms determines both wavelength and amplitude of fluctuations in the controlled system; longer lags produce longer waves with wider swings away from long-term trends. It has been well-publicized since at least the time of Kondratieff's studies in the early 1920s that modern industrial societies have a **half-century wave running through their economic systems**. Such a long wavelength would only result from a time lag in the control mechanism of several years.

Longer lags produce longer waves with wider swings away from the long-term trend.

⑤ The fifth argument for focussing on wholesale fuel price indices (WFPI) as the cause of economic cycles is the **observed correlation between high fuel prices and subsequent depressions**. The bottom panel in Fig. 7-5 depicts trend-adjusted WFPI, 9–13 years later than years on the x-axis. Pronounced energy price spikes occur after the ends of major wars. Further, there is a fairly constant time lag from the year of the peak energy price to the nadir year for the subsequent depression (Table 7-1). Thus there is reason to postulate that pig iron shipments are regulated by average wholesale fuel price indices over the period 9–13 years previous.

⑥ Major economic-political-resource-cultural waves of a half century are very large-scale phenomena. It seems reasonable to suspect that some very major phenomenon occurring on a global scale explains them. It is widely understood that mines, oil refineries, and oil and gas storage facilities are extremely high priority targets during wars. Yet oddly, it seems to have occurred to few people that the **massive wartime destruction of energy resources** was a phenomenon that would have global, massive, and long-lasting aftereffects. One has only to look at the reduced circumstances of Kuwait following the oil-well fires after the Iraqi-Kuwait War. Fig. 7-2 also illustrates the scale and duration of this effect. The figure shows the U.S. ratio of year-end stocks of oil and coal to their respective production rates the following year. Either rapid rates of decline in these ratios, or unusually low levels of the ratios would coincide with times of peak stress of demand on supply. The ratio was unusually low for coal

Massive wartime destruction of energy resources has global, massive, and long-lasting aftereffects.

in 1919 and 1946; for petroleum, the ratio dropped rapidly from 1915–1922 and from 1941–1947.

Summary

The preceding discussion identifies two key features of modern societies: (1) A causal pathway extends backwards from end effect to ultimate cause, and (2) the pursuit constantly crosses boundaries between disciplines and subdisciplines, which exist in our minds and our institutions, but not in real world phenomena. Thus the flow chart in fig. 7-1 combines information from resource geology, knowledge about the delays in capital investment programs, history, political science, economics, and stability theory developed in engineering and ecology.

Bringing the pieces together

We can now assemble a theory of the process that generates long waves in modern industrial nations.

Energy shortages start the cycle

Some wars and other events (such as depletion of U.S. crude oil reserves in the 1970s) create massive shortages of global energy resources. Whether a war will or will not create massive draw-downs in world stocks of fuels depends on supply/demand trends and investment in fuel production prior to the war. Thus development of world oil reserves was much further along before World War II compared with World War I; the impacts of WW II on world stocks of petroleum were therefore much less than was the case for the earlier war.

Massive global energy shortages have twin effects:

- Sharply increasing overhead costs for any investors who might want to increase production capacity for manufactured goods, while
- Enormously increasing incentive to invest in energy production capacity.

The response of the economic system is to divert available capital away from investment in manufacturing capacity towards investment in energy production capacity.

Other industries decline

Specifically, as we saw in fig. 7-5, the wavelike oscillations of pig iron shipments about their long-term trend are regulated by wavelike oscillations of wholesale fuel price indices about their long-term trend. Further, unusually high fuel prices depress investment in manufacturing capacity, which after a lag is reflected in inadequate supplies of goods on sale, which drives up prices relative to wages. In the language of economists, war-induced fuel shortages and excessive fuel prices mean that after a lag, the product of price times quantity of goods on sale (**Q**) is too great for the product of money supply times the velocity with which it circulates, so **Q** must be decreased, which implies employee layoffs, and the initiation of **the vicious cycle that starts depressions**. In the language of economics this is expressed as:

$$P\,Q = M\,V$$

In economics textbooks, the variables in the equality **P Q = M V** stand for:

P the average price of all goods and commodities on sale

Q the total quantity of all goods and commodities on sale

M the total money available for purchase of everything on sale, and

V the average velocity of circulation of money amongst the public.

The trend for production of energy, although still growing, is slowing down as additional fuel resources become scarcer, more inaccessible (as in the case of outer continental shelf crude oil) and more expensive to discover and produce. Wars stimulate the search for new fuel sources, but this stimulus has less effect as more and more of the fossil resources have already been used up. Thus the impact of the Vietnam War on the energy production growth rate was far less striking than the impact of the Civil War on energy production growth rate.

Two scenarios of events after war.

The first of these scenarios describes the sequence for a country that still has superabundant fossil or other energy resources. I will illustrate this scenario with **1**. the U.S. after the Civil War and **2**. the U.S. after after World War I.

A different, and sadder scenario is when a nation cannot increase supply because it does not have the potential to increase resource production—either because it has neither superabundant fossil or energy resources nor the capital infrastructure to make optimal use of the resources they have. This is the scenario that led **3**. Nazi Germany into World War II and **4**. Czarist Russia into World War I. (We will begin by describing Nazi Germany, for which most of the relevant statistics are available (Mitchell, 1975) and for which there can be little ambiguity or controversy about the causal pathway.)

① The U.S. Civil War created a fuel shortage, which was becoming serious in any case because of firewood was running short. This produced a surge in fuel prices in 1865. That, in turn, had two consequences, which appeared by about 1876:

- Capital investment in manufacturing depressed below its trend, and
- Marked growth in coal production.

The fuelwood shortage and surge in energy prices in 1865 created the perception of an imminent bottleneck for the economy in fuel availability, implying that there was profit to be made in eliminating that bottleneck. That perception triggered a period of sustained, steep growth in fossil energy production that lasted from 1865 until 1890. A period of rapidly increasing capital investment began in 1876 and lasted until 1893. Fuel prices, meanwhile, declined steadily from 1872 until 1894.

During the whole period 1885–1915, capital investment rates were far above their long-term trend values. This implies a high degree of market supersaturation. That produced the depression of the mid 1890s, when capital investment was the farthest above its long-term trend. This scenario did not lead to a major world war in the 1890s, however.

② World War I also created a fuel shortage in the U.S.; as a result, fuel prices shot up. Fuel production sharply increased in the 1920s, which had led to market supersaturation by 1926. Wholesale fuel prices steadily fell after that until the bottom of the depression. Depressions occur because of market supersaturation—when **Q** (quantity of goods on sale) x **P** (unit prices) is too high for **M** (the quantity of money in circulation) x **V** (velocity of circulation of money).

The 1890s depression occurred because **Q** was too high (excessive capital investment in manufacturing in response to depressed fuel prices). The 1930s depression occurred because **P** was too high (elevated average fuel prices, resulting in inadequate capital investment in manufacturing). In either case, the dollar cost of everything on sale was too high, given the sum of all dollars available to buy it and given the velocity of circulation of money. The notion that there was market saturation by 1929 was documented in fig. 4-17.

After each of these wars, the U.S. system was eventually able to come back into balance because in both cases the nation had the resource potential to raise supply enough to balance with demand.

③ World War I created extreme shortages of fuel for Germany. Production of hard coal in 1923 was only 33 percent of

> production in 1913; total 1923's coal production was only 65 percent of 1913's. This resource shortage—in combination with the punitive terms of the Versailles peace treaty—caused a commodity price explosion in Germany that became progressively more extreme from 1913–1923. The result was inadequate capital investment in Germany and stagnation of the economy from 1923–1932. By 1932 the unemployment rate in Germany was 30.1 percent of the work force. Under such circumstances there is a high probability that a significant proportion of the electorate will turn to an extremist political leader. In this case the choice was Hitler.

One means by which an extremist political leader can mobilize political support in a shattered economy is to stimulate enormous growth in basic industries in association with the manufacture of armaments. From 1932–1938, pig iron production in Germany increased 4.59 times; the unemployment rate had fallen to 2.1 by 1938 from 30.1 in 1932 (Mitchell, 1975). This is a principal reason for Hitler's widespread support among the German people.

By 1932 German unemployment was 30.1 percent; the electorate turned to an extremist leader—Hitler.

This history illustrates several causal pathways in fig. 7-1, ending with **13** and **14**: after a war, resource shortages led to a price explosion that depresses capital investment, causing a particularly severe depression. The social tensions resulting from inadequate supply and increased prices, in turn, led to a political shift to an extremist government that renewed economic growth and reduced the unemployment rate by preparing for war.

In Germany in the 1910s and 1920s, fuel shortages and increased fuel prices did not lead to a surge in fuel production as in the U.S. in the late 19th century or 1920s, simply because Germany was not so rich in potential fossil fuel resources as the U.S. was then. Thus

Why cumulative production?

We use cumulative domestic production of fossil energy, (rather than cumulative *consumption*) because it's cumulative production that determines cumulative investment in capital infrastructure, education, research and technological development, and hence the standard of living. The reason that is so is that *excess consumption does not add to the standard of living in a society, but subtracts from it* because the excess must be paid for by exporting cash from a nation, in some form.

This cash export may occur in the form of actual money (petrodollars), commodities, goods or services sold to other countries, or in a transfer of ownership rights in the U.S. capital stock to foreigners. We are, in effect, living off credit borrowed from other countries. In all of these cases, the long-term impacts on the resident U.S. population are negative, although for a long time these negative effects are veiled, or masked, in various ways. One negative effect is a gradual long-term erosion in value of the currency relative to other currencies, which gradually robs Americans of purchasing power in the world market.

Some readers may wonder why Japan, Switzerland and other countries are so successful economically when they are short of domestic fossil fuel reserves. This problem will be addressed in a later volume. At this point, it is sufficient to note that economic success depends on the product of two variables:

- The amount of energy available per capita, and
- The efficiency with which that energy is used.

Japan, Switzerland, and other countries have compensated for low domestic fossil energy reserves by having very highly efficient energy use. This has been accomplished by making the society very knowledge-intensive, which in turn is accomplished by having very high quality elementary and secondary public educational systems.

increased price could not produce the same dramatic stimulus to increased production as in the U.S. after the Civil War.

④ The scenario for Czarist Russia leading to mobilization of its armed forces in August, 1914, was probably similar, although the statistical evidence is less complete than for Nazi Germany. The Czarist economy stagnated after the 1904–1906 war with Japan, then grew explosively from 1906–1913. This growth could not be met by domestic production, so coal imports grew very rapidly from 1902–1913 (Mitchell, 1975). It is reasonable to guess that this was accompanied by an increase in fuel prices within Russia in that period, which would have resulted in an increase in all other prices relative to wages. By the late summer of 1914, there was labor unrest throughout Russia; there were massive workingmens' strikes in the streets of most cities (e.g. Ferro, 1973; Lincoln, 1983); and the ruling elite perceived an urgent need to redirect the hostility of the citizenry outwards—toward a foreign, anti-Slavic foe—rather than towards the Czarist government (e.g. Fay, 1928, page 305).

Depression or war?

Now we've seen that two wave-generating mechanisms can produce long-term cycles of war–depression or war–depression–war. Which scenario is experienced by a country depends on its potential to increase fuel production rapidly in response to sharply increased fuel prices. If a country still has vast reserves of unexploited energy sources *and* the capacity to increase productive infrastructure rapidly to exploit those resources, a war will lead to large (and ultimately excessive) increases in capital investment and a new, but mild depression. Simultaneously, war-induced fuel shortages will lead to a surge in fuel production, which sets the stage for growth of the economy after the postwar depression.

Depressions and wars—alternative responses of industrial societies to systemic crisis.

If, on the other hand, a country lacks either energy resources or energy production capacity, a war or a depression will lead to a very serious economic and political crisis from which the most likely outcome is another depression, then another war. As some scholars have noted, depressions and wars are simply alternative systemic responses of modern industrial societies to systemic crisis. Further, **depressions and very large wars involve many nations, because of the tight international linkages that have existed between major trading nations** increasingly since at least 1800.

Significance of the wave-generating process

Many recent large capital projects were trapped in a cost explosion that was predictable from fuel shortages that began in the 1970s.

Because the effects of this wave-generating mechanism permeate every aspect of society, it would be impossible for any FP activity to produce realistic output unless its underlying assumptions incorporated the mechanism. Many recent large capital projects were trapped in a cost explosion that was predictable from fuel shortages that began around the 1970s. Deflationary forces appearing in the late 1980s are radiating outwards from excessive capital investment of 1970–1982.

This wave is not by itself sufficient for FP, however. It is also necessary to understand high-frequency, short-wavelength fluctuations in society, the topic to which we turn in the next chapter.

Conclusion

When energy is either too expensive or too cheap, it has a deleterious effect.

This chapter leads to a curious finding: when energy is either too expensive or too cheap, it has a deleterious effect on society. Either leads to market supersaturation: too high, and average price of commodities on sale becomes too high for the average consumer; too cheap, and the volume of products on sale becomes excessive for the market, given the number of people who can afford to buy the products at the current price. The notion that markets can be supersaturated may seem like a strange concept to some readers. Reexamination of fig. 4-17 may make the point more convincing.

Energy and culture

To illustrate how the long waves permeate all aspects of society, I note that "popular music" around 1950 implied going to an evening concert, presented by 16–40 musicians who were brought to the concert in one or two buses.

By the 1980s, "popular music" implied a concert presented by 3–7 musicians who were driven to the concert in limos, followed by two moving vans full of amplifiers and loudspeakers, lighting equipment and complex electronic gear.

Why did the ratio of performers to energy-consuming equipment change so dramatically from 1950 to the 1980s? Why was there such a change in the method of producing all music and in the character of the music? The answer is simply that the ratio of labor costs to energy costs increased enormously during much of that interval, and the meaning of "popular music concert" is an effect for which that ratio is the cause.

In perhaps ten years, when the cost of labor relative to the cost of energy has fallen to 1950 levels, "concert" will have the same meaning as in 1950.

Chapter 8

The World Market for Crude Petroleum

By now, readers will be interested in applying the methods of this book to evaluate prospective business ventures or investments. Our first example, the world market for crude petroleum, is particularly interesting for five reasons.

- Oil is an important element in world trade and a major source of income for many nations or regions within nations (i.e., Texas, Alaska).
- Oil illustrates both typical and certain atypical features of market behavior.
- Crude oil price is an important determinant of a wide variety of other markets and processes in modern societies.
- No other phenomenon appears to have the same potential to throw a startling perturbation into the world system over the next 10 years.
- Finally, projections of the likely trend in world oil prices from now on vary enormously and are highly controversial.

The oil market is a simple, clearcut subsystem for illustrating the dynamics of supply, demand and price; in modern societies there is only one link in the causal chain from the oil market back to a fundamental system driver (FSD). That FSD is the status of the fossil fuel energy resource. Therefore, this market is almost entirely under endogenous control and is far less vulnerable to disturbance by exogenous perturbations than subsystems that are many causal links removed from the FSD.

The reason for long time lags

Business cycles have greatest amplitude (widest swings away from the trend) for manufactured goods and capital investments with long useful lives, along with commodities used to build them or fuel them. This fact provides a major insight into the mechanism generating cycles. Having purchased something with a long useful life, the purchaser is unlikely to replace it soon—even if the purchase was unwise for some reason; too much capital has been tied up in the purchase. The item will only be replaced after many years, because of the long time over which the purchase price must be depreciated. **This is a phenomenon with a long lag built in**; we shall see that such lags

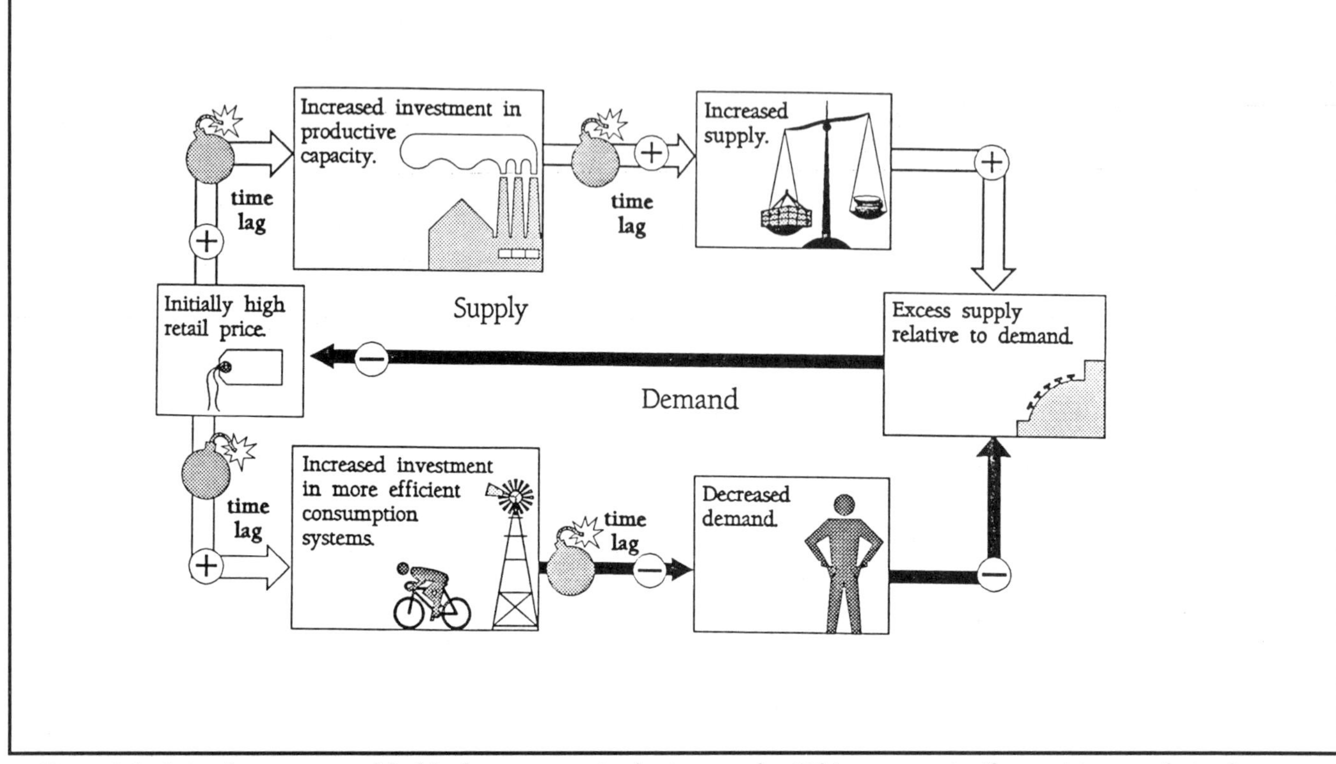

Figure 8-1. A simple systems model of the forces generating business cycles. White arrows signify a positive correlation between a cause (the origin of an arrow) and an effect (to which the arrow points). Black arrows signify an inverse causal relation between a cause and an effect. **Time delays indicated will, for many business cycles, be years, not months.** *Thus increased supply will raise the supply relative to demand (supply:demand ratio), but decreased demand will also increase the ratio. Either way, the result is to drive retail prices down. See text discussion of real-world complications.*

are much longer than most people realize. It is these lags that account for the large amplitude and long wavelength in economic fluctuations.

When an investment of any size has proven unwise, it may be several years before the full effects of that error are revealed

To explain the existence of the long time lags that generate large-amplitude cycles in socio-economic systems, we need to examine the way in which people make decisions. Consider what the typical owner of a 3-year-old car would do if energy prices suddenly doubled. Three options can be compared.

① Keep the car and drive as much as one would have done without the fuel price increase.

② Keep the car, but drive less; replace it when one normally would have done that, such as when the car is seven years old.

③ Trade in the car immediately for a new car that uses half as much gasoline per mile.

Each year, the federal government publishes tables showing the estimated cost of driving cars—by type, per mile, by category of expenditure, and by age of car. This information can be used to choose among options 1, 2 and 3.

Table 8-1. Hypothetical comparative costs (cents per mile) of keeping, vs. trading in a 3-year-old car

Expense	Costs		
	This year	Next year: 4-year-old car	New car
gasoline cost at old price	4.5	4.5	2.25
gasoline cost if prices double	9.00	9.00	4.5
depreciation	8.04	7.30	11.00
repairs & maintenance	2.48	4.00	.31
total cost per mile (at higher prices next year)	—	20.30	15.81
net gain in switching to new car	—	—	4.49

Table 8-1 shows the benefit of switching to new car immediately—4.49 cents per mile. This would be weighed against a major disincentive to purchase a new car: interest on a car loan. The economically optimal strategy (if automobile transportation yields a value) would be to keep the old car and drive it half as many miles per year. Then, at the end of the normal useful life of the car it would be traded in for a new, much more energy-efficient car. Because of reduced driving, repairs and maintenance for the old car would tend to be no more than the increment in depreciation from switching to the new car. If large numbers of people actually behaved this way after a major energy price increase, only a small part of the society-wide response would be noticed immediately. The bulk of the response would show up after a lag of many years.

More generally, this line of reasoning suggests that whenever an investment of any size has been rendered unwise by subsequent events, it may be several years before the full effects of that error are revealed. Bearing in mind that many major investments have very long lives, the lags could be decades. Electrical generating plants, fleets of jet airplanes, steel mills, automobile manufacturing plants and similar investments illustrate this principle.

A typical business cycle

The principle is illustrated in fig. 8-1 by a flow chart of causal pathways involved in a business cycle. Using energy as an example because it is a fundamental system driver, an increase in retail price of gasoline leads to increased investment in productive capacity infrastructures: oil exploration equipment, drilling rigs, refinery and tankship fleet expansion, and the like. Time lags occur both from the time of price increase to the time of increased investment, and from then until the supply has increased. Increased retail prices also increase investment in energy-conserving systems: more energy-efficient vehicles and integrated transportation systems, space heating and cooling of buildings, manufacturing, lighting and refrigeration, and so on. After a lag, this investment pattern reduces demand for energy. Increased supply relative to demand for energy (higher supply:demand ratio) would decrease retail prices.

Note that there are two negative signs in the demand loop. These cancel each other's effects, so that increased price also raises the supply:demand ratio via the demand side. There is a negative sign on the feedback from the supply:demand ratio back to retail prices, so the entire subsystem depicted in fig. 8-1 is under negative feedback control, and stable. (More generally, if there is an odd number of negative controls (minus signs) along a causal pathway, the net effect is negative feedback control, and the pathway fosters stability. An even number of negative feedbacks has the net effect of producing positive feedback. That is, a continued trend upward, with larger values of the output tending to produce ever-larger values.)

Much of decreased demand in response to price increase occurs after a long lag.

Complications arise in this simple picture, however. The *apparent* stability may not be around a constant (non-existent) equilibrium level, but may actually flucuate about a changing long-term trend. Along both supply and demand causal pathways, there may be subdivisions into multiple causal mechanisms, each with different time lags. That is, if retail prices increase suddenly, some countermeasures could be adopted immediately, such as economizing on use of the higher-priced commodity or good. Others could be adopted quickly (as by carpooling). Still others would take many years, such as trading in the old car or making the manufacturing plant for vehicles more energy-efficient. That is, much of the decreased demand in response to a price increase occurs after a long lag.

Consumption of crude oil

To illustrate the analytic procedures and the results, we can use a simple model (Appendix A) to account for year-to-year changes in U.S. consumption of refined petroleum products. Two variables are responsible for fluctuations of crude oil consumption about its trend: a large depressing effect of the ratio of the crude oil price to a measure of the U.S. average wage one year earlier, and a weaker depressing effect of the same ratio averaged over the period 4–6 years earlier. That is, **price by itself is not the key determinant of demand, but rather price relative to the mean wage**. The purchasing power of wages determines demand for a commodity or good. If the retail price doubles, coincident with a three-fold *increase* in the average wage, demand would increase, not decrease.

Fig. 8-2 depicts the trend in actual U.S. consumption of crude oil (dots), the trend computed from the model (thick line), and the computed long-term trend for consumption of refined petroleum products (thin line). Crude oil consumption rose rapidly until 1978, because wages were rising constantly relative to petroleum products. Then crude oil prices shot up relative to wages, and demand decreased sharply. This meant that there had been huge over investment in oil discovery and production, given the new high ratio of oil prices to wages. Further, the excessive capacity had a very long useful life, and it would take many years before demand for oil caught up with the new, enlarged capacity to produce supply.

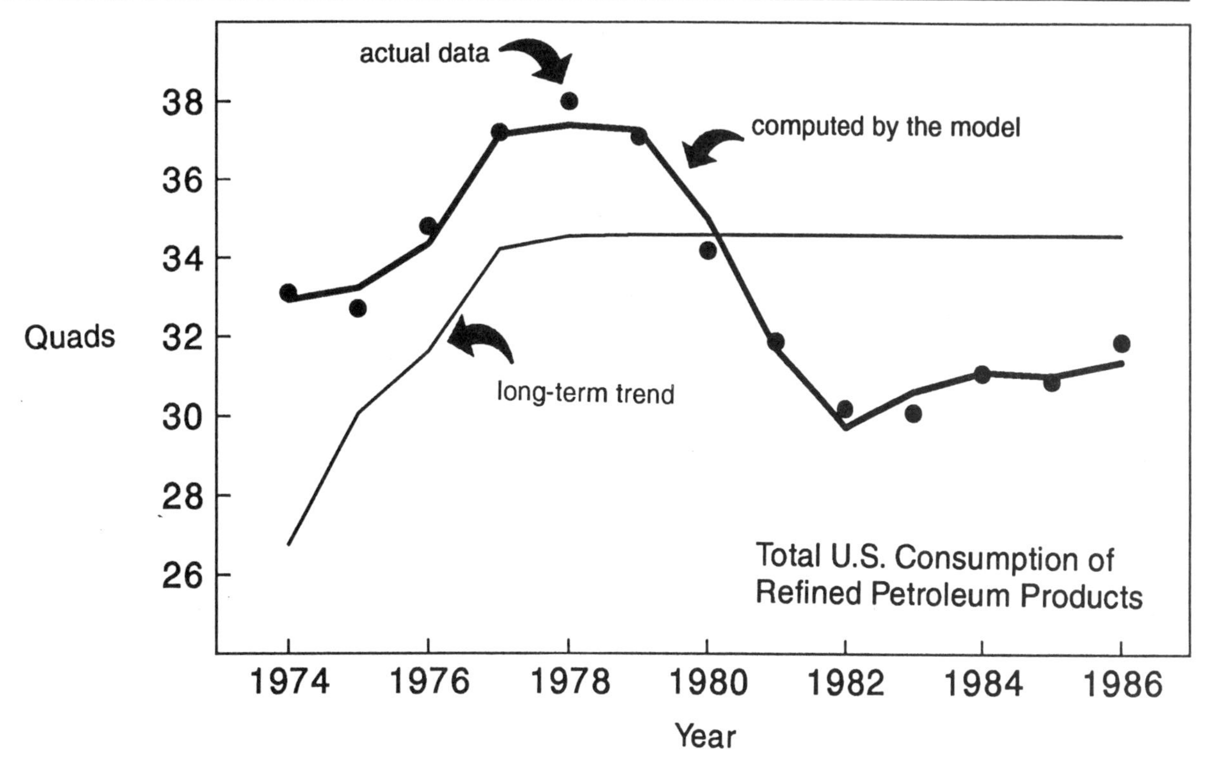

Figure 8-2. U.S. total consumption of refined petroleum products in quads (dots). (Data from SA 1979, Table 1012; SA 1987, Table 903; Energy Information Administration Annual Report to Congress, 1978, Vol. 2, Table 3.) The thick line was calculated from the simple model in Appendix A. The thin line is the computed long-term trend.

Current or Constant dollars?

Economists and accountants distinguish between "current dollars" and "constant dollars" to clarify the effect on prices of inflation (increase in the money supply).

- Any price or economic statistic for a particular year expressed in *current* dollars is the actual average price in that year.
- The *constant* dollar price makes a correction for inflation. It gives us the price as if there had been no change in the value of money due to inflation.

To illustrate, suppose we take 1967 as the base year for defining the purchasing power of the dollar for wholesale commodities. The wholesale commodity price index (a measure of the purchasing power of money) is taken as 1.000 for 1967. By 1982, the corresponding purchasing power had dropped to .356. Therefore, a wholesale item which cost $100.00 in current dollards in 1982 only cost .356($100.00), or $35.60 in the far more valuable "constant" dollars of 1967. Typically, the base year for such calculations is indicated thus: $35.60 (1967 = 1.000).

Behavior of the international oil market

The world oil market has an odd feature. Many of the oil-producing nations are poor, and oil is either a principal source of national income or almost the only source. Instead of responding to low prices by cutting back on supply so as to drive up price, the poor nation increases production to maintain income. Thus we have a positive feedback loop temporarily replacing a negative feedback loop. Lower prices lead to increased production, which leads to still lower prices. To explore the likely future scenario resulting from this situation, we can use a model for the year-to-year change in world crude oil prices (Appendix A).

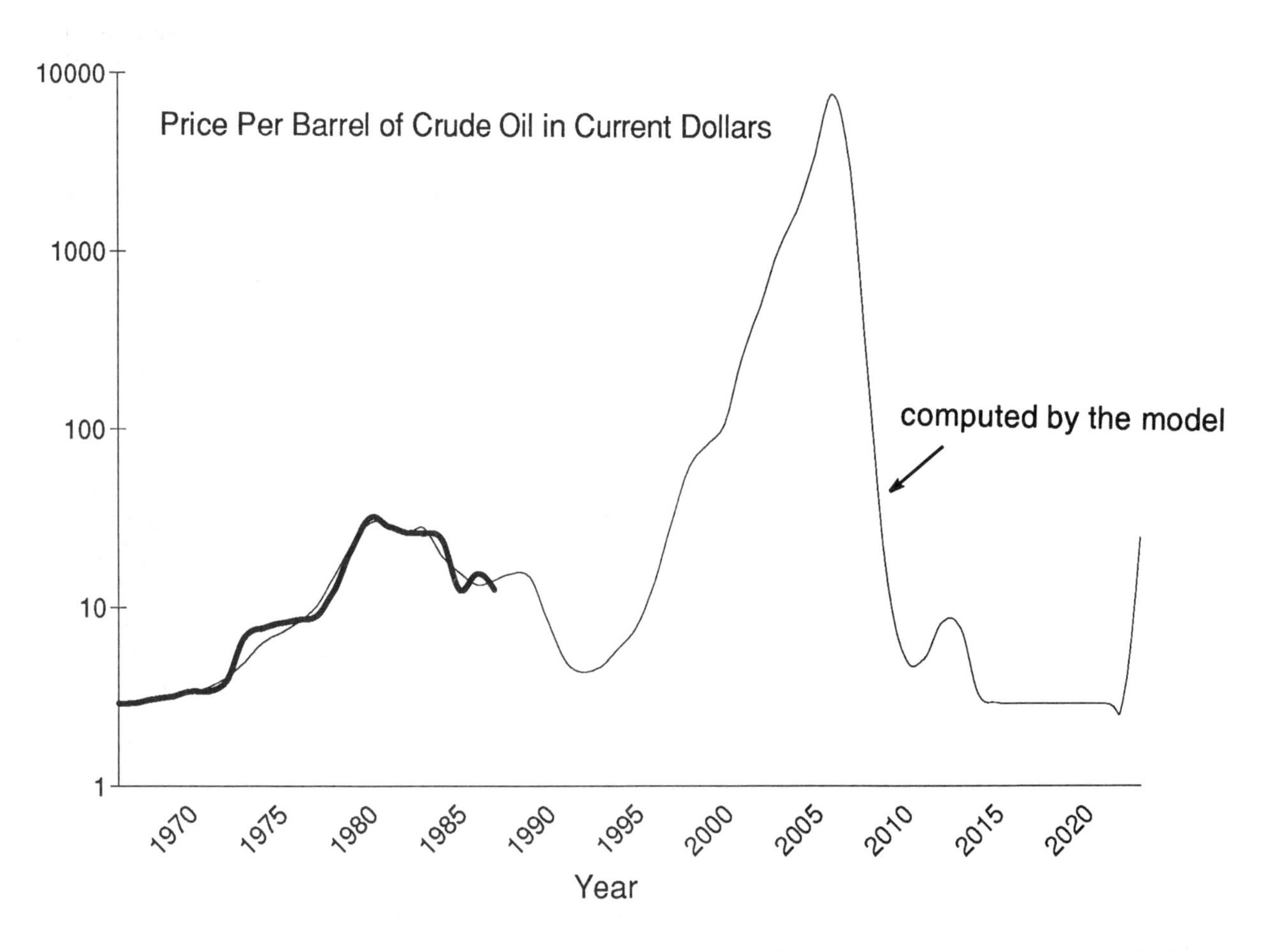

Figure 8-3. Past and projected future world oil prices, in current dollars. Actual: thick line. Projected: thin line. Projection after 1988 generated by program listed in Appendix A. Note that the predicted dip in prices indicated did not occur because Iraq was embargoed from exporting, and subsequently Kuwait's oil fields were burned and knocked out of production. (Data to 1978 from Energy Information Administration Annual Report to Congress, 1978, Vol. 2, Table 26; thereafter, SA 1987, Table 1166.)

A simple model accounted for 96.8 percent of the year-to-year change in world oil price from 1967–1988 (data from SA 1990 Table 1213). In fig. 8-3, actual oil price data are represented by the thick line. The forecasting model generated the thin line for 1967–2024,inclusive. I found that three variables in combination provided the most accurate prediction of the world oil price.

- Cumulative U.S. production of domestic fossil fuel, in quadrillions of BTUs. This variable generated a long-term rising trend in the oil price.
- Averages of oil price over the period 11–16 years earlier.
- Averages of oil price over the period 2–4 years earlier.

In each case, **high past prices produced low present price and vice versa**. Further, the intensity of this **inverse effect was greater for the longer time lag**.

We can interpret these results to mean that excessive investment in oil discovery, production, transportation, refining and marketing capital infrastructure supersaturates the world oil market after a lag and has a depressing effect on prices 2 to 4 years later and 11–16 years later.

This **system is very delicately balanced between two opposing forces**:

- Long-term effect of progressive depletion of world fossil fuel resources, which increases prices in the long run, and
- Intermediate and short-term effects of capital overinvestment in the global oil business, which depresses prices.

This is a system with enormous instability.

Further, because of the 11–16 year time lag, once a wavelike oscillation begins, it is many years before it reverses itself. For example, oil prices rose almost constantly from 1970 until 1981, when they began to decrease. When that decrease began, it continued to at least 1991, apart from the upward movement caused by the Persian Gulf War. The fit of the model to data up to 1988 shows that a change in crude oil prices has only a slight immediate effect on consumption, production and price of oil. **The lagged effects** of deviations of crude oil prices about their long-term trend line **are so large that they completely mask the slight, immediate effects of a change in prices.**

Are these results credible, and what do they mean?

We projected world oil price from 1989–2024 as if the Persian Gulf War never occurred, using the model that fitted the data well until 1988. The price drops steadily to $4.36 a barrel in current dollars by 1993, then gradually increases to $7423 dollars a barrel by 2007, then undergoes a tremendous drop to $2.92 a barrel before rising again in 2024.

The result does not violate either observation or common sense. The price did drop from about $32 in 1981 to about $20 in 1991. As of 1991, about 10 percent of the world's exportable supply is being withheld from market, because of the oil well fires in Kuwait and the embargo on exports from Iraq. Given a market as volatile as this, it is credible that the world oil price drop would probably have been far greater if those two countries had been able to export.

Once oil prices began to move up in 1970, they continued to increase until 1981. Governments make it possible for people to afford higher oil prices by printing money faster. It is reasonable to expect that to happen any time in the future that oil becomes scarce. After a while, however, the public will respond by a massive move to more energy efficient systems, and the oil price will collapse after 2007. Readers who wish to explore the consequences of modifying the oil forecasting model will find the program listed in Table 13-4. The huge drop in oil prices forecast after 2007 should come as no surprise.

Conclusions

More generally, the following conclusions apply.

- There is a great deal of inertia in complex socio-economic-environmental systems. Almost all of the response of demand to changes in the wage:price ratio is delayed by several years. Prices many years ago may be more important than prices one year ago in accounting for year to year variance in consumption. Failure to grasp the significance of these long lags is the single most important reason why so much demand forecasting has been badly off the mark. It is noteworthy that **in 1988, U.S. consumption of petroleum products was still lower than it had been in 1973, even though the oil price had been dropping since 1982**. The system was still adjusting to energy price increases that ended in 1981.

Failure to grasp the significance of long time lags is the single most important reason why so much demand forecasting has been badly off the mark. In 1988, U.S. consumption of petroleum products was still adjusting to price increases that ended in 1981.

- Complex socio-economic-environmental systems are characterized by cumulative effects. It can be demonstrated statistically that the most important measure of oil prices in accounting for year-to-year variability in current oil prices is the average price over a series of previous years. We see this phenomenon repeatedly in complex systems: the true independent variable is the mean of a series of values extending over a particular time interval. In other words, many variables in complex systems function as a storage (or reservoir) rather than as flow (e.g., over the spill-way). The current impact of the storage is determined by the net inputs to the storage over a series of years, not the net input to it in a single year. Perhaps the clearest example of why this must be so is an inventory, such as the excessive housing inventory in a housing market. **It does not matter in which past year houses were added to the inventory; the important variable is the total number of houses in the inventory.**

The current impact of a storage is determined by net inputs over a series of years, not net input in a single year.

Present day fuel use is so profligately wasteful in certain countries, particularly the U.S., Canada and Australia, that slight price increases, in constant dollars, will inevitably produce major reductions in fuel use with very little change in life style and virtually no pain or discomfort. To illustrate, in 1983 the average mileage per gallon (mpg) of all U.S. cars was only 16.7, yet experimental cars are being developed with fuel economy of up to 105mpg. Thus, even with no alteration of the present life style (high percentage of all passenger transportation in the form of one rider per car), a switch to more energy-efficient cars would decrease fuel use by a factor of six. Simply doubling the number of riders per car in a very half-hearted effort at car pooling would decrease passenger transportation fuel use by a further factor of two. Any really serious effort at increasing energy efficiency in passenger transportation would decrease fuel use per passenger mile by a factor of twenty.

This astounding capacity for increased energy efficiency in society permeates all aspects of fuel use; coupled with the long time lags in response, this sets the stage for a future oscillatory pattern in price trends. The extraordinary self-regulatory behavior in the oil price market results from the interplay between two phenomena.

- First, mass publics need to see a sustained price increase for at least three years before they become convinced it is likely to last and worthy of a permanent behavioral change. This introduces a delay into the response to oil price increases.
- Secondly, once the public becomes convinced that the oil price increase is likely to last, their response has the potential to be violent, because there are so many relatively painless means to achieve major fuel economies.

Once corporations and governments become convinced of the potential for serious instability inherent in the world oil market, steps may be taken to dampen the oscillations.

Once a mathematical model has been developed that describes the historical behavior of any system, it can be used to construct a computer simulation game, for forecasting likely future trends and exploring likely responses to various policy options. Once corporations and governments become convinced of the potential for serious social and economic instability inherent in the world oil market, steps may be taken to dampen the oscillations. One means would be to put a floor under constant-dollar oil prices, using national sales taxes. **Vigorous efforts to dampen oil price oscillations would be successful**. Many games can be invented to explore the consequences of future oil pricing policies. The upper or lower oil price could be forced to fall within certain limits, or the dynamics of the game can be altered by introducing various rules or relationships.

Summary and implications

This chapter has presented the fundamental principles basic to all business cycles. In all cases, the system includes some kind of storage or inventory that can be filled to overflowing or depleted too far. That storage should be understood in a very general fashion. (It might represent, for example, the sum of all worldwide investment in oil production and refining capacity over a previous series of years.) The oscillatory behavior is regulated by the size of this storage, **after a delay**. It is the excess inventory of any good, commodity, or production capacity built up over a series of years in which supply exceeded demand, that depresses market prices. The lag in this process is the source of the oscillatory behavior.

In chapters 6–8 we have seen examples of simple oscillatory mechanisms at work. **In all these cases, the pattern of oscillation resulted from a single wave-generating mechanism**. For any reader who accepts the argument of this chapter as proved, the implications for business or government planning are enormous. We live in a culture for which the basic premise is never-ending growth, yet almost everything around us has either already stopped growing or will soon stop growing. Few institutions have grasped the implications of this simple observation for strategic planning.

We live in a culture whose basic premise is never-ending growth, yet almost everything around us has either already stopped growing or will soon stop growing.

No matter whether we consider oil price, population growth, consumer purchasing power, or net profit in agriculture, they and **a host of other examples suggest that growth is over**. From now on, money will be made by improving the quality of life in an oscillating, not a growing system. Oddly, the standard of living, quality of life, and gross national product per capita in U.S. dollars are highest in parts of the world where most variables have shown little growth for years. Most people have not noticed that fact or understood its meaning.

Standard of living, quality of life, and GNP are highest in parts of the world where most variables have shown little growth for years.

Chapter 9

Forecasting Behavior of Volatile Markets

Modern society is full of highly volatile markets that don't simply rise steadily. For example:

- The price farmers receive for agricultural commodities fluctuates wildly. A bushel of corn sold for $3.21 in 1983, but only $1.50 in 1986 (SA89 T1121).
- The earnings-to-price ratio for the average share of 500 Standard and Poor common stocks was 12.66 percent in 1980, but only 5.48 percent in 1987 (SA89 T826). This would suggest a startling drop by 1987, which did, in fact, occur.
- The price of an ounce of gold was $148 in 1977, $613 in 1980, and $376 in 1982 (SA89 T767).
- New car sales in the U.S. were 9.2 million in 1977, 5 million in 1982, and 8 million in 1985 (SA89 T1013).
- House sales in the U.S. Midwest were 1.14 million in 1978, .49 million in 1982, and .96 million in 1987 (SA89 T1235).

With prices, earnings, and sales jumping up and down this way, all decision makers—from individual investors to corporate planners—could benefit from realistic forecasting models. Suppose the price for something increases by a factor of four times over three years, as with gold from 1977–1980, or by 3.3 times over five years, as with wheat from 1969–1974. Models can help with questions such as these:

- What is going on?
- Is this simply an 8- or 10-year cycle at work, or
- Are the prices likely to stay high for a longer period?

The answers affect our strategic decision-making. If a sudden price jump is part of a short-term oscillation and no more, we do not invest more in the commodity or our capacity to produce it. Sales and prices will shortly be sinking, not rising. We might even decide to leave this line of trade or production. If we believe the price jump portends higher prices for at least a decade, then we might consider it worthwhile to invest in greater productive capacity. If we perceive a recent price run-up as signalling an indefinitely growing sales trend, we would invest a lot in increased productive capacity.

Also, we would like to know how price and sales trends are behaving relative to trends in other sectors. If computer software sales or specialized medical and clinical services are growing more rapidly than anything else in the economy, then perhaps we should move to that area of the economy, permanently. Given all the different markets, activities, or types of education and training in which we could invest, which are the most profitable? The most sophisticated strategy of all is to shift from one activity to another, moving towards steepest rates of growth in demand.

An important point is worth mentioning before moving on. Prices in apparently unrelated parts of the economy move together. Adages of ancient origin reflect this observation:

Prices in apparently unrelated parts of the economy move together.

> *"A good suit for a man, or dress for a woman costs an ounce of gold;*
> *A good house costs a thousand ounces of gold."*

This fact provides a clue in developing forecasting models. Over the 11 years 1977–1987, inclusive, the prices of gold, oil and wheat varied by factors of 4.14, 3.70 and 1.68 times, respectively. The *ratios* of those prices, however, varied by less than the fluctuation in gold prices. During that period an ounce of gold never cost less than 13.2 barrels of oil or more than 28.4, as shown in Table 9-1. It never cost less than 63 bushels of wheat, or more than 176. These coincidental movements suggest the possibility of causal connections between apparently unrelated sectors.

Over 1977–1987, an ounce of gold never cost less than 13.2 barrels of oil or more than 28.4.

Table 9.1. Coincidental price movements in diverse markets.

Year	Price of one ounce of gold (current dollars)	Price of one barrel of oil (current dollars)	Price of one bushel of wheat (current dollars)
1977	148	8.57	2.33
1978	194	9.00	2.97
1979	308	12.64	3.78
1980	613	21.59	3.91
1981	460	31.77	3.66
1982	376	28.52	3.55
1983	424	26.19	3.53
1984	361	25.88	3.39
1985	318	24.09	3.08
1986	368	12.51	2.42
1987	448	15.40	2.57

Developing a forecasting model for wheat prices

In fig. 9-1, I've used price (current dollars) of a bushel of wheat in the U.S. to illustrate the creation of forecasting models for volatile markets. For most phenomena we wish to forecast, a very high proportion of year-to-year variability is under control of systemic, predictable, non-random causes. Consequently, we are able to forecast up to 99.8 percent of year-to-year variation consistently for most markets. In the case of wheat, however, an extraordinarily high proportion (17 percent) of the year-to-year variation in price is under the control of weather phenomena. Thus, the trick in forecasting is to separate out the causative agents, and focus on the effects of *predictable*, rather than unusual events.

The unusual forces affecting wheat prices fall into two categories: geophysical and geopolitical. The top panel of fig. 9-1 depicts year-to-year variations in actual current-dollar prices of wheat (K508), superimposed on the calculated long-term price trend. The bottom panel depicts the price trend (thin line) projected from a simple forecasting model. The differences between the price trends in the top and bottom panels illustrate unusual forces of both types—geophysical and geopolitical.

Geophysical force

As I've mentioned before, the effect of the volcanic eruption at Krakatau in 1883 dropped world surface temperatures everywhere over the period 1883-1888 (e.g. J254,J266). Consequently, wheat production took a severe downturn over the period 1885–1888 (K507), resulting in high prices during that interval, particularly in 1888 (K508). This shows up as a clear upward blip in price (top panel, 1890–1891). No presently-existing model could predict that blip; the timing of volcanic eruptions is unpredictable. The model produced simulated wheat prices (bottom panel) around 1890 below the 1890–1891 data. Thus, the simulated prices imply a slight undersupply, whereas the actual data imply that supplies were quite short relative to demand.

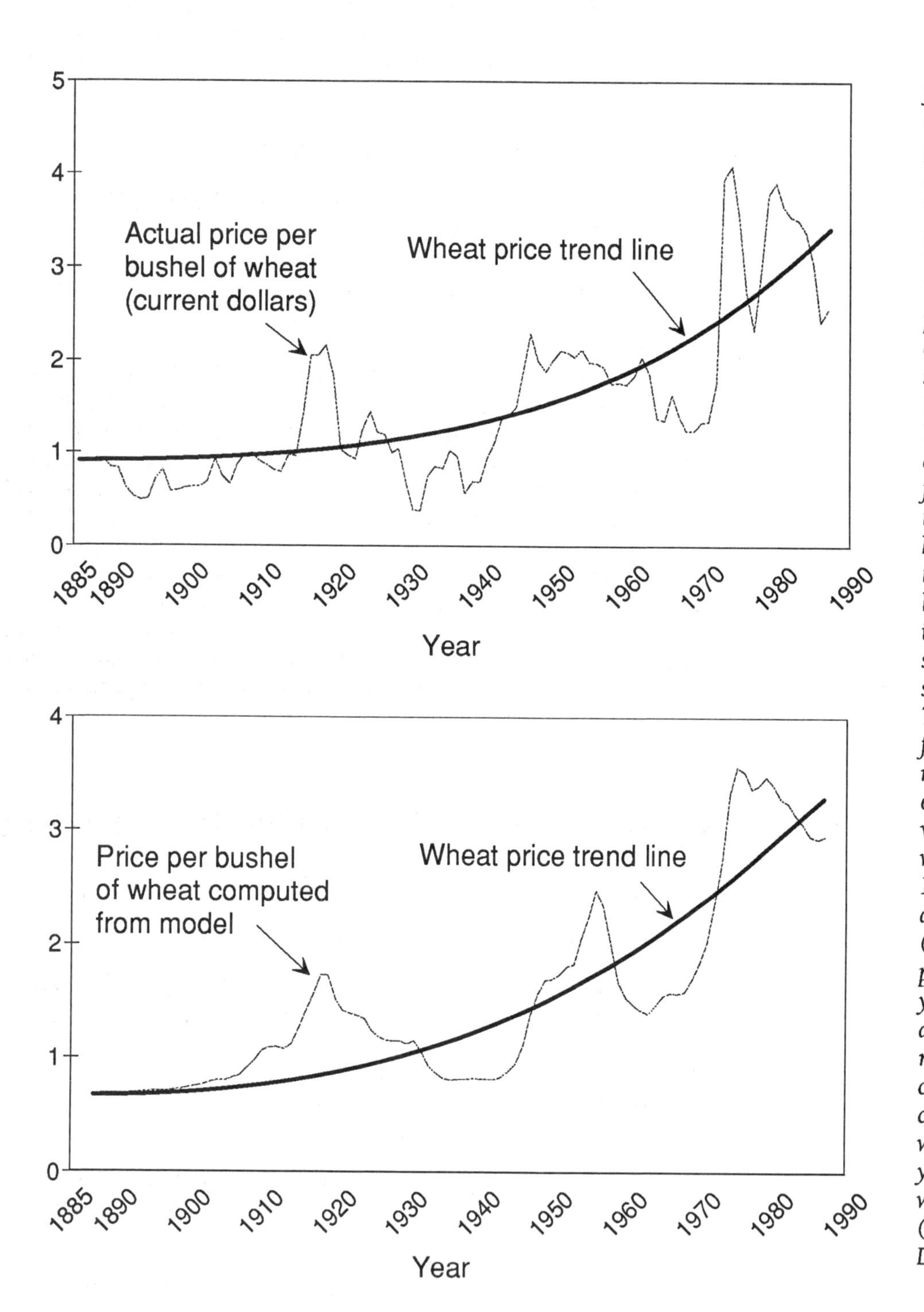

Figure 9-1. Year-to-year fluctuations in current dollar price of a bushel of wheat. The top panel depicts actual data since 1880 (K508). The bottom panel depicts output from a simple model (Appendix A.). To facilitate comparison of fluctuations in the top and bottom panels, the calculated long-term trend in wheat price is shown (thick, smooth lines). The startling feature of the model is that the explanatory variables are: wheat prices 13–15 years ago; WFPI (wholesale fuel price index) 25 years ago (E29); and the average ratio of the contract construction wage 21–23 years ago to that wage in 1856 (D745, D735, D719).

Geopolitical effects

By far the most startling unusual perturbation to wheat prices over the last 110 years occurred from 1973–1975 (sharp upward spike in top panel, fig. 9-1). It came about for geopolitical reasons, which, in turn, occurred because of a historically unique coincidence of three events.

① The U.S. was beginning to deplete domestic reserves of crude oil by 1971, and the dollar cost to import crude oil began to explode at about that time, particularly beginning in 1973 (SA 1978, Table 1521). This severely impacted the U.S. merchandise trade balance with other countries, with the cost of imported crude oil jumping by $24 billion over a four-year period.

Remarkably, this fuel shortage coincided with

② Large U.S. stocks of wheat and corn in 1972 (SA 1978 Tables 1227 and 1229), and

③ A small Soviet Union wheat crop in 1974, and an even smaller one in 1975 (SA 1978, Table 1570).

From this unusual trio of coinciding events developed the idea of exporting U.S. agricultural commodities to communist block countries, to benefit our foreign exchange position, so we would be better able to purchase crude oil from oil-exporting nations. The resulting enormous decrease in U.S. wheat inventories (SA 1978 Table 1229) caused a great reduction in domestic wheat supply relative to demand. This, in turn, caused the great blip in wheat prices between 1973 and 1975, appearing as the price spike in the top panel of fig. 9-1. No other unexpected perturbation of comparable scale appears in the historical record. Unexpected perturbations of this magnitude provide the ultimate challenge to forecasters, and require that we make a clean separation between predictable and less predictable components of the causal systems generating effects on markets.

Requirements for better forecasting

In order to develop forecasting models, we need two things:

- Data on history of the markets, and
- Some understanding of the behaviors of the players in each market in response to either unusually high or low prices.

This information can be obtained in government historical statistical documents, or industry publications. We need details on the two standard responses to unusual prices.

- Unusually **high prices cause increased production**, so as to gain the unusually high profitability from a unit of commodity, goods, or services sold.
- Unusually **low prices cause a cutback on production**, and productive capacity may be diverted to production of alternate goods or services.

Behavioral responses to price changes

The complication for the development of forecasting models comes about because these behavioral responses occur on four very different time scales: 3–8 years, 16–26 years, 34–44 years, and several centuries (summarized in Table 9-2). These time scales are associated, respectively, with economic, investment, demographic, and energy resource phenomena.

Business cycle

In the shortest (3–8 year) case, producers respond to unusually high or low prices by adjusting their utilization of available productive capacity up or down. If prices are very high, available capacity is used at close to 100 percent of its productive potential. If prices are very low, utilization of productive capacity falls very low. This process is known as the short term business cycle. For example, new car sales peak every fourth year.

Investment cycle

In the intermediate (16–26 year) case, producers respond to unusually high prices by investing in more productive capacity. This process takes time, because years may go into planning, research and development, site preparation, factory or heavy equipment construction, tooling up for manufacturing, then selling new products or services until the market has been saturated. Examples are the conversion of the U.S. transportation system from train-dominated to car and truck-dominated, conversion of the agricultural sector from horse-drawn to tractor-drawn, or installation of new types of energy-producing systems, such as refineries or electrical energy generating systems, or factories.

Table 9-2. Systemic behavioral responses occur on different time scales.

Prices	Response	Sector responding	Time lag	Example
high	productive capacity nearly 100% used	economic (short-term business cycle)	3–8 yrs	new car sales
low	low use of productive capacity			
high	greater investment in productive capacity	investment	16–26 yrs	conversion of U.S. transportation from trains to cars and trucks
low	diversion of investment capital to other areas			
high	workers move into the primary industry	demographic	34–44 years	depression-associated drop in labor force in agricultural, mining, other industries
low	workers move into different primary industries			
high	over-exploitation of resources	energy resources	several centuries	rise and fall of major civilizations
low	decreased exploitation when resources become depleted			

The long time delay from initiation to completion of such processes—leading to supersaturation of their markets,—explains wavelike oscillations in all economic and social systems, with wavelengths of about 30–40 years (fig. 7-1). As we shall see, much of the year-to-year variation in market behavior usually attributed to the business cycle is in fact being driven by these longer time-delayed processes.

Much variation in market behavior usually attributed to the business cycle is in fact being driven by longer time-delayed processes.

Demographic cycle

An even longer cycle (68–88 years) enters markets associated with movement of workers between different sectors of the economy. Depressions produce their severest effects on primary industries: agriculture, forestry, fishing, mining, fossil fuels and production of raw metals. These industries are also characterized by a strong sense of tradition in the labor force: sons do the same work as their fathers, grandfathers, and great-grandfathers. If the sons should leave such traditional occupations, they are unlikely to be replaced by young men migrating into these primary industries from service industries in the cities. When a depression strikes, the sons of traditional workers leave these occupations as soon as possible.

When depression strikes, sons of traditional workers leave traditional occupations as soon as possible.

Throughout history, **the "new work opportunity" that arose shortly after a depression was a war**. After the war, surviving sons of primary industry laborers could seek new occupations in cities. For a while, their absence in the labor force of primary industries can be compensated for by increases in labor productivity brought about by technological revolutions. The day of reckoning comes when the fathers retire. Because many of their sons are missing from the industry because of death in war or migration to cities, there are no sons to replace them. Suddenly no amount of technological revolution can mask or veil the mysterious contraction of the labor force in primary industries.

The time lag from depression to marked contraction in the primary industry labor force is 34–44 years. The reality of this postulated mechanism can be checked by inspecting data series on the farm population (K1) and the number of people engaged in mining (M5). The depression of 1932 produced a rapid reduction in primary industry labor forces in 1957. The depression of 1894–5 produced a huge drop in the number of coal and metal miners after 1919, and the depression of 1932–3 produced another huge drop in the number of coal miners about 1959–60 (M297).

Resource cycles

The longest cycle of all (a wavelength of several centuries) describes the rise and fall of economic and political power of a nation, as it goes through the cycle of building up the rate of exploitation of its natural resources, then decreasing that rate as its resources become depleted. This is the cycle that was traced out by the rise and fall of Phoenicia, Palmyra, Mesopotamia, the Roman Empire, the Incas, Mayans, and the empires of Imperial Spain and Britain.

Fine tuning our model

We need to make several adjustments to our model, based on the four cycles just covered.

Business cycle

The absolutely simplest assumption we can make about future market conditions is that managers adjust capacity utilization rates upward to exploit high prices, and downward to avoid low prices over the very short term. Upward adjustment would increase the flow of goods, shortly supersaturate the market, and drive down prices. Downward adjustment would decrease the flow of goods, demand would shortly overwhelm supply, and prices would increase. If this reaction were vigorous and widespread over four years, a graph of prices each year against prices four years before would drop from the upper left corner to the lower right corner, as in the top left panel of fig. 9-2.

We would expect the price reaction to have become even more vigorous after six years, as in the bottom left panel. Testing this idea on the wheat price series from 1850–1987 (K508), we produce on the computer screen a graph of wheat prices for each year plotted against wheat prices four years previously. Fig. 9-2, top right panel depicts a computed trend line and all the data points, which show great scatter about this trend. Even more startling, the curve has the opposite slope to that expected. That is, prices tended, if anything, to go up in the short term in response to higher prices.

Waves and time lags

Note that when we speak of wave, it is from peak to peak, or trough to trough. The associated time lag, however, is from a peak to the next low point. Thus, the 78-year wave has a 39-year time delay.

There is only slight evidence of a response to previous prices in this graph. Over the 138 years, low prices tended to follow low prices. Intermediate prices tended to follow intermediate prices. Only when prices four years ago were very high does there appear to be a slight price decrease four years later. Presumably, when prices were very high, this resulted over the short term in increased production, supersaturation of the market, and a slight depression in prices four years later.

We also note an important phenomenon: years of outlier data that do not follow the general pattern. The years 1866, 1973, 1974 and 1975 are clearly aberrant with respect to the rest of the data (top right panel of fig. 9-1). The first—1866—represents an explosion in demand relative to supply, characteristic of the period just after a war. The equation describing the effect of prices 4 years ago on current prices accounts for only 64.5 percent of the year-to-year variability in wheat prices over the 138 years of data. This is scarcely the type of forecast reliability that would give us a basis for making business decisions with any confidence.

Therefore, we consider the possibility that it took somewhat longer to make capacity utilization adjustments in response to unusually low or high prices.

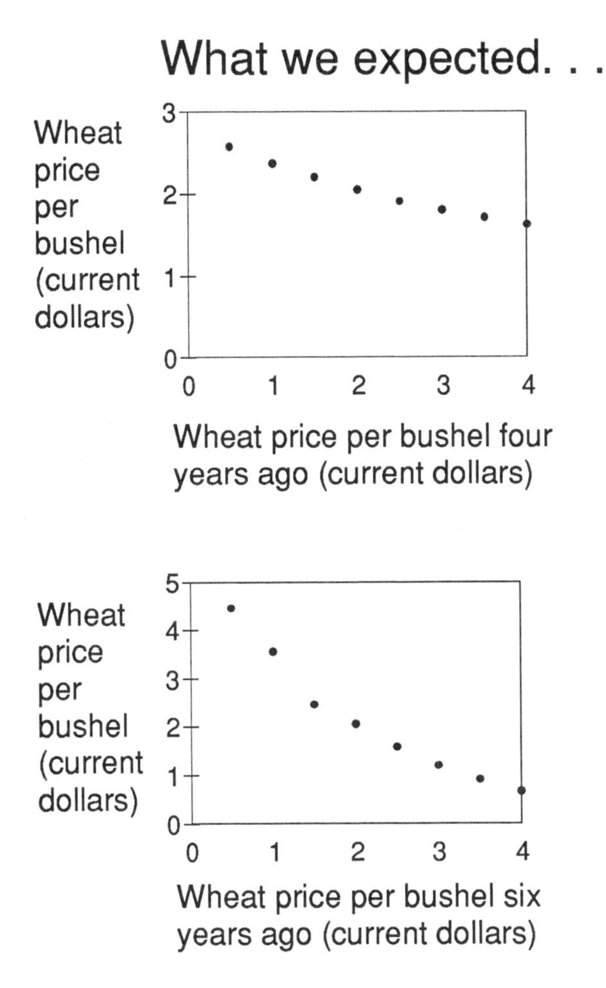

Figure 9-2. Hypotheses and findings concerning the short term business cycle in data on the current dollar price per bushel of wheat in the United States (K508). The left hand panels depict the self-regulatory process we hypothesized in the wheat market over four years (top panel) and six years (bottom panel).

The right hand panels depict the corresponding patterns actually observed. There is virtually no short-term self regulation operating in this market. The labelled data points are values for extreme outlier years.

Investment cycle

Accordingly, we examine the possibility that the adjustment required six, not four years. When we produce this graph on the computer screen, we get the pattern in the bottom right panel of fig. 9-2. Again, the data for 1866 and 1973–5 stand out as outliers. Compared with prices 4 years ago, this relationship is even less useful for prediction. Even with the four outliers removed, it only accounts for 59 percent of the year-to-year variation in wheat prices over 138 years.

Adjustment of data for long run trend

Therefore, we need to introduce a refinement—adjusting both present and past wheat prices relative to the long-run upward price trend that is so apparent in the top panel of fig. 9-1. As we've shown in earlier chapters, an equation was tuned to the historical data, to express the long-term effect on wheat price each year of the cumulative U.S. production of fossil fuel. As we've found already, the status of a nation's fossil fuel reserves has the effect of a fundamental systems driver on all long-term trends in a modern society.

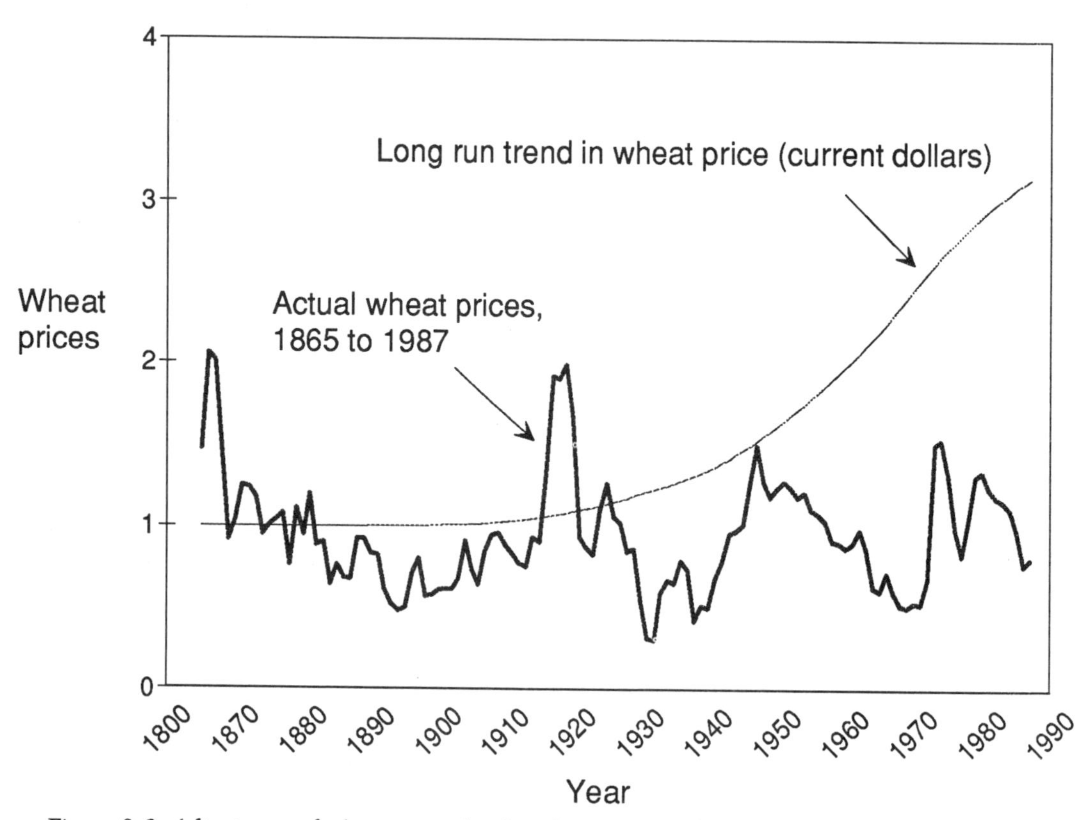

Figure 9-3. Adjustment of wheat prices for their long-term trend. The smooth curve is the long-term price trend, computed from the cumulative U.S. production of fossil fuel, expressed in quads (computed by adding up M76 from the earliest date, less M81). The trend in wheat prices was obtained by dividing the data for each year by the value of the long-term trend.

The severity of another major downturn in 1968 has been masked because the long-term trend was steeply rising at that time.

The fitted equation (Appendix A) produces the upward-rising, long-term trend in fig. 9-3 (thin line). This equation accounted for 65 percent of the year-to-year variation in wheat prices from 1865–1987. When the actual data are divided by the values computed from this equation, we obtain the pattern of year-to-year fluctuations (thick line) in fig. 9-3. This graph clearly exposes four major upward price spikes: those produced by the Civil War in 1866, World Wars I and II in 1919 and 1946, and a fourth period of intermittently high prices in the 1970s and 1980s. Also, we discover that, in addition to the well-known depressions of 1893 and 1932, another major downturn appears at 1968 in the bottom panel. The severity of this downturn had been masked because the long-term trend was in a steeply rising phase at that time.

Predictions based on recent data

When we plot trend-adjusted wheat prices against adjusted prices four or six years ago, we obtain the same patterns as in the two right-hand panels of fig. 9-2. Some of the more extreme outliers are indicated. These two panels suggest that this approach is virtually worthless in accounting for major market perturbations. From statistical analysis, adjusted wheat prices four years ago only account for 8 percent of the year-to-year variation in wheat prices.

The data for 1973,1974, and 1975 are extreme outliers. When these data are excluded, however, adjusted wheat prices four years ago still only accounts for 14 percent of the year-to-year variation in adjusted wheat prices. Combining the trend equation with the equation for explaining departures about the wheat price trend, we can only account for 62 percent of the variation over the last 138 years. Clearly, this approach is almost useless in accounting for major fluctuations in wheat prices. Using a similar approach applied to the relation between adjusted wheat prices each year, and adjusted prices six years ago produces a similar result: it only accounts for 65 percent of the year-to-year variation in wheat prices.

Most forecasting assumes that causes can be found in the recent past. These results suggest that causes of the current state are either non-existent (that is, a random process), or are found much further back in time.

This is an extremely important finding. Almost all modern forecasting is based on the assumption that the causes of an effect now can be found in the recent past. The results just presented suggest that the causes of the current state of a system are either nonexistent (that is, we have a random process), or are found much further back in time. Therefore, we need to discover the factor or factors causing longer cycles than those just considered, and which account for major market excursions from the trend line.

Capital investment cycle

Simply by examining historical time series, we see hints that adjustments in capital investment are crucial in producing major fluctuations in all measures of economic, resource-utilization, social, political, industrial, agricultural and cultural variables.

For example, wheat prices peaked in 1919, then hit a low in 1932—a lag of 13 years. They were high from 1947–1954, then hit a low in 1968 and 1969, 14 or 15 years after the high plateau. This suggests a hypothesis: extreme price spikes lead to massive overinvestment in productive capacity, which then after about 14 years leads to market supersaturation, and a price collapse (see also fig. 7-1). In industry after industry, we find data to support this hypothesis.

For example, the price spike in wheat from 1916–1920 resulted in the agricultural sector converting from a horse-drawn system to a tractor-drawn system. There were 37,000 tractors on farms in 1916, and 1,022,000 in 1932 (K184). The result was a gradual increase in wheat production per acre until by 1931, it was 29 percent higher than in 1916. This supersaturated the market, and the price collapsed in 1932.

Further, analysis of the process involved in major capital investments in many industries has pointed out the existence of time lags lasting many years. The processes of planning, approval, site preparation, research, development, tooling up for manufacturing, production, then buildup in the new capital stock takes 10–40 years for major capital items, with the longer times being for national deployment of new types of energy-generating or transportation systems (Hirsch, 1987; Watt, 1982).

Two wavelengths associated with labor force migration

This process has been described earlier in the chapter. A variety of types of evidence suggest that this time lag is 34–44 years, not 16–26. Now we explore the utility of forecast models that combine self-regulatory mechanisms with both **21- and 39-year time lags. We discover that these are, in fact, the mechanisms that produce major societal fluctuations**. This is demonstrated because models based on this assumption account for the fluctuations in markets actually observed, as in the correspondence between the two panels of fig. 9-1. Specifically, the presence of these two wave-generating mechanisms explains a major puzzle: why have time lags between depressions, or between wars, varied through history. To illustrate, early in the history of the Industrial Revolution, depressions occurred 52 or 53 years apart: in 1739, 1791, 1843 and 1896. Later, however, the time between economic downturns shortened to 36 or 37 years: 1933–1969 (E23, E40, E52, E97).

The relative strength of the two control mechanisms has altered during and after the Industrial Revolution—the 78-year wave gradually increasing relative to the 36-year wave.

The explanation for this shift in wavelength is that the relative strength of the two control mechanisms has altered through the Industrial Revolution and the post-industrial phase, with the 78-year wave gradually increasing both in absolute strength, and relative to the 36-year wave. In the forecasting model, we deal with this increase in the importance of the 39-year delay mechanism by making its effect stronger with increasing year number.

There are two ways to demonstrate this change through time in the relative strength of the two wave-generating processes. The first is to depict the values of their effects through time, as in fig. 9-4. The two panels show that wheat prices 34–44 years ago, and 16–26 years ago, respectively, produce departures of wheat price above and below its trend line. The violent societal oscillations from 1880–1920 were clearly largely the work of the short cycle-generating mechanism operating with a 21-year lag. After the late 1950s, however, the mechanism with the 34–44 year delay became of overriding importance and was responsible for both the severity of the depression of the 1930s and the violence of the upswing in the 1940s. Putting it differently, just after the industrial revolution a capital investment cycle-generating mechanism was dominant in producing waves in wheat prices, but after the 1950s, a demographic cycle-generating mechanism became dominant.

Another way of examining the mechanisms depicted in fig. 9-4 is presented in fig. 9-5. There, the relationships depicted are:

- The effects of wheat prices 39 years earlier on the multiplier that produces departures of wheat price from its trend line, and
- The effect of wheat prices 16–26 years earlier on its multiplier.

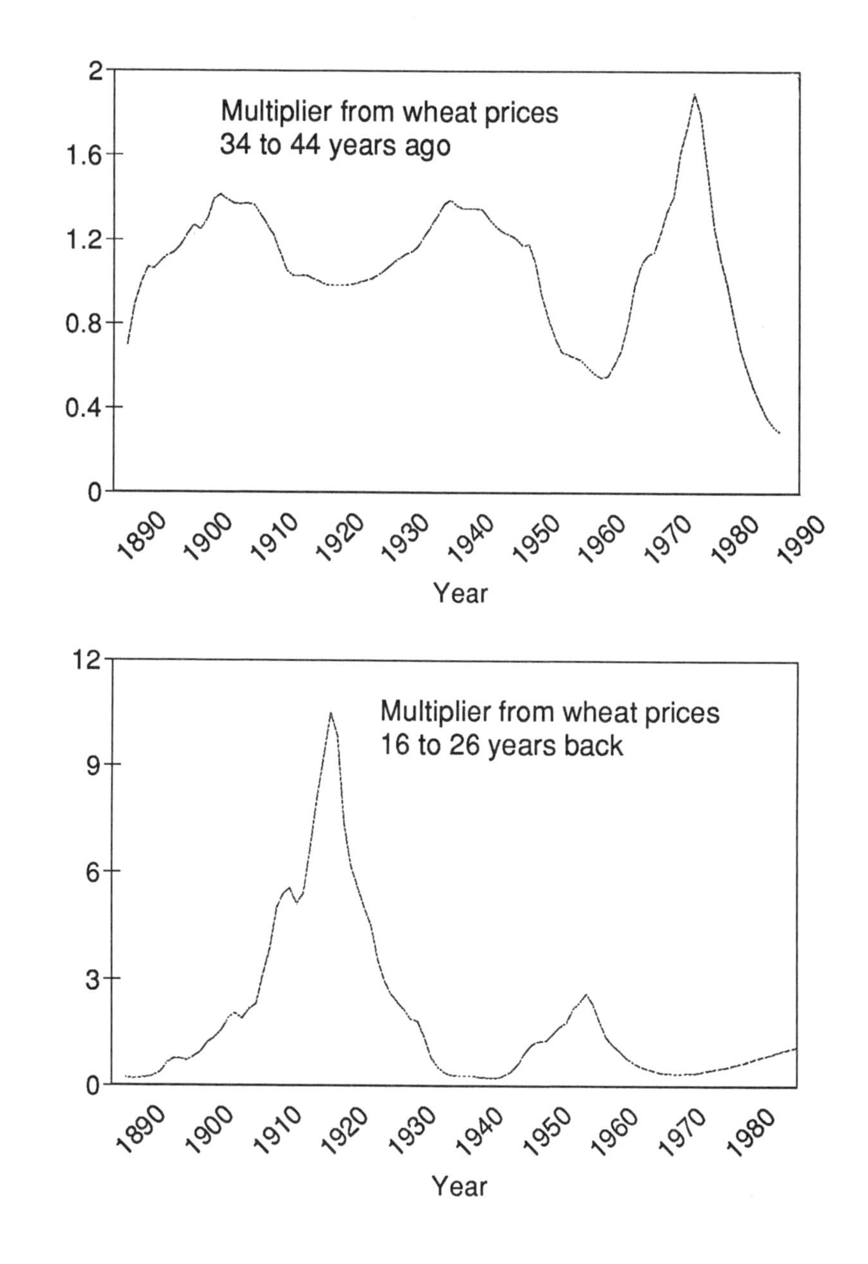

Figure 9-4. The trend through time in the strength of the two multiplier terms that produce deviations in wheat price around its long-term trend line. The top panel depicts the strength of the self-regulatory mechanism operating with a 34–44-year lag.

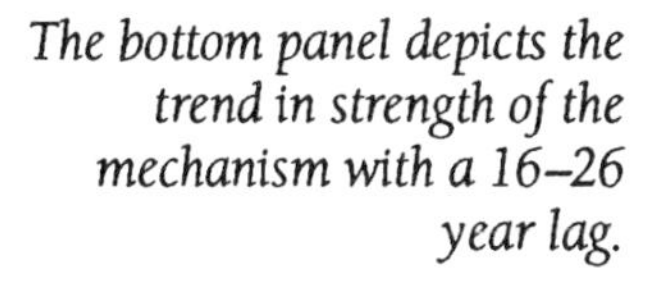

The bottom panel depicts the trend in strength of the mechanism with a 16–26 year lag.

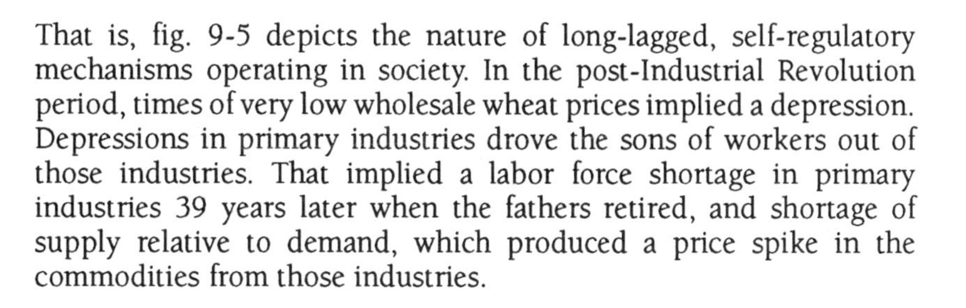

That is, fig. 9-5 depicts the nature of long-lagged, self-regulatory mechanisms operating in society. In the post-Industrial Revolution period, times of very low wholesale wheat prices implied a depression. Depressions in primary industries drove the sons of workers out of those industries. That implied a labor force shortage in primary industries 39 years later when the fathers retired, and shortage of supply relative to demand, which produced a price spike in the commodities from those industries.

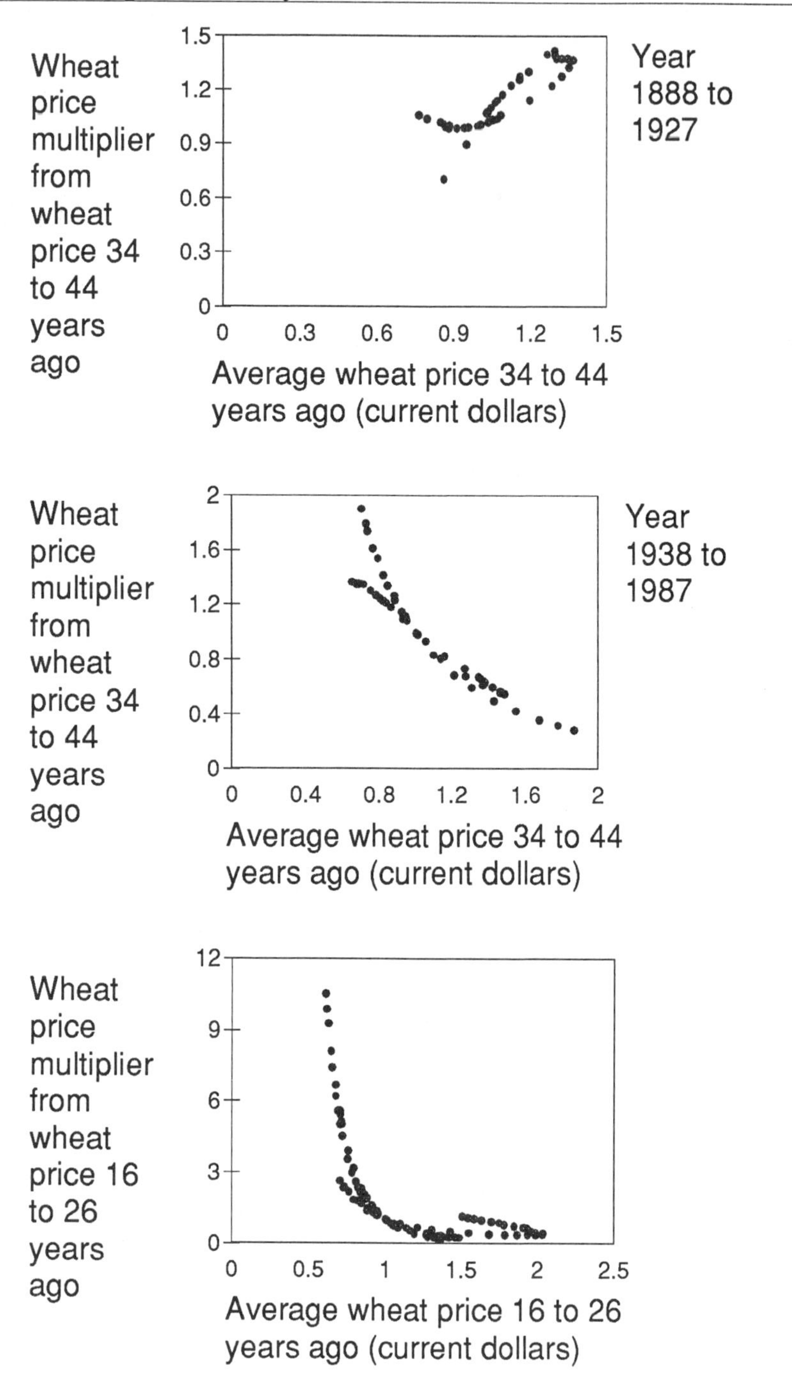

Figure 9-5. The relationship between wheat price multipliers and the system drivers which regulate them. Top panel: the labor force migration mechanism with a 34–44-year lag, before and during the Industrial Revolution.

Center panel: the dampened 34–44-year lag mechanism in post-Industrial Revolution times.

Bottom panel: the capital investment mechanism with a 16–26 year lag.

In each case, the mechanism operates to self-regulate the societal system, but the long time lags produce wave-like oscillations in wheat price and many other societal variables.

On the other hand, price spikes in primary industries' commodities had the effect of reducing the rate of labor force emigration from those industries. This resulted in a price collapse 39 years later because of excessive supply relative to demand. That mechanism became important after 1938, as the second panel of fig. 9-5 shows. The first panel demonstrates that the mechanism with **the 39-year time lag had been weaker and of opposite sign from 1888–1927**. The third panel of the figure depicts the relationship between wheat prices 16–26 years ago, and the multiplier expressing departures of wheat prices about their trend line.

The strength of this mechanism has not dampened.

Chapter 10

The Bottom Line

A Likely Scenario for the Future

We have demonstrated two types of forces can affect the future:

① Long-term, fundamental system drivers (FSD) that govern evolution along long-term trend lines into the future, and fluctuations about those trends, and

② Statistical "Acts of God"—major, unexpected perturbations that produce surprisingly large deviations about trend lines, or system leaps on to new, different trend lines.

There is a third type as well:

③ Decisions by managers, mass publics, politicians or any other group with the power to shape events.

The most likely future scenario comes about because of interplay between all of them—the fundamental system driver being cumulative production of fossil fuel.

The effects of the FSD

To forecast any system variable, we first identify its causes by following backwards along the causal pathways that lead to it. This identification begins with the proximate causes, then the causes of those causes, until we arrive at the ultimate causes, or FSD.

The ratio of energy prices to the costs of labor and all other factor inputs will govern all economic substitution processes, such as substitution of labor for energy.

Forecasting is done by using mathematical computer models to project, for each year into the future, the behavior of variables in the causal sequence just described, in *reverse* order: first ultimate causes, or FSD, then the proximate causes affected by the FSD, then finally, ultimate effects. To forecast societal changes, we first project cumulative fossil fuel production in the U.S., which determines prices of all forms of energy here and elsewhere. The ratio of those prices to the costs of labor and all other factor inputs will govern all economic substitution processes, such as the rate of substitution of labor for energy. **Knowing the future trend line for cumulative U.S. fossil fuel production allows us to project trends for wholesale fuel prices, which then allows us to project capital investment, wages and retail prices.** Then, because we can project the wavelike oscillation of demographic variables (e.g. fig. 6-5), we can project wages. We can also project prices—from the likely high-frequency oscillations introduced into the U.S. and world economies by the dynamics of the world oil market.

The trend in cumulative U.S. fossil fuel production

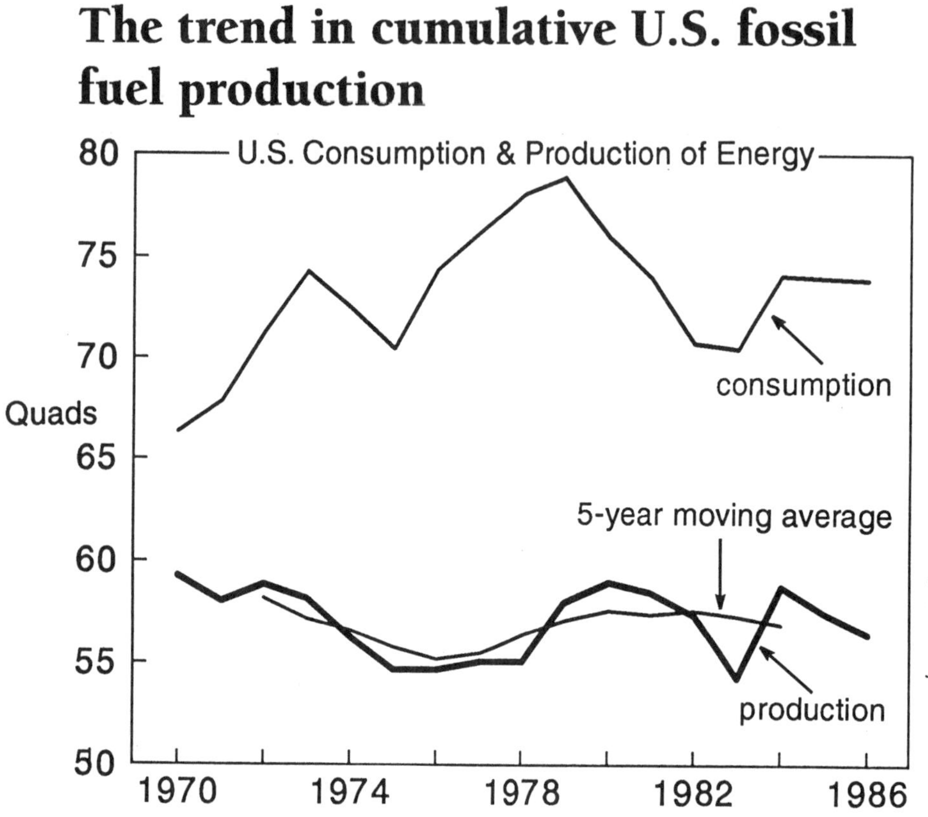

Figure 10-1. The recent trend in consumption and production of energy in the U.S. Consumption, top line, production, bottom line, both measured in quads (quadrillion BTUs). The thin line through the production trend is the 5-year moving average of annual production. (Data from SA 1987, Table 904.)

In order to project cumulative U.S. fossil fuel production, we must understand the system of forces regulating production of fossil fuel energy in the U.S. each year into the future. It turns out that this is a simple problem. Fig. 10-1. depicts the trends since 1969 in the U.S. in both total consumption of energy in all forms (top line), and total production of fossil fuel energy (bottom line). The thin line drawn through the production trend line is the 5-year moving average for U.S. fossil fuel energy production.

While there is a great deal of variation in energy consumption in the U.S., there is far less variation in U.S. fossil fuel production.

The striking feature of this graph is that while there is a great deal of variation about that trend through this 17-year period in energy consumption in the U.S.—from 66.4 quads in 1970 to 78.9 quads in 1979—there is far less variation in U.S. fossil fuel production—from 54.3 in 1983 to 59.2 in 1970. This is because two forces are at work to produce self-regulation in U.S. fossil fuel production.

- This production does not decrease much, because in years when domestic oil production decreases, there is a compensatory increase in domestic coal production. That mechanism has the effect of preventing too much U.S. currency from leaving the U.S. to pay for imported crude oil.
- U.S. fossil fuel production will not go much higher than it is at present, because if it did, the sharply increased cost to produce a marginal unit of energy in the U.S. would depress both profitability and demand for energy.

As a result, total U.S. domestic fossil fuel energy production is remaining rather constant, and large swings in energy demand are being accommodated largely by swings in energy imports. To illustrate, U.S.

energy consumption was very high in 1988, and oil imports in many weeks near the end of the year were running well over 50 percent of input to refineries. The thin line for the five-year moving average U.S. fossil fuel production shows how constant domestic fossil fuel production has been recently, when we eliminate the effect of high-frequency oscillations. There is no perceptible trend in the thin line. Accordingly, I assume that a reasonable scheme for projecting future annual U.S. fossil fuel production is to assume that quantity, every year for the foreseeable future, will be the average value for the period 1970–1986, inclusive: 57.1 quads.

Domestic production cannot increase much above its present level because production has been so high in the past.

Production of fossil fuel in the U.S. illustrates one of the **key features of a FSD: a high degree of stiffness, or inertia, because its present and future behavior is largely constrained by its own past history**. The reason why such a high proportion of U.S. fossil fuel consumption is imported is because of the past history of fossil fuel production. The large prior cumulative production means that much of our remaining domestic fossil fuel reserves are expensive to discover and produce relative to reserves in countries that have still only exploited a small proportion of their original total resources. Thus the reason why our domestic production cannot increase much above its present level is because that production has been so high in the past. We are now in a situation where the cheapest way to meet marginal increments of domestic demand is by marginal increases in importation of foreign oil. Ironically, large prior use of domestic fossil fuel is also the reason why our domestic fossil fuel production can not sink much below its present level: the incremental increase in our already negative balance of trade would be too great.

Variables such as cumulative U.S. fossil fuel production enormously simplify the problem of forecasting. So much of their future variation is governed by their own past history that they are relatively invulnerable to being strongly affected by other variables. This is the essence of an FSD.

Because the FSD (domestic fossil fuel production) is declining, it implies that all other variables are now approaching a stable state or declining.

The trend in cumulative U.S. domestic fossil fuel production was illustrated in fig. 4-7. Because this variable is the FSD regulating long-term trends of all other variables in modern socio-economic systems, then its declining growth rate implies that all the other variables are now approaching a stable state or declining. The **consequences of this gradual disappearance of growth will pervade society**, with the effect radiating out from countries that have first depleted their reserves of cheap fossil fuel to countries that still have large reserves of fossil fuel.

This decline in growth is masked by phenomena such as massive immigration by young women with high birth rates and by substitution of debt for income.

This decline in growth shows up in a plethora of statistics on the U.S., from population growth rates (SA 1987, Table 82) to real wages in private nonmanufacturing industries (SA 1987, Table 648). The rate of decline is masked, however, by such phenomena as massive immigration by young women with birth rates much higher than those of women born in the U.S. (SA 1987 tables 95 and 99), and increasing substitution of debt for income to support standard of living. The ratio of outstanding consumer credit to disposable personal income rose from 17.7 in 1982 to 23.6 in 1986 (SA 1987 Table 795). In general, a **collapse in the purchasing power of the U.S. citizenry and the U.S. government is being masked by using debt as a substitute for internal return on investment**. Also, the appearance of affluence is being maintained by indefinitely deferring investment in such items as education, research and development.

The consequences of this deferred investment show up gradually as decreased international economic competitiveness.

The trend in wholesale fuel prices

Earlier, I identified average WFPI 9–13 years ago—as a ratio of the values computed from their trend equation—as the FSD for economic waves. Because of the long lag, we already know the values for that variable to 1999. These can be inferred from fig. 4-17. The WFPI 9–13 years ago, adjusted for long-term trend, will rise steadily until 1993, when it will reach its highest level ever, implying a depression then. Then it will drop precipitously, at least until 1999, implying recovery. Further, we know from the theory and analyses of chapters 5 and 7 that this variable will oscillate for a long time, although with gradually dampening amplitude.

Think of the period 1977–1985 as equivalent to a war in its effect on wholesale energy prices.

A simple way to understand the likely future scenario is to think of the period 1977–1985 as being equivalent to a war, with respect to the effect on wholesale energy prices. Therefore, the period we are in now corresponds to the postwar periods of the early 1870s and late 1920s, with respect to overinvestment in global energy production capability and underinvestment in manufacturing. As would be expected, therefore, we also see the pattern of collapsing wholesale energy prices at present that characterized the 1870s and 1920s. The period around 1993–1994 will therefore be similar to the periods around 1878–1879, and the early 1930s, if the pattern of the last 110 years persists.

Batra (1987) has pointed out that the period leading into a depression involves a complex of societal changes in culture as well as the economy. It is astonishing how **many statistical series suggest that the period since 1984 is a replay of the period after 1924**. For example, the period after 1926 was characterized by a decline in the number of U.S. doctorates awarded per bachelors degree 9 years previously (H765). Since 1971 we have had a similar decline in this statistic, from .062 to .036—**the 1926 level**. In the period just prior to a depression, there is a shift away from investments that only pay off over the long term.

Trends in wages and prices

Since the industrial revolution, the worldwide growth of average per capita affluence was fueled by a long-term gradual increase in consumer purchasing power: the ratio of earnings to costs of consumer items. The FSD driving this changing ratio was the decreasing unit energy cost to discover and produce a marginal BTU of fossil energy. This cost decrease occurred because the higher costs we would expect to be associated with a depleting fossil resource were more than compensated for—in the short term—by technological innovations in discovery and production, and economies of scale as larger and larger quantities of energy were discovered and produced. By the early 1970s, however, the cost-increasing effects of a depleting resource finally overwhelmed these compensatory effects.

By the early 1970s, a historical turnaround occurred worldwide: more labor per unit of energy being used to increase energy productivity, rather than using energy to increase labor productivity.

Up to the early 1970s, because energy had become progressively cheaper, and labor became progressively more costly relative to energy, each year more units of energy were used with a unit of labor: labor productivity increased. Affluence grew steadily until the early 1970s. The major historical break occurred then because the energy cost to discover one additional unit of energy began to increase rapidly in the world's largest consumer of energy, the U.S. This meant that a historical turnaround occurred worldwide in the ratio of energy prices to labor costs. After the early 1970s, more labor per unit of energy was being used to increase energy productivity, rather than more energy being used per unit of labor to increase labor productivity. The result has been a **dramatic and historically unprecedented decline in the ratio of earnings to energy prices, and hence in the ratio of earnings to all consumer prices**. The magnitude of this change is demonstrated in Table 10-1.

This **dramatic decline in consumer purchasing power has attracted little attention because it has been largely veiled by explosive growth in use of credit cards**, which has given consumers an artificially elevated perception of their purchasing power.

Table 10-1. The steady decline in consumer purchasing power resulting from increased costs of discovering and producing fossil energy. All statistics are U.S. national averages (earnings from SA 1987, Table 648; CPI from SA 1987, Table 740).

Year	Average weekly earnings in private non-agricultural industries (current dollars)	Consumer price index (CPI)	Consumer purchasing power: the ratio of earnings to the CPI
1974	154.8	147.7	1.048
1975	163.5	161.2	1.014
1976	175.5	170.5	1.029
1977	189.0	181.5	1.041
1978	203.7	195.4	1.042
1979	219.9	217.4	1.011
1980	235.1	246.8	.952
1981	255.2	272.4	.937
1982	267.3	289.1	.925
1983	280.7	298.4	.940
1984	292.9	311.1	.941
1985	299.1	322.2	.928
1986	304.9	328.4	.928

The ultimate cause for the increase in consumer prices (a worldwide, not just national phenomenon) is geological: the decreasing average global availability of fossil fuels that can be discovered and produced at low unit energy cost. As more and more of the readily accessible worldwide fossil energy resources are used up, on average the remainder will be in deeper, more inaccessible geological sites. Therefore, the energy cost to discover and produce them will be greater, per unit of energy produced. This will be reflected in a progressively increasing level of consumer prices to wages, since energy prices are a determinant of all other prices. Thus, Table 10-1 shows the beginning of a trend that will continue from now on. This trend will be temporarily veiled, also, by the competition between otherwise poor oil-rich countries to seize a large share of the world oil market, by selling oil at very low prices (Tanner, 1990). As more and more nations deplete their readily accessible oil resources, however, this competition will ease, and sellers—not buyers—of oil will control the world oil market.

There is a limit to the extent that credit can be used to veil a decrease in consumer purchasing power. This limit is reached when the interest on consumer debt becomes equal to the proportion of the monthly family budget than can be spent on credit card purchases.

Thus, gradually, there will be a perceptible decrease in economic growth that can be fueled by consumer spending.

Population trends

A really insightful projection of future trends in the ratio of wages to prices (consumer purchasing power) requires that we be able to project population trends, because when populations of young people are unusually large or small relative to their trends, this elevates prices, thus depressing purchasing power. Accordingly, we now turn to the prospects for population growth.

The key to projecting population is projecting the number of live births. Having done this, it is relatively straightforward to project the numbers of people in each age group. Chapter 6 demonstrated that population cycles are under strong self-regulatory control: after correcting for the long-term trend, large numbers of births tend to be followed by small numbers of births, about 16–24 years later, and vice versa. The last year of peak births was 1957, which was followed by a period of unusually low births in the middle and late 1970s. Thus we would expect the cycle in births to peak again around 1997 and 2037.

Figs. 6-2 and 6-5 suggest that any business or government agency banking on a sustained future increase in population growth needs to proceed with caution. If our analysis is correct, the largest number of births that will ever occur in the U.S. will be 4.5 million in 1997. The next peak in birth numbers will be 4.3 million in 2037, and the peaks in birth numbers will become gradually lower from then on. This implies that **the largest group of 20-year olds we will ever see in the U.S. will be the survivors from the year class of babies born in 1997**. The *peaks* in numbers of 20-year olds will on average decrease in the U.S. every year from 2017 to 2115, even without figuring in the effect of AIDS. Years of unusually large numbers of 20-year olds will be seen again about 2017 and 2057, with the second of those peaks being smaller.

Growth of the world system is now finished.

This type of projection leads to a most important conclusion: growth of the world system is now finished. Powerful self-regulatory forces are now coming into play, such as the huge cost of raising children and providing them with an education. The thesis that the trend for U.S. population growth has reached an asymptote can be verified by examination of statistics on trends in the intrinsic rate of natural increase in different demographic subgroups (e.g. SA 1990, Table 84).

Also, all institutions are going to be faced with huge planning problems associated with oscillations in numbers of people in particular age groups. It needs no imagination to foresee the gigantic problems for educational institutions, pension plans, and manufacturing and service industries of all types. The characteristics of the culture with respect to music, art, fashion and entertainment are enormously affected by population age structure and average age of the people in a population. Huge oscillations in the numbers of young people also have enormous implications for law enforcement and criminal justice systems: both are taxed to the limit when the number of people in their late teens and early 20s are far above long-term trend lines.

Figs. 6-2 and 6-5 also allow us to forecast future fluctuations in consumer purchasing power (the ratio of wages to consumer prices). There will be a gradual downward trend in wages with respect to prices from now on as labor is substituted for energy. Oscillations will occur in the ratio of wages with respect to prices, as can be inferred from fig. 6-5. Prices are highest, and consumer purchasing power is lowest when populations of young people are either unusually low or high relative to their long-term trend line. Consumer purchasing power will fluctuate in accord with the scheme described in Table 10-2.

Table 10-2. Changes in consumer purchasing power related to demographics.

Year	Birth numbers relative to their long-term trend	24 years later	Consumer purchasing power
1965	intermediate	1989	high
1977	nadir	2001	low
1987	intermediate	2011	high
1997	zenith	2021	low
2005	intermediate	2029	high
2015	nadir	2039	low

The oscillatory tendency introduced into society by this mechanism will interact with the other oscillatory mechanism resulting from cycles in wholesale fuel price indices. The severity of the effects from either would be greatest if they coincided with those produced by the other mechanism. That happened in the 1930s, and will likely happen again in the 1990s.

Statistical "acts of God"

Before we can proceed in developing a scenario for the future, we need to explore possible consequences of big surprises. Five big perturbations appear imminent in the world at the moment:

- AIDS.
- An explosive increase in energy prices.
- Total transportation gridlock.
- A gradual cooling of high-latitude climate.
- Pollution-triggered increased mortality.

Acquired immune deficiency syndrome

The AIDS pandemic is worldwide. The trend in the cumulative number of new AIDS cases reported each month worldwide is behaving as a regular growth process (fig. 6-11). If the projection in fig. 6-11 is at all realistic, then AIDS has much larger implications for planning in all fields than most people expect. Projections of future demand for fossil or electrical energy, transportation systems capacity, housing demand, and land for urban purposes have to this point typically ignored the future impact of AIDS. By four or five decades from now, population growth in the entire world may have been converted to population decline by AIDS. This would clearly have a tremendous impact on worldwide levels of resource demand relative to supply, on pollution, wages, economic growth, and a great many other measures of society.

Thus we need to view with caution projections of any variable—such as global demand for fossil fuel or global levels of pollution—that overlook projections of AIDS death.

Explosive increase in energy prices

A second factor will have the potential to have a dramatic, and unexpected impact on the world: the sharp run-up in crude oil price in the latter half of the 1990s. This will cause a violent lurch away from the car toward public transportation, shove the world to alternative energy sources, decrease long-haul movement of people and goods, and foster high densities in cities. In terms of spatial location and interspersion of activities in cities and towns, life will become more like that of the middle ages. Most of a person's activities will occur in a ten-mile by ten-mile square that will include home, workplace, and shops. There will be a shift from trucks to trains, ships and barges, which decrease the energy cost per ton-mile to ship goods.

Transportation gridlock

One of the curious features of the future is that large problems will often solve another large problem. Over the very short term (to 1998), developing traffic gridlock will be an enormous problem, but higher energy prices and lower populations brought on by AIDS mortality will solve that.

Gradual cooling of high latitudes

Contrary to the widely promulgated view of climate trends, the world appears to be getting colder, not warmer, at high latitudes (Wood, 1988). For the last few years, the tables in daily newspapers reported many days when at least 48 percent of the world's largest cities were colder than their long-term means for that day, and only 33 percent or fewer were hotter. Those very large cities would be the first places to heat up if the world were indeed warming. This phenomenon is possibly caused by a developing positive feedback loop: cold weather at high latitudes lowers the photosynthetic rate of trees at those latitudes, so that they remove less carbon from the atmosphere. The resulting increase is probably related to the mass deforestation now occurring in the third world tropics and that happened earlier in the developed world, concurrent with the industrial revolution.

Pollution-triggered mortality

A fifth factor that could produce a great surprise is the global increase in environmental contamination with toxic wastes. During 1988, a rather alarming pattern occurred on a more intense and widespread scale than before: masses of marine organisms washing up dead on ocean beaches in widely separated locations:

- Much of the coast of northwest Europe.
- Off the coast of northern Ireland.
- On a thousand miles of the Adriatic coast.
- The Gulf of St. Lawrence.
- Along great stretches of the east and west coasts of North America. Different diseases were implicated in different places, and in some instances the cause was mysterious. The common denominator in all such cases was probable depression of the immune systems of the organisms by toxic chemicals in the environment. Sometimes these were metals, and sometimes organic molecules. In some cases, autopsies of dead animals revealed a soup of different toxic chemicals in their organs.

The problem is that we eat many of the ocean foods those organisms eat, and in any case, the oceans are an alarmingly large proportion of the global environment to have become so toxic to life. At some point we may succumb also, on a surprising scale. Some estimates are that 90 percent of all seals off the coast of Northwest Europe died in 1988. We should be alert to evidence that we are also becoming affected.

Civil disturbances

A final possible surprising development would be massive civil disturbance of the type we associate with Lebanon, as the standard of living decreases, and the average incomes of "haves" and "have-nots" widens. This has already occurred in China.

Obviously, all of these problems could be dealt with before they become catastrophic, by appropriate policy decisions.

The effect of decision-making on the future

Events in the future will be shaped, in part, by the way that decision-making by managers, politicians, and electorates responds to the state of the world as produced by the FSD and "Acts of God."

Two features of the philosophy underlying decision-making can have a particularly large and pervasive effect in shaping events. The first of these concerns beliefs about the appropriate time period to use as a basis for extrapolating past trends into the future. The approach advocated in this book has been to use a very long period, so that waves and fluctuations about long-term trend lines can be distinguished from the trends themselves.

Down the garden path

The other, and more common approach is to use a very short recent period as the basis for extrapolation of trends into the future. This approach makes one vulnerable to confusing a recent upward wavelike oscillation about a long-term trend line with that line itself (fig. 10-2). The long-term trend line in this figure is indicated by the dashed line; the actual growth pattern is indicated by the solid line. If one were unfortunate enough to use a short recent time period of upward oscillation around the trend for extrapolating the trend, one's forecasts would be the dotted lines **A** or **B**. Alternatively, if one were unfortunate enough to use a short recent period of wavelike downswing below the long-term trend line for the purpose of projecting the future, the projected trend would be the dotted line **C**.

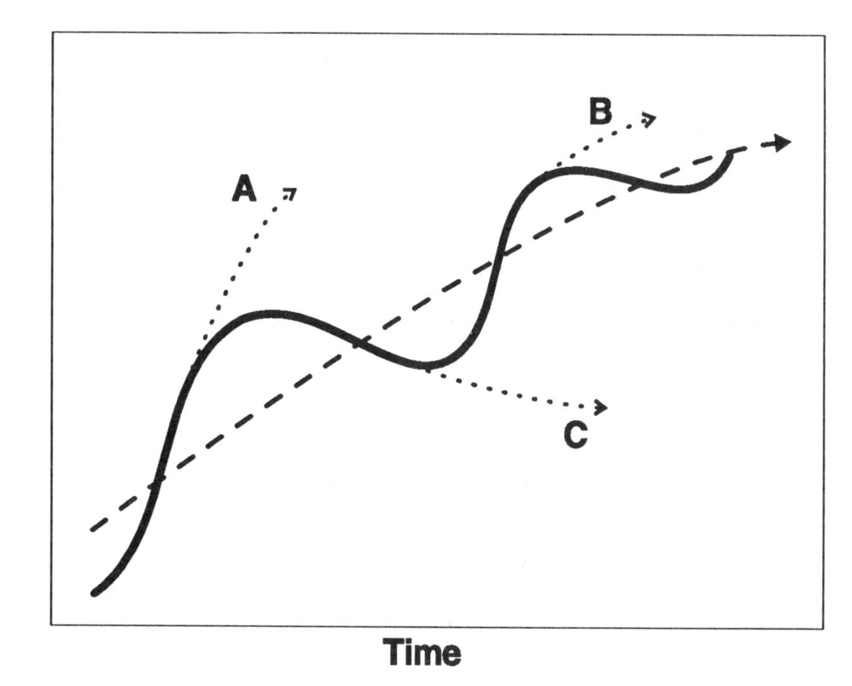

Figure 10-2. One of the fundamental errors made by most people forecasting the future is to use too short a time horizon, resulting in faulty forecasts A, B, or C.

The dashed line is the long-term trend line. The solid line depicts the actual pattern of fluctuations about the long-term trend line.

A realist is someone who bases forecasts on the solid line and the dashed line. At those times when most people are making forecasts like **A** and **B**, the dominant paradigm will be considered "realistic" and the people forecasting an extension of the solid line or of the actual trend will be considered "pessimists" or "doomsayers." Conversely, people forecasting that the solid line will be the trend, when most people are forecasting along the dotted line at **C** will be considered "incurable optimists." **It is precisely these substitutions of the dotted line (short-term) for the solid line in forecasts that produces the wavelike oscillation of the solid line about the dashed line in the real world trend.**

What might happen to shift the dominant forecasting paradigm from making forecasts like the dotted lines to making forecasts like the solid line? One possible source of rapid instruction for everyone will be the world oil market. Recent history has abounded with forecasts of prices per barrel, demand, and supply analogous to the dotted lines in fig. 10-2. After a few violent oscillations about the long-term trend, however, large numbers of expert forecasters for the oil business may come to realize that the system is under strong self-regulatory control with a very long lag, as in the solid line.

Until such wisdom becomes widespread, wavelike behavior in many important phenomena in society will be the norm, not the exception.

Dare we say it—Limits to growth

A second important belief underlying decision-making is the denial of limits. In fact, **the world seems to have now reached a limit to growth**, although the mechanisms operating to limit further growth are different in developed than in developing nations.

- In developed nations, growth is being limited both by the cost to raise and educate children, and a gradually increasing ratio of resource costs to average wages.
- In developing nations, growth will be limited by starvation and pandemic disease.

Evidence of these phenomena at work are already clearly visible in statistical compendia. The end of growth is being masked in some countries by use of debt. Growth based on debt comes to an end when the budget for all expenditures is largely consumed by the interest on old debt.

Implications

The analyses reported in this book all point in the same direction. Whether we consider the world oil price, population growth, consumer purchasing power, demand for energy, or demand for anything else, **the future appears to hold something between very slow growth or decline**. The rapid growth of the last century is over, because a variety of self-regulatory mechanisms have come into play vigorously, from decreased birth rates and AIDS to lowered demand brought on by a decline in consumer purchasing power.

As discussed in the Prologue, in the modern world information about the state of the system is at least as important in affecting the behavior of most people as is the actual state of the system. Realistic information about change in the state of the system tends to become available to most people some time after the change has actually occurred. This information-caused time lag can only increase the wavelength and amplitude of oscillation in the world system, which we have seen, already oscillates because of system time lags.

Accordingly, the optimal strategy for prospering in the future is to profit from meeting the needs of a stabilizing world system, with gradually dampening oscillations, and stabilizing local society, rather than a constantly growing system. In the next chapter, we turn to the tactics of doing this.

Pivotal decisions that could shape the future

The future is not something that happens to us, but rather something over which we have partial control, within the constrains imposed by the FSD and the statistical "Acts of God." Further, over a time horizon of decades or more, we have the power to alter the FSD—for example, by a sharp increase in efficiency of energy use.

Given the relationships presented in previous chapters, we can identify certain key policy decisions that would have a crucial impact on the future of the U.S. and the world.

Perception that climate is a critical problem, and that vegetation is critical in climate control.

This planet can have a stable physical environment if, and only if there is a balance between the strength of processes that remove carbon dioxide from, and those that add it to the atmosphere. Animal life (through respiration) and humans (through combustion) add carbon dioxide to the atmosphere; plant life removes it. For there to be a balance, the total mass of global vegetation must surpass a critical level. Civilization is now acting as if this proposition were not true, and in the process is eroding the habitability of the planet. If the truth of the proposition is recognized by mass publics and their elected representatives promptly, and mass reforestation results, then the problem will be ameliorated. Otherwise, nations in the highest latitudes will experience a significant cooling, and there will be other surprising effects worldwide.

Energy efficiency

A second important cluster of issues relates to the efficiency of energy use by nations. Readers will have noted that entirely different types of analysis highlight the significance of this issue. A shift to emphasizing efficiency of energy use away from maximizing the amount of energy used would increase gross national product per capita. For example, Sweden, Switzerland, Germany and Japan all demonstrate that high levels of GNP per capita are attainable with a fraction of the energy consumption per capita of the U.S. Such a shift would have three principal components.

① A significant proportion of "cutting edge" or "state-of-the-art" high technology in a nation would be shifted from military research and development to R & D on high-speed, technologically innovative mass transportation systems that made highly efficient use of minerals, energy, and land. This would have a most beneficial impact on economic growth and the standard of living through a remarkable variety of causal pathways. Since fewer resources need to be produced or imported, this decreases the strain on capital markets, decreases the demand:supply ratio for venture capital, and decreases interest rates. It frees up a great deal of human time and energy by eliminating time lost in traffic congestion.

② Car technology is an old technology. Further development of cars will have a minimal impact in pushing the "envelope of technology" of a nation. High-technology mass transportation, on the other hand, is like space exploration; it has a high impact on the rate of technological innovation in a wide diversity of technologies, from electronic control systems and computer-controlled system management to tunneling technology.

③ Cars have reached the limit of their ability to facilitate the mobility of populations in large, high density metropolitan areas. Further improvements in mobility and improved access of a high proportion of the prospective labor force to a diversity of job opportunities will require a technological leap in transportation technology.

In any case, fossil energy will shortly become too expensive for most people to afford the waste of commuting to work by themselves in an energy-inefficient car. These issues are developed at length elsewhere (Thomson, 1977; Yago, 1984; Sperling, 1988). The speed with which nations convert from a car-dominated to a transit-dominated policy will have a huge impact on the relative economic competitiveness of nations from now on. Similarly, the shift to a more energy-efficient society implies mass social revolutions in passive and active alternative energy systems, from home design to small home energy-generating systems using wind, sun, or small hydroelectric generating plants in streams.

At its roots, a shift from brute force to ingenuity in society implies a significant increase in investment in research, development and education. Major improvements in mass education will be required to produce a population-wide increase in the average level of ingenuity. The relative economic competitiveness of nations will be significantly affected by the speed with which electorates and policy makers grasp this idea.

Chapter 11

Taming the Future

This chapter offers some advice to individuals, investors, corporations, government agencies, or universities on how to apply the methods and approach of this book.

For investors and business executives

It is critically important not to overestimate the length of upturns or downturns in the economy. The best insurance against excessive optimism at the crest of an inflation or excessive pessimism at the end of a depression is to visualize the past in terms of cycles, not the recent trend. One way to become wealthy is to buy when others are selling, and sell when others are buying. Both strategies imply an understanding of the cyclical nature of events.

Common sense, and observations of events and processes can be used to reason out the identity of the FSD that drive sales and profits for a corporation. Then, using the projections in previous chapters, you can reason out the likely future trend in the FSD that affect your business. Then think through the effects those trends will have on trends in your likely sales and profits. From this, decide corporate strategy.

Sources of information

One way to gain improved forecasting skills is to practice reasoning by analogy. The relationship between the FSD and business in the past can yield clues about likely future changes in the FSD. Extremely useful documents for this purpose are *The Historical Statistics of the U.S.* and the *Statistical Abstract of the U.S.* Anyone concerned about the future would be well advised to buy the *Statistical Abstract* each year, when the current volume becomes available (about June).

Response to depression

Fig. 11-1 reveals how the Great Depression and the 1979–1981 surge in energy prices affected a wide range of businesses in the past. The solid bars show the percentage of 1929 sales volume, in current dollars, that had been lost by 1933, the bottom business year for the Great Depression. The thatched bars show how much the dollar volume of sales increased from 1979 to 1981, a period when there was a spectacular increase in both wholesale and retail energy prices.

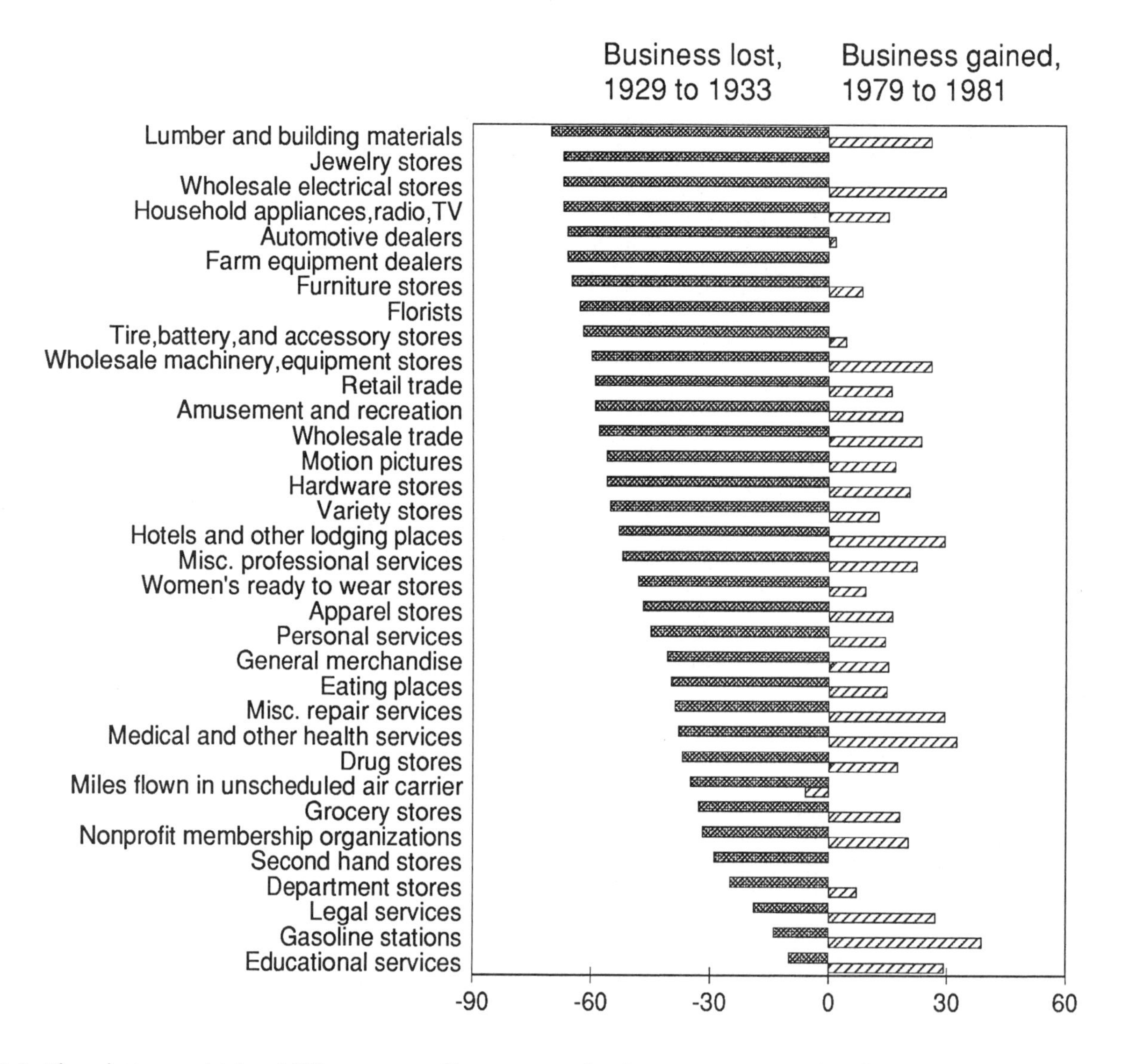

Figure 11-1. The relative sensitivity of different types of businesses to the Great Depression and to the 1979–1981 surge in energy prices. Black bars to the left of zero indicate the percentage of 1929 sales volume, in current dollars, that had been lost by 1933. Thatched bars to the right of zero show how much the dollar volume of sales increased from 1979 to 1981.

Clearly, different types of business have had remarkably different responses to these two classes of perturbations. We note, for example, that lumber and building materials retail outlets lost 70 percent of their business in the depression; gasoline stations only lost 14 percent of their business, and educational services lost only 10 percent of their business. The dollar bought about 29 percent more in 1933 than in 1929. Thus, for several classes of business, the dollar volume of business actually rose, in constant dollars, from 1929 to 1933.

Another way of doing detective work on the effect of past perturbations is to calculate the ratios of two prices, or two other measures, then plot those ratios against year number. In fig. 11-2, the top panel shows the trend in a production index for printing and publishing as a multiple of the corresponding production index for manufacture of primary metals. The bottom panel depicts the trend in the ratio of the printing and publishing production index to the index measuring production of petroleum and coal.

In a depression, people cut back far more on purchases of large items than on small. People buy less and spend more on maintenance of existing goods. Also, a depression is a time for upgrading educational qualifications.

The top panel suggests that during the last depression there was a shift of capital away from manufacturing metal products (such as cars) to production of reading materials. The bottom panel does not suggest any such shift from consumption of energy to reading. Putting the information in these panels together, we conclude that during a depression, family finances are shifted from purchase of large durable goods to reading, but that there is no comparable shift from energy use in durable goods to reading. Thus families economize by holding off on purchases of new durable goods, but continue to operate the durable goods they already have at close to the normal use rate.

What are the fundamental principles revealed by the patterns in Figures 11.1 and 11.2? In a depression, people cut back far more on purchases of large items than on small items and necessities (shoes, discount clothing stores, drug stores). People buy less, and spend more on maintaining or preserving existing goods and products. Also, a depression is used as a time for upgrading oneself, so as to be better able to take advantage of new opportunities in the boom following the depression. That explains the only 10 percent current dollar decrease in educational services.

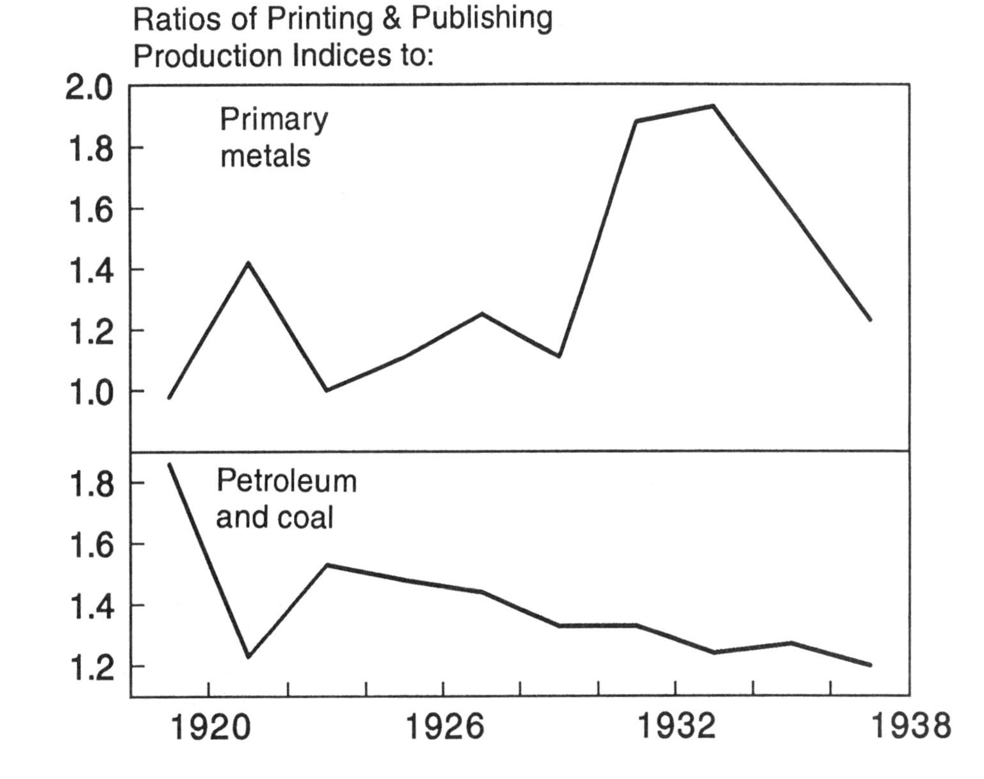

Figure 11-2. Top panel: the trend in the ratio of production indices for printing and publishing to production indices for manufacture of primary metals.

Bottom panel: the trend in the ratio of production indices for printing and publishing to production indices for petroleum and coal. (Raw data from HS P53,P41, P55.)

Response to high energy prices

An energy price increase produces a pattern of effects similar in some respects to a depression, but different in others.

- As with a depression, automobile sales are hurt hard, but gasoline sales are benefited: a unit of gasoline costs more, and there is a limit to the extent that people can economize on car use.
- Energy-intensive luxuries are hurt, such as travel on unscheduled air carriers: the energy cost per passenger mile is too costly.
- There is a big increase in sales of electronic appliances: people stay home and play with computers, video recorders or compact disc players.
- Motion pictures are hurt badly in an energy price crisis; it is cheaper to stay home and watch television than to drive to a theater.
- Discount clothing stores are not benefitted as much by an energy price shock as by a depression.

Similar tables and graphs show how either a depression or an energy price shock would affect any business or investment.

From data to conclusions

A useful next step is to write down a description of the steps in the chain of logic leading to your conclusion as to how your business would be affected. Do those steps hold up when you reread them? Can you think of counterarguments? Do you know of any data or observations that could be used to test the logic underlying the sequence of steps you wrote down? After going through this exercise, you may decide to branch out into another type of business, or invest in another business less sensitive to a possible depression or an energy price shock.

Ride the trends

Another way to adjust to the future is to "ride trends." For example, almost all goods and services are sold to people of a particular age and sex for their own use or to be given to, or used on another. One does not want to be selling or investing in baby food or toys at a time when numbers of births are about to start a multi-year decline, as in 1957. Similarly, it would have been a very good idea to begin selling to or investing in products or services for people over 75 in 1960. That group doubled in size from 1960 to 1984, while the numbers of people in the U.S. up to 13 years of age actually declined.

All human activities and sales volumes are sensitive to changes in population age composition. For example, men aged 20–35 drive far more miles per year in cars than men aged 50–65. Therefore, if the average age of American men were to increase markedly, the total amount of driving done per million men per year would decrease markedly.

The graying of America

Over the period 1970–2000, the typical age of the U.S. population could increase from 27 to 37 or more. The most recently available information suggests that **aging of the population will be faster than previous estimates, because birth rates are dropping more than expected**. If there should be a depression, birth rates will drop much more than most forecasters expected, and the average age of the population will increase faster than almost anyone expected. That has enormous implications for all retailers and wholesellers—and for the Social Security system. Therefore, for each type of business or investment, one should be considering whether it will be hurt or helped by such a change in the age of the population.

Shift to less expensive inputs

Another type of trend to "ride" is concerned with changes in relative cost of different intersubstitutable inputs to manufacturing, or service operations. One way to exploit such trends is to keep track of the relative costs of broad categories of factor inputs, such as innovative technology, information, educational programs to increase the productivity of labor, capital, labor, land, energy, lumber and minerals. As one of these begins to be more expensive relative to others, wise managers shift from using that input to using less expensive inputs.

Thus, until 1973, the history of farming in the U.S. was a history of progressively substituting cheap energy for more expensive labor. The labor productivity of each person was increased by using more units of energy, capital and land to increase the productivity of each unit of labor. From several decades ago until 1973, we saw this same substitution and conversion process going on all around us. Since then, there has been an alteration in the trend in ratios of costs of different factor inputs, and wise business managers and investors have profited by riding those changes.

This principal, of maximizing profits by minimizing overhead, can be made very sophisticated indeed when we explore the possibilities for making substitutions within a category of factor inputs, such as materials. Suppose we consider material for either industrial pipes or the tanks carried by specialized trucks for transporting liquids (pure foods or corrosive industrial chemicals). In either case, we require material with a set of specific properties in terms of corrosion-resistance, strength, rigidity, leak-resistance, and so on. Those characteristics could be obtained in any of plastics, metal alloys, ceramics or glasses. As energy becomes more expensive relative to other input costs, we seek the material that does the job we need to do, at the lowest energy cost to manufacture the amount of material required to perform the job. Specialty manufacturers are constantly seeking to optimize profits by substituting one material for another, or one way of doing a job for another.

Pursuing this line of argument, innovative managers would seek to maximize profit by minimizing overhead costs associated with transporting messages, parcels, or quantitative data by exploring costs of very different alternative means of doing this: mail, parcel post, dataphone, facsimile, and so on.

Location, location, location

Another way to optimize profits by riding trends is through altering the spatial distribution of retail outlets, factories, energy generating systems, or transportation hubs or nodes for airlines or express systems, and so on. When energy is cheap, we want a small number of large retail outlets, to maximize economies of scale; when energy is expensive, we want a large number of evenly dispersed outlets to minimize travel cost to our outlets for prospective customers.

Transportation

The cost to transport one person, or one ton mile of freight is cheapest by boat or barge, more expensive by rail, still more expensive by truck or bus, and most expensive of all by small truck or car. Certain specialized forms of transportation—notably helicopters—are extremely energy-inefficient. Against the increased fuel-efficiency of larger vehicles must be traded off the increased cost of logistics and inflexibility. That is, several refrigerated train cars containing fresh food may arrive in Chicago from the west coast, bound for the northeast. The time it takes those foodstuffs to arrive at their destination depends not only on the speed with which the train moves, but it may also depend on the time it takes to locate a new locomotive to pull these cars away from Chicago, if the train from the west coast was broken up there and those cars became separated from the locomotive that brought them from the west. There is no such logistical delay in the case of a truck that carries its entire contents from the west to east coasts.

Transportation relative to location

The relative benefit:cost ratio of high fuel-efficiency, logistically difficult transportation systems, relative to low fuel-efficiency, logistically easy systems will vary from year to year in response to changes in the relative cost of fuel and national average wages. That benefit:cost ratio, in turn, will determine the relative attractiveness of siting warehouses and wholesale outlets adjacent to rail sidings, or truck transportation hubs.

Hotels are now found in several different types of locations in large metropolitan areas: downtown, near rail stations, near bus depots, near major freeway interchanges, and near airports. The relative attractiveness of different sites for hotels in the future will be determined by trends in the cost of energy relative to wages. If energy should become much more expensive, society will switch to innovative-technology, high-speed, energy efficient rail systems, particularly for trips of under 400 miles. That development would enormously increase the relative attractiveness of hotel sites near downtown, and at station sites for the rail lines.

In general, increase in the price of energy relative to wages will increase the value of downtown real estate relative to the value of real estate at the edge of metropolitan areas. Increased energy costs make long commute round trips prohibitively expensive.

Pest control

Future changes in the relative prices of different factor inputs will change the relative attractiveness of completely different means of achieving the same objective. One of the most interesting examples in modern society is control of insect pests: there are many different ways of doing this, and their relative attractiveness is extremely sensitive to changes in the ratios of costs of different factor inputs. Chemical control of insect pests is economically very attractive if the petrochemical feedstocks for the poison molecules are cheap. If the price of crude oil escalates, however, chemical pesticides will become uneconomic relative to pest control methods dependent on labor-intensive inputs of time of scientific researchers.

Labor-intensive methods include insect pest control using biological agents, such as insect species that are parasitic or predacious upon the pests. A great deal of research effort is required to locate and test parasitic or predacious species that will have the maximum beneficial impact in reducing the density of the pest insects. Other biological control methods include bacteria, fungi and viruses. Discovery of and testing biological control methods consumes a great deal of time on the part of highly trained research scientists. Field application of the methods often requires considerable labor by technicians or farm workers.

Applying what we've learned: a case example

To illustrate decision-making about substitutions in more detail, suppose we are running a machine tool plant, and our specialty is metal cutting.

Find the data

We look up "machine tools" in the index of the current volume of the *Statistical Abstract of the U.S.* and are directed to two tables. The first trick we need to know is that footnotes to the tables provide clues as to where we can obtain much more complete information. In this case, we discover the following useful sources:

- National Machine Tool Builders Association, McLean, Virginia.
- U.S. Bureau of Economic Analysis, *Business Statistics*, for years 1965–1978.
- After 1978 the monthly *Survey of Current Business*.
- U.S. Bureau of the Census, *Census of Manufactures*, and *Annual Survey of Manufactures*.

Identify trends

The first step is to inspect the data tables, and make graphs of trends, so that patterns can be spotted as readily as possible. We discover that there are marked fluctuations in new orders for metal tools, and that for the last 15 years the amplitude of oscillation year to year has been much more violent for metal-cutting tools than for metal-forming tools. The *Statistical Abstract* gives us trends in new orders, shipments, order backlogs, employments, wages, value added, cost of materials, new capital expenditures, inventories, assets, rents, exports, and imports. Now we have some data with which to start developing a planning, forecasting and management model.

Look for causal factors

We can make a first trial experiment to answer questions such as the following.

- What explains downturns or upturns in business in certain years or months?
- Why do orders fluctuate more in one region of the country, or for one type of product or service than another?
- What FSD appear to drive trends in this business?
- What affects the intensity of foreign competition?
- What kinds of external factors coincide with years when demand for our business is strongly elevated or depressed?
- How long are the time lags between causes and effects?
- What do the answers tell us about our plans for the future?
- What steps should we take to buffer ourselves against possible effect of a future energy price increase?

- How does the likely magnitude of the price increase affect the tactical details of our planning?

Whether or not a statistical analysis or modeling program is required depends on how obvious the answers are to these questions, and many others that might be put.

The Role of Free Will

Most people like to believe that they are masters of their own destiny: that through exercise of their free will they decide what they are going to do, and do it. Some scholars suggest, however, that people may have less control over their individual and collective fates than they think. If, indeed, the behavior of large numbers of people appears to be explicable as the operation of natural forces operating on society, then this raises the most disturbing questions about the real role of free will. Tolstoy, the psychohistory school (e.g. deMause, 1985), and much of this book suggest that masses of people typically do what they do in response to large-scale historical forces of which they are only dimly aware.

If, in fact, the behavior of people was an expression of their own free will, then their actions would result from the following sequence of events.

- Each person would gather the necessary accurate information so as to become completely informed about the consequences of pursuing each of a number of different courses of action.
- Then each person would make a rational decision as to which present course of action would produce the optimal future consequences for them, on the basis of the available evidence.
- The choice made would be correct, and the resulting scenario would turn out as expected.

This hypothetical sequence makes three assumptions.

① That each individual is prepared to expend the effort required so that exercising their free will becomes an actuality, rather than a potentially available possibility.

② That each individual seeks, and is successful in finding the accurate information necessary to make a rational choice.

③ That each individual has the necessary information and conceptual model required to perceive, correctly, the relation between present choice and future consequences, for each of the available present choices.

Clearly, each of us has the potential option of exercising free will, but in practice, something like this rarely occurs. What more usually happens is that someone tells us what to do, and we do it. If we are unlucky, the someone is a Napoleon or a Hitler. It is my deepest desire that this book will assist readers to exercise their free will.

For government policy and planning

It is important to keep FP staff housed together in one adjacent suite of rooms, even though their institutional affiliations might be with several different subdivisions of the institution. A great deal has been learned about the importance of intimate contact between different people working on various components of a large model. This point is important, because FP staff must have their primary allegiance to a completely pragmatic and interdisciplinary effort on development of the forecasting model, rather than the policy positions of operating departments.

FP staff must have their primary allegiance to a completely pragmatic and interdisciplinary effort on development of the forecasting model, rather than the policy positions of operating departments.

One of the most researched and analyzed cases dealing with the phenomenon of physical separation of staff occurred during the development of the White House *Global 2000 Study* under President Carter. The following quotations tell the story.

> *"Each of the various agencies and departments of the executive branch of the federal government has always had some capacity to make long-term assessments of global trends....*
>
> *"Prior to the Global 2000 Study, such reports were generally prepared independently of each other. Little formal attempt was made to ensure that the assumptions used by one agency were consistent with those used by another. Little consideration was given to mutual interactions and feedback over time. Little heed was paid to intersectoral problem areas and concerns that were not the immediate responsibility or a special interest of that particular agency. Instead, it was implicitly assumed that long-term issues relating to population, natural resources, and the environment could be studied and analyzed on a largely independent basis.*
>
> *"A signal indication of the relative lack of direct interaction among the elements and associated experts (prior to the Global 2000 Study) was provided when the Global 2000 staff met with the agency experts responsible for the maintenance and operation of the 11 elements of the government's global model. With one or two exceptions at the most, none of the agency experts had met each other previously, and none knew anything about the assumptions, structures, requirements, and uses of the others' calculation procedures—although on occasion they were required to make use of projections developed by the other elements."*

For all of us

Most sources of information about the threat AIDS poses to each of us are simply useless. Official government statistics are in many cases extremely misleading. Published statistics are often based on census data that are up to several years out of date. Also, information about the real severity of the epidemic is being suppressed because of potential adverse effects on tourism and investment. Three types of information sources are useful, however.

- Eyewitness accounts by recently returned visitors to other countries.
- For developed countries, AIDS deaths are often misclassified. The statistical fact that can not be concealed is that a death occurred. Thus statistics on changes in the age-specific mortality rates for people 15–34 years of age are a more certain indicator of the impact of AIDS on the population.
- A few recent books are very accurate assessments of the AIDS threat to all of us (Johnston and Hopkins, 1990). Perhaps the most penetrating, novel, and revealing analysis of the AIDS pandemic appears in a most unlikely place: the entire issue number 18 of *Los Alamos Science* (Colgate et al., 1989). (This is an interesting illustration of what happens when a group of highly trained and talented people move into what is for them a new field.) They present an entirely new perspective on AIDS by assuming that the human population divides itself into subgroups on the basis of sexual preference and number of sexual outlets per week. This analytic refinement leads to a view of AIDS as being a historically novel type of epidemic, in which there will be waves of new cases, one after the other. The first waves will involve relatively small numbers of people with a high level of sexual activity. Subsequent waves will be separated from each other by progressively longer time intervals, and will involve progressively larger number of people. Thus everything about this disease produces a false sense of security in the general population.

I strongly recommended that readers base their own behavior and their guidance to their children on the three types of information sources mentioned.

This is the time to reconsider where one wants to live and work.

Supersaturation of the world oil market has resulted in a large drop in retail gasoline prices since 1981. The result has been a big increase in freeway traffic volume since then, which is leading to complete traffic gridlock in many metropolitan areas. This excess of oil supply relative to demand is temporary, however, and within a few years gasoline prices will again jump up sharply. Long distance daily **round trips from home to workplace are unpleasant for many people now because of the gridlock; by 1997 they will be horrendously expensive**. This is the time to reconsider where one wants to live and where one wants to work.

Climate change is something we can all help avoid. Each of us can plant trees that take carbon dioxide out of the air. We can take a number of steps so that less carbon dioxide waste enters the atmosphere from unnecessary combustion of fossil fuels:

- Buy more energy-efficient cars and appliances.
- Avoid waste travel.
- Insulate our homes.

We can all adjust our lifestyles and select the products we buy so as to minimize toxic waste being added to our underground aquifers, and the ocean.

Epilogue

How You Can Apply This Material to Your Own Interests

We all need some means of gauging what will happen to our business interests or our investments in the future. We also need to know when to buy and sell, particularly in the case of costly items such as houses or office buildings, or four-engine jet transports. If you don't know anything about mathematics or statistics, proceed as follows.

1. Get some quantitative historical data on your business, or on the national population of businesses of this type (from government documents). Make a graph of the prices or volumes of business plotted against time (as with figs. 4-1, 4-2 or 4-3).

2. Draw a freehand curve through the data points, so that half the data points are on either side of it. This represents the long-term trend line.

3. Now look for patterns in the deviations about the smooth long-term trend line. Do you see a repeating cycle? Look particularly carefully for a cycle with a half-wavelength of 12–16 years. Does it appear that there is a recurring pattern of cycles, in which high deviations follow low deviations, and vice versa, with roughly constant time lags?

4. If you do spot a pattern, try to find out what is affecting it. Does it have anything to do with energy cycles, capital investment cycles, or population cycles?

5. If you think you see patterns, and if you do not know how to analyze your data, we recommend that you seek help from someone in your own organization, or a consulting firm who will help you develop a formal approach to forecasting.

Train yourself to interpret newspaper and magazine articles, and business magazines in terms of the ideas in this book. Stay on the alert for evidence of economic substitution forces at work. For example, in August of 1992, a developing theme was concern about the decline in number of high-technology jobs in the United States, and the migration of high-technology activity to other countries. Why should that be a surprise? If the United States constantly undervalues petroleum, then that encourages the substitution of cheap petroleum and petrochemical feed stocks (energy and matter) for high technology. In one specific instance, that implies use of cars, trucks and buses instead of very high technology trains. The implications for waste of energy, space, and human time in congestion delays, production of pollution, and employment of engineers to design the trains are obvious. This constant replacement of high-technology engineering talent by under-priced petroleum could lead to a massive unemployment problem among engineers in the United States, with obvious effects on national average consumer purchasing power.

Appendix A

Validating the Analysis and Deriving the Equations

This chapter presents the mathematical foundation for the entire book, so readers can check the analysis and see how the equations are derived. The material is arranged by the chapter to which it refers.

Chapter 4. Long-term trends

The equation for the long-term trend (dashed line) in fig. 4-1 is

$$WPI = 38.06 + \exp(-132.2 + .0700Y) \quad (1)$$

where **WPI** represents the wholesale price index, and **Y** represents year number. This is a useful type of equation for processes that oscillate about a constant level for a long time, then begin to grow exponentially after some threshold is exceeded.

The equation for the long-term trend in fig. 4-2 is

$$D = \exp(-4.39 + .0700Y) \quad (2)$$

where **D** represents the federal government public debt in billions of current dollars, and **Y** represents year number, less 1819.

It is thought-provoking that the exponent for both equations is .0700. A plausible explanation is that prices are ultimately driven by cumulative fossil fuel production, and the debt is then driven by prices. The debt also indicates the rate at which the government must print money to keep the system functioning normally, given the increasing energy cost of extracting one more BTU (British Thermal Unit) of fossil fuel. This hypothesis becomes more credible as one reads through the book.

The equation for the long-term trend in fig. 4-3 is

$$P = .104 + \exp\{18.43[.253 - \exp(-.0219Y)]\} \quad (3)$$

where **P** represents the thousands of tons of pig iron shipped, and **Y** represents the year number, less 1800.

The equation for the long-term trend in fig. 4-16 is

$$\ln WFPI = 3.534 + 0.0008364C \quad (4)$$

where **WFPI** represents the wholesale fuel price index (E29,100.9 for 1967), and **C** represents the cumulative U.S. production of fossil fuel in quads (quadrillions of BTUs), obtained by cumulating M76, beginning in 1800. For early years with missing data, the data were obtained by interpolation.

Chapter 5. The mechanisms that produce fluctuations

A computer simulation model is described for determining the effect of population growth rate **R** and time lag **L** on the pattern of oscillation in snowshoe hare populations.

In the program in fig. A-1, **I** represents year number, and **N(1)** to **N(100)** represent the population sizes per 100 hectares from the first to last years in each century. At the outset of each run the operator supplies **R** and **L**. Recommended starting values: **R=1.271**, and **L=1,2** and then **3**. The data for the hare populations for the first 15 years came from Cary and Keith (1979).

The first step in developing a model to mimic lynx fluctuations is to compute an equation for the long-term trend line. As explained in Chapter 5, we must make a clean separation of the variation through time attributable to the force causing the trend, and that due to the force or forces causing fluctuation about the trend. Otherwise, attempts at statistical analysis of the causal system generating change through time will be bedevilled by confounding. Part of the variation we attempt to assign to the causal system generating fluctuations about the trend will, in fact, be due to the forces causing change in the trend, unless we remove the latter at the outset of the analysis.

```
5    DIM N(200)
6    N(1)=254
7    N(2)=104
8    N(3)=43
9    N(4)=22
10   N(5)=24
11   N(6)=39
12   N(7)=93
13   N(8)=144
14   N(9)=340
15   N(10)=510
16   N(11)=245
17   N(12)=78
18   N(13)=23
19   N(14)=4
20   N(15)=9
21   PRINT "R?"
22   INPUT R
23   PRINT "L?"
24   INPUT L
25   LPRINT " GROWTH RATE R=";R; "TIME LAG L=";L
26   FOR I=16 TO 100
27   N(I)=N(I-1) + R*N(I-1)*(1-N(I-L)/129)
28   LPRINT I; N(I)
29   NEXT I
30   END
```

Figure A-1. Simulation of snowshoe hare population.

Over the period 1821–1934, Mackenzie River District lynx fur returns varied from 39 to 6991. In dealing with data sets such as this, where the largest number is almost 180 times the smallest, the values of the dependent variables should be converted to logarithms. Otherwise, in any curve-fitting procedure to estimate parameter values, the effect of large values will overwhelm the effect of small values, and the "best-fitting" parameter estimates will only be best fits to the largest data values. Here

$$\log N_C = 6.4764 + .00270Y \quad (5)$$

where N_C represents the calculated number of lynx fur returns, and **Y** represents the actual year number, less 1800.

Equation (5) only accounted for .48 percent of the variance year to year in **N**. This seems insignificant, but it was significant in terms of antilogs. The long-term trend values increased from 693 in 1824, to 933 in 1934.

In subsequent stages of the analysis, all values were expressed as deviations about their long-term trend:

$$D = \log N_O - \log N_C \quad (6)$$

N represents the actual number of lynx returns.

In statistical analysis to determine the origin of fluctuations in **D**, it became apparent that the datum for 1917 fell out as an outlier. The observed value was far too low relative to the calculated value. This is to be expected: the trappers were away fighting the first world war in Europe. The equation that proved most useful in accounting for variation in **D** over the period 1824–1934 was

$$D(Y) = .151 + 1.404\,D(Y\text{-}1) + .0711\,D(Y\text{-}1)^2 - .8034D\,(Y\text{-}2) - .1547\,D(Y\text{-}2)^2 \qquad (7)$$

A simple test of the realism of equation (7) was to compute **N** each year, using (7) to compute **D(Y)**, then (6) and (5). The results are plotted in the second panel of fig. 5-3. Equation (7) accounted for 87.6 percent of the variance in **D(Y)**, and as we might expect, therefore, the computed lynx fur returns in the second panel are similar to the actual returns in the top panel.

This is not a very strong inferential test of the hypothesis that equation (7), in fact, describes the wave-generating mechanism in the lynx populations, however. Each year, **D** is computed from the actual **D** values for the two previous years. This would mask a systematic drift of calculated values away from their real-world counterparts. A much more stringent test of the realism of equation (7) is to use a computer simulation model provided with only the **D** values for the first two years, and equation (7). After the first two simulated years, the input **D** values for one year back and two years back would be those generated by the model for previous years. The model is listed below, and the results are plotted in the third panel of fig. 5-3.

The following is the revised version of the equation to account for fluctuations in the lynx population, when the parameters were estimated from a data set from which eight outlier years were removed. These outliers were all associated with volcanic eruptions. This analysis yielded the equation

$$D(Y) = .206 + 1.390\,D(Y\text{-}1) + .0957\,D(Y\text{-}1)^2 - .804\,D(Y\text{-}2) - .183\,D(Y\text{-}2)^2 \qquad (8)$$

which accounted for 90.6 percent of the variance in **D(Y)**. While the coefficients of the linear terms in this equation are similar to those in equation (7), the coefficients of the squared terms are 35 and 18 percent higher, respectively. The **D(Y)** values computed from a simulation model based on this equation (fig. A-2) are displayed in the fourth panel of fig. 5-3.

Figure A-2. Simulation of lynx fur returns.

```
1    DIM N(4)
2    N(1)=-.167
3    N(2)=.2283
4    YEAR=1824
5    YEAR=YEAR+1
6    X1==N(2)
7    X2=N(1)
8    X3=.2057 + 1.3904*X1 + .0957*X1*X1 -.804*X2 -
         .183*X2*X2
9    N(3)=X3
10   G=EXP(X3 + 6.476 + .002704*(YEAR-1800))
11   LPRINT YEAR,G
12   FOR I=1 TO 2
13   N(I)=N(I+1)
14   NEXT
15   IF YEAR-1935 GOTO 5 ELSE END
```

N(1) and **X2** represent the size of the return two time steps back; **N(2)** and **X1** represent the size of the return one time step back. **N(3)** and **X3** represent the size of the return in the present year. All of these numbers are expressed as deviations of logarithms about the logarithm of the trend for the corresponding year. In line 10, the deviation and the trend values are added, and the actual number of lynx returns is computed as the antilogarithm of that sum.

The simulation program in fig. A-3 is used to generate the future projections for the WPI values depicted in fig. 5-7. The first WPI value simulated is for 1989. Therefore the program begins by creating a table of all actual WPI values from 40 years prior to 1989 (1949) to 1988. At each cycle, the program computes and prints a new WPI value, then updates the value for the year number, and the 40 WPI values in the data table. The equation used to compute each WPI in this program is the same equation that was used to compute the WPI values depicted in the bottom panel of fig. 5-5.

```
10    DIM P(9)
20    DIM W(41)
30    FOR I = 1 TO 40
40    READ W(I)
50    NEXT I
51    DATA 78.7,81.8,91.9,88.6,87,4
52    DATA 87.6,87.8,90.7,93.3,94.6
60    DATA 94.8,94.9,94.5,94.8,94.5
70    DATA 94.7,96.6,99.8,100.0,102.5
80    DATA 106.5,110.4,114.0,119.1,134.7
90    DATA 160.1,174.9,183.0,194.2,209.3
100   DATA 235.6,268.8,293.4,299.3,303.1
110   DATA 310.4,308.9,299.9,307.7,320.0
120   FOR I = 1 TO 8
130   READ P(I)
140   NEXT I
150   DATA 37,9.243,.08721,-1.628,5.558E-5
160   DATA -5.914E-3,-2.33E-5,793.7
180   Y=1989
190   YC=Y-1800
195   YC2=YC^2
200   CLS1=0
210   CLS2=0
220   CLS3=0
230   FOR I=1 TO 11
240   CLS1=CLS1+W(I)
250   NEXT I
260   FOR I=21 TO 31
270   CLS2=CLS2+W(I)
280   NEXT I
290   CLS1=CLS1*.09091
300   CLS2=CLS2*.09091
320   T=P(1) + EXP(-P(2) + P(3) * YC)
330   M1=CLS1^(P(4)+P(5)*YC2)
340   M2=(CLS2^(P(6)*YC+P(7)*YC2))*P(8)
360   W(41)=T*M1*M2
370   LPRINT Y,W(41)
380   Y=Y+1
390   IF Y=2030 THEN 450
400   FOR I=1 TO 40
410   W(I)= W(I+1)
420   NEXT I
430   GOTO 190
450   END
```

Figure A-3. Simulation of future projections of Wholesale Price Index in fig. 5.8.

Chapter 6. Fluctuations in human populations

From this point on, variables are modelled as if their value at any point in time is the product of one term, **TREND**, expressing the value of the trend, and another term, **MULT**, for multiplier, expressing the deviation about the trend as a proportion or multiple of 1.

The equation fitted to the data for birth rates in U.S. women was

$$R = [TREND][MULT] \quad (9)$$

$$TREND = 330.3 - 316.8/[1.0 + 4.328\exp(-.03392T)] \quad (10)$$

$$MULT = 24.94 - 23.97/[1.0-.8120\exp(-.01638X)] \quad (11)$$

Here **R** represents the 3-year moving average of birth rates per 1000 women 15–44 years old, **T** represents year number, less 1799, and **X** represents the average of birth rates 20 to 28 years ago. Moving averages of **R** were used to facilitate convergence of the curve-fitting algorithm, given the high level of high-frequency fluctuation in the raw birth rate data produced largely by wars.

This equation and the fitted parameters itemized above accounted for 98.81 percent of the year-to-year variance in the moving averages of birth rates, over the 159 years 1828–1986, inclusive.

The equations describing year to year change in the number of live births in the United States are

$$B = [TREND][MULT] \quad (12)$$

$$TREND = 13.73 /[1.0 + 3.266\exp(-.001581C)] \quad (13)$$

$$MULT = .857 - .673/[1.0+4.609\exp(-.852X)] \quad (14)$$

where **B** represents the 5-year moving average of the number of live births each year, in millions, **C** represents the cumulative U.S. domestic fossil fuel production to, and including each year, in quads, and **X** represents the average annual number of births over the period 16–24 years ago, inclusive, in millions.

Moving averages of **B** were used to facilitate convergence of the curve-fitting routine. This was done to smooth out high-frequency oscillation in the raw data for **B** associated with the effect on conception rate of wartime service abroad by large numbers of servicemen, as explained in Chapter 6. This relationship and the fitted values itemized above accounted for 96.2 percent of the year-to-year variance in 5-year moving averages of birth numbers from 1934 to 1985. The 3.8 percent residual variance is largely due to perturbations associated with wars, as we shall show.

We now explain why the particular forms of the above functions were selected. We consider **TREND** first. From inspection of fig. 6-5, the trend for birth numbers appears to be a logistic function. When growth rates are high in the middle of a growth period and lower at the end and beginning, this suggests a growth function in the logistic family of equations. Wide-amplitude oscillation tends to obscure the trend, but even so, fig. 6-5 suggests that the trend for birth numbers was growing much more rapidly between 1940 and 1960 than between 1900 and 1940, or after 1960. For example, the ascending slope of the wave between 1975 and 1985 is less steep than for the ascending wave between 1935 and 1955.

Our postulate that the logistic was a good descriptor of the growth pattern for number of births proved correct. When estimates of all the parameters for **TREND** and **MULT** were obtained in a single fitting procedure, the values of **TREND** computed from the estimated parameters produced the long-term trend depicted in fig. 6-6. The trend for numbers of births rose at an increasing rate until about 1960, after which the rate of growth decreased markedly. By about 2010, the trend for number of births each year will have ceased growing.

The interpretation is that growth of any population is governed by the status of its currently most critical limiting resource, which in the case of the U.S. population at present is domestic reserves of fossil fuel. The best measure of that status is cumulative production of U.S. fossil fuel, measured in quads. **TREND** is a logistic function of this cumulative fuel production, as demonstrated by the computed trend plotted in fig. 6-6.

Now we consider the appropriate mathematical formulation for **MULT**. From study of the oscillatory pattern depicted in fig. 6-5 it appears that the deviations of the number of births each year around their trend are determined by the sum of the lagged values of birth numbers 16–24 years ago. Birth numbers are far above an imaginary trend about 1958 and far below it about 1978. That is, birth numbers are governed by birth numbers in the previous generation. The reason for describing **MULT** by a reverse logistic is that one would not expect birth numbers to rise indefinitely as the standard of living of young mothers improved, and one would not expect it to drop indefinitely as their standard of living worsened.

The equation for the apparent survival rate to age 22 takes the form

$$S = B(y-22)\{.0154 + 1.050/[1.0 + .743\exp(-.000969C)]\} \qquad (15)$$

where **B(y-22)** represents the number of births 22 years ago, in millions, and **C** represents cumulative U.S. production of fossil fuel, as before. This equation accounts for 98.2 percent of the year to year variance in the smoothed "apparent survival rates."

The equation for the growth in the cumulative number of diagnosed AIDS cases worldwide was

$$A = -2.2337 + 2.258 \times 10^{-10} Y^{9.4334} \qquad (16)$$

where **A** represents the cumulative number of people diagnosed as having AIDS, worldwide, in thousands, and **Y** represents year number - 1970.

This equation accounts for 99.986 percent of the year to year variance in cumulative worldwide number of people newly diagnosed as having AIDS each year since 1981.

Chapter 7. The mechanism producing the long wave

The measure of lagged WFPI values that best accounted for fluctuations in pig iron shipments was the sum of trend-adjusted values 9–13 years ago. We will designate this variable as **F**. The parameter estimates in equation (17) were obtained using the data for the period 1869–1981, inclusive, with the values for 1927–1931, inclusive, being ommitted as outliers. These values were excluded because of the extraordinary increase in the amount of money tied up in loans by banks relative to their cash on hand in that period. The measure of tonnage of pig iron shipments used was the 5-year moving average, to minimize the effect of short-term fluctuations and to facilitate convergence of the curve-fitting algorithms.

The fitted equation was

$$\ln PIS = \{11.0\,[1.0 - \exp(-.162C)] - 3.00 - \exp(-50.5 + .808C^2)\}\{.975 + .0145F - .115F^2\} \qquad (17)$$

This equation accounted for 98.98 percent of the variance in *ln* **PIS**.

The first line of (17) allows us to compute the long-term trend for **PIS**; the second line represents the multiplier term that generates the wavelike oscillations about the **PIS** trend.

Chapter 8. The world market for crude petroleum

The equation to account for change in **Q**, the U.S. consumption of refined petroleum products in year **Y**, in quads, is

$$Q = 34.59X1^{-.211}\,X2^{-.0438}\{1.0/[1.0 + 1.19 \times 10^{19}\exp(-.0170G)]\} \qquad (18)$$

where **X1** represents the ratio, in year **Y-1**, of the crude oil price to an index of the average wage and **X2** represents the average of that ratio, over the years **Y-6** to **Y-4** and **G** represents the GNP in 1982 dollars.

The index used for the ratio of crude oil price to average wage was obtained by dividing the price per million BTUs of crude oil in current cents by the average gross weekly earnings, in current dollars, of workers in private nonagricultural industries. The numerator was obtained from the *Annual Reports to the Congress* of the U.S. Energy Information Administration (e.g. Table 6 in Volume 2 of the 1978 report). The denominator comes from tables on average weekly earnings in the SA (e.g. SA1979 Table 688).

This equation accounts for 97.3 percent of the year-to-year change in **Q**.

Of various simple mathematical models tested as descriptors of the past trend in current dollar oil prices **P**, the one that best described the data was

$$P = 2.92 + B1(B2) \tag{19}$$

where

$$B1 = .00169(X1^{-.5.227})(X2^{-5.227}) \tag{20}$$

and

$$B2 = EXP(-6.349 + .01023C) \tag{21}$$

X1 and **X2** represent average oil prices in current dollars over the periods 11–16 years ago and 2–4 years ago, respectively, and **C** represents the cumulative U.S. fossil fuel production to and including the present year, in quads. This relationship accounted for 96.4 percent of the variance in the oil prices over the period 1967–1988, inclusive. The equation means that the oil market is under strong negative feedback control over the short term.

The computer program in fig. A-4 was used to project oil prices into the future. Readers might wish to experiment, so as to explore the consequences of varying the structure of the equations, the lag lengths, and the values of the parameters.

```
10   REM THE FIRST YEAR SIMULATED IS 1989
20   REM P(1) IS THE CURRENT DOLLAR OIL PRICE IN 1973
30   DIM P(20)
40   P(1)=3.89
50   P(2)=6.87
60   P(3)=7.67
70   P(4)=8.19
80   P(5)=8.57
90   P(6)=8.96
100  P(7)=12.6
110  P(8)=21.6
120  P(9)=31.8
130  P(10)=28.5
140  P(11)=26.2
150  P(12)=26.0
160  P(13)=24.1
170  P(14)=12.5
180  P(15)=15.4
190  P(16)=16.6
200  YEAR=1992
210  CUM=3086
220  X1=(P(1)+P(2)+P(3)+P(4)+P(5)+P(6))/6.0
230  X2=(P(13)+P(14)+P(15))/3.0
240  A1=.000169
250  A2=-5.227
260  A3=-1.255
270  A4=6.349
280  A5=.01023
290  A6=2.92
300  B1=A1*(X1^A2)*(X2^A3)
310  B2=EXP(-A4+A5*CUM)
320  P(17)=A6+B1*B2
330  LPRINT YEAR, P(17)
340  YEAR=YEAR+1
350  CUM=CUM+1
360  FOR I=1 TO 16
370  P(I)=P(I+1)
380  NEXT
390  IF YEAR <2031 THEN GOTO 220 ELSE END
```

Figure A-4. BASIC computer program for simulating future oil prices.

Chapter 9. Forecasting Behavior of Volatile Markets

Where **P(Y)** represents the current dollar price of wheat in year **Y**, the following parameter values were computed from the wheat price data since 1844.

$$P(Y) = .336 + .853P(Y-4) - .0332(Y-4)^2 \quad (22)$$

$$P(Y) = .530 + .627P(Y-6) + .0253(Y-6)^2 \quad (23)$$

The model used for the bottom panel of fig. 9-1 was

$$P(Y) = .687 + TREND[MULT1][MULT2] \quad (24)$$

where

$$TREND = EXP(-9.61 + .0619Y) \quad (25)$$

where **Y** represents the year number, less 1800

$$MULT1 = X1^{12.39 - .146Y + 3.69 \times 10^{-4} Y^2} \quad (26)$$

where **X1** represents the average price of a bushel of wheat 34–44 years back, and **Y** represents the number. The term for MULT1 shows how to describe the situation where the influence of one variable, **X1**, on a dependent variable weakens with increase in another independent variable, **Y**.

$$MULT2 = X2^{.696 - .122Y + 6.40 \times 10^{-4} Y^2} \quad (27)$$

where **X2** represents the average price of a bushel of wheat 16–26 years ago.

GLOSSARY

Codes such as D745 refer to a data series that has been recorded and published in a uniform fashion for a long time by the U.S. Department of Commerce, Bureau of the Census. The most elaborate compilation and explanation of these codes is in the two-volume document found in the government documents section of most large libraries: *Bicentennial Edition. Historical Statistics of the United States. Colonial Times to 1970* (HS). Current statistics for these data series are published each year in the *Statistical Abstract of the United States*, from the same agency.

aggregated This is the property of a statistic that pools information from many data sources, as by combining them into a sum or an average. The average birth rate of women 15–44 years old is a highly aggregated statistic. The average birth rate of women 20 years of age is a highly disaggregated statistic. Aggregated statistics compensate for a loss in precision with a gain in robustness. The higher the degree of aggregation in a statistic, the less sensitive it will be to unusual, extreme perturbations at a particular time or place, or befalling a particular group. A 9-year moving average is a highly aggregated statistic, relatively uninfluenced by violent short-term perturbations.

asymptote An asymptote is an upper limit above which a variable cannot grow, or a lower limit below which it can not fall. A line on a graph describing change in a variable bends and flattens as it approaches an asymptote. Upper and lower asymptotes are caused by supersaturation or total depletion, respectively, of some storage.

BTU British Thermal Unit. This is the quantity of heat required to raise the temperature of one pound of water 1°F. Such an energy measure is important in systems analysis of society because it allows us to convert the energy from diverse sources (coal, fuel wood, hydroelectricity, nuclear power, etc.) to a common base so they can be added up. This addition is illustrated for M 76–92 in HS.

C The value of **C** in any year for any country is the cumulative production in that country of all fossil fuels in quadrillions of BTU, since the first year of production. For the U.S., it is the sum of the energy in M77 (bituminous coal), M78 (Pennsylvania anthracite), M79 (crude petroleum), M80 (natural gas, wet). This variable expresses both the amount of fossil fuel already used up, but **also** the amount still left in the ground.

D The public debt of the U.S. federal government (Y493).

D745 Average annual earnings per full-time employee in the construction industry.

datum (plural: data) Fact(s). A single unit of quantitative information (e.g. the U.S. national average wellhead price for a barrel of crude oil in 1982). "Data" refers to assemblages of such units.

demographic
Pertaining to human population(s). Birth, death, survival and migration rates are demographic statistics.

E23
Annual estimate of the U.S. wholesale price index for all commodities (1967=100.0). I use the item compiled by the Bureau of Labor Statistics, but extended back to 1720 by Ethel Hoover and George R. Taylor (Shirk, 1985).

E52–63
The wholesale price index computed by George Warren and Frank Pearson, and its subcomponents.

E135
The consumer price index.

empirical
A quantitative estimate, an equation or parameter estimates derived from actual data, rather than being derived from theory. This makes the distinction between induction and deduction as sources of knowledge. This book places heavy emphasis on induction and empiricism, in contradistinction to deduction, theory or ideology.

endogenous
Pertaining to some force, system driver or perturbation originating within the system of interest.

equilibrium
The state, trajectory or long-run trend line to which a system returns after a perturbation has caused a deviation.

exogenous
Pertaining to some force, or perturbation originating outside the system of interest. Particularly clearcut examples are disruptions of the economic or political systems by volcanic eruptions or large meteorites.

externalities
Sources of economic costs or benefits that lie outside "the economic system," given present conceptions as to how that system should be bounded. Moderate weather and ocean water off the coast of New Jersey suitable for bathing are externalities as the economic system is understood and bounded now. If the "economic system" boundary were enlarged so that every activity entailed the total cost of its end effects on the economic system, we would say that we now had "equitable internalization of costs and benefits".

F
The sum of trend-adjusted values of the wholesale fuel price index from 9 years ago to 13 years ago, inclusive.

flow
The rate of addition to, or subtraction from a storage. Typical rates are the birth rate, which measures the annual rate per 1,000 women at which babies are added to the number born in that year (which is a storage).

FP
Forecasting and related activities of policy, planning and management.

FSD
Fundamental system driver. This is a system variable at the heart of the driving mechanism of the system. Such variables override all other system variables in their effects on the dynamic behavior on the system.

global stability region This region would be the state to which a system would invariably return after a perturbation, if the system were too stable to evolve or transform. If England had returned to a system of stage coaches and horse-drawn canal barges after attempts to introduce railroads failed, we would say the societal system was trapped in a global stability region.

hectare Metric measurement of land, approximately equal to 2.47 acres.

inflection point Point on a curve or arc where curvature changes from concave to convex and vice versa.

J254, J256 The average annual temperatures for New Haven, Conn., and New York City, respectively.

K1 The U.S. farm population.

K184 The number of tractors on U.S. farms.

K507 The production of wheat on U.S. farms (millions of bushels).

K508 The average price per bushel of wheat in the U.S.

leading indicator A variable that gives advance warning of subsequent changes in other variables.

linear model A mathematical model to describe a phenomenon or process in which the combined effects of the subcomponent terms can be expressed as a sum.

M5 The number of production and development workers in the U.S. mineral operations industry.

M76 Total U.S. production of mineral energy fuels and electricity from waterpower.

M92 Total U.S. consumption of energy from fuel wood.

M217 Total U.S. shipments of pig iron (thousands of long tons).

M297 Man-hours worked in U.S. coal mines.

market supersaturation see *supersaturation*

mpg Average mileage per gallon of gasoline.

nadir A low point in a graph.

net energy cost The energy cost of an activity after subtracting the energy produced by the activity. Any activity with a net energy cost would not be economically worthwhile over the long term. If such an activity were economically worthwhile over the short term, this would imply that the current market price of the energy being used to obtain more energy did not correctly value the cost to replace the former in the energy inventory.

nonlinear equations — Equations in which the combined effect of the constituent terms can not be expressed as a simple sum.

outlier data — Data points representing extreme departures from a trend or equilibrium.

P — Pig iron shipments.

P41 — The index of manufacturing production by all manufacturing industries.

P53 — Index of manufacturing production in printing and publishing industries.

P55 — Index of manufacturing production in petroleum and coal products

paradigm — In this book, the word is used in a very broad sense, to mean a world view or belief system

PIS — Pig iron shipments.

point source — A source of energy for society concentrated at a very small geographical location, such as a coal mine, oil or gas well, or refinery. The opposite condition would be a geographically diffuse source of energy, as in solar, wind, or tidal energy.

quads — A very large unit of energy, the short form for quadillions of British Thermal Units.

SA (e.g.) 1987, Table 1168 — The Statistical Abstract of the United States, a compilation of statistics published annually by the U.S. Department of Commerce, Bureau of the Census.

state variable — One of a small number of system variables that collectively carry the full information about the current transient state of the system. These state variables have three important characteristics: (1) Their current values can be computed using only past data on their own values or the values of other state variables; (2) Therefore, they impose a high degree of inertia, or rigidity on dynamical systems. In effect, they are the "skeleton" of a system that maintains its basic character as it changes through time; (3) State variables measure the status of storages, not rates of flow.

state-dependent variable — System variables whose current values can be computed from the current values of state variables.

steady state values — The values taken by system variables under equilibrium conditions.

storage The quantity of an inventory stored at any particular time. This is not the capacity of the container. An example is the number of square feet of floor space in U.S. office buildings in 1992.

supersaturation, market The condition in any market when supply exceeds demand, as in the U.S. car market in 1930, or the U.S. market for space in office buildings in 1992.

surrogate variable A variable used as a substitute for another, as when year number is used in place of another variable that changes through time, for which there is difficulty in obtaining measurements for all years.

system A set of subcomponents collectively united by some form of causal interaction, or interdependency. Also, a system can be visualized as separated from its environment by some real or imaginary boundary, as in "The U.S agricultural system."

system variable Any variable describing the current state of a system Note, however, the distinction between state variables, and state-dependent variables. Only the former carry the full information about the current state of the system.

variable A quantity that changes through time.

variable, state See state variable.

variable, state-dependent See state-dependent variable.

variable, surrogate See surrogate variable.

variable, system See system variable.

Y Year number. In mathematical models of society, and in statistical curve-fitting operations, this quantity is typically "scaled" by using year number less 1800, for example, in lieu of the actual year number.

WFPI Wholesale fuel price index (E29), a composite index of the wholesale prices of all types of fuel computed by the U.S. Bureau of Labor Statistics. One of the most important state variables measuring the status of U.S society.

WPI U.S. Wholesale Price Index, a composite index of the prices of all wholesale commodities.

zenith Peak year(s) in a graph of some variable plotted against time.

REFERENCES

Albion, R.G. 1926. *Forests and Sea Power.* Harvard University Press, Cambridge, Mass. xv + 485 pp.

Allen, T.F.H., and T.B. Starr. 1982. *Hierarchy. Perspectives for Ecological Complexity*. University of Chicago Press, Chicago. xvi + 310 pp.

Anderson, D.V. 1985. *Illusions of Power. A History of the Washington Public Power Supply System.* Praeger, New York. xiii + 159 pp.

Anderson, R.M., R.M. May, and A.R. McLean. 1988. Possible Demographic Consequences of AIDS in Developing Countries. *Nature* 332:228–233.

Armstrong, J.S. 1978. *Long Range Forecasting: From Crystal Ball to Computer.* Wiley Interscience, New York. xviii + 612 pp.

Ascher, W. 1978. *Forecasting: An Appraisal for Policy-makers and Planners.* Johns Hopkins University Press, Baltimore, Md. xiv + 239 pp.

Ascher, W. and W.H. Overholt, 1983. *Strategic Planning and Forecasting. Political Risk and Economic Opportunity*. Wiley Interscience, New York. xxi + 311 pp.

Auburn, J.S. 1988. Decentralizing the Distribution of Fresh Agricultural Produce. *Transportation Research*-A 22A(2):109–119.

Ball, H. 1986. *Justice Downwind. America's Atomic Testing Program in the 1950's*. Oxford University Press, New York. xviii + 280pp.

Batra, R. 1987. *The Great Depression of 1990.* Simon & Schuster, New York, New York. 235 pp.

Becker, E. 1971. *The Birth and Death of Meaning.* Second Ed. An Interdisciplinary perspective on the problem of man. The Free Press. Macmillan, New York. x1 + 228 pp.

Becker, E. 1975. *Escape From Evil. The Free Press.* Macmillan, New York. xix + 188 pp.

Bergesen, A. (ed.). 1983. *Crises in the World System.* Sage Publications, Beverly Hills, California. 311 pp.

Boffey, P.M. 1988. NASA Urged to Improve Forecasting. *New York Times*, July 28, A9.

Braudel, F. 1972, 1973. *The Mediterranean and the Mediterranean World in the age of Phillip II.* Vol. 1–2. Harper and Row, New York.

Bremmer, S.A. (ed.). 1987. *The Globus Model. Computer Simulation of Worldwide Political and Economic Developments.* Westview Press, Boulder, Colorado. xxiii + 940 pp.

Broad, W.J. 1986. Effects of Cold Emerge as Focus of Shuttle Panel. *New York Times*, Feb. 23:1.

Browne, M.W. 1988. In Math, the Language of Science, Americans Grow Ever Weaker. *New York Times*, Oct. 30. Section 4:24.

Butler, L. 1953. The Nature of Cycles in Populations of Canadian Mammals. *Canadian Journal of Zoology* 31:242–262.

Cary, J.R. and L.B. Keith. 1979. Reproductive Changes in the 10-year Cycle of Snowshoe Hares. *Canadian Journal of Zoology* 57:375–390.

Churchill, W.S. 1948. *The Gathering Storm*. Houghton Mifflin Co., Boston. xviii + 713 pp.

Churchill, W.S. 1949. *Their Finest hour*. Houghton Mifflin Co., Boston. xvi + 652 pp.

Churchill, W.S. 1950a. *The Grand Alliance*. Houghton Mifflin Co.,Boston. xviii + 777 pp.

Churchill, W.S. 1950b. *The Hinge of Fate*. Houghton Mifflin Co., Boston. xviii + 873 pp.

Clark, J.M.. 1931. *The Costs of the World War to the American People*. Yale University Press, New Haven, Conn. xi + 316 pp.

Clark, W.C. (ed.) 1982. *Carbon Dioxide Review:1982*. Oxford University Press, New York. xix + 469 pp.

Clark, W.C., and R.E. Munn (eds.). 1986. *Sustainable Development of the Biosphere*. Cambridge University Press, Cambridge. vi + 491pp.

Cobb, C.E., Jr. 1987. The Great Lakes' Troubled Waters. *National Geographic* 172(1):2–31.

Colgate, S.A., E.A. Stanley, J.M. Hyman, C.R. Qualls, and S.P. Layne. 1989. AIDS and a risk-based model. *Los Alamos Science* 18:2–23.

Cook, E. 1976. *Man, Energy, Society*. W.H. Freeman & Co., San Francisco. xi + 478pp.

Cook, J. 1985. Nuclear Follies. *Forbes*, Feb. 11:1–100.

Darby, M.R., J.R. Lothian, A.E. Gandolfi, A.J. Schwartz, and A.C. Stockman. 1983. *The International Transmission of Inflation*. The University of Chicago Press, Chicago. xv + 727 pp.

D'Arrigo,R.D., G.C. Jacoby, and I.Y. Fung. 1987. Boreal Forests and Atmosphere–biosphere Exchange of Carbon Dioxide. *Nature* 329:321–323.

Deevey, E.S., D.S. Rice, P.M. Rice, H.H. Vaughan, M. Brenner and M.S. Flannery. 1979. Mayan Urbanism: Impact on a Tropical Karst Environment. *Science* 206:298–306.

Demause, L. 1982. *Foundations of Psychohistory*. 1982. Creative Books, Inc. P.O. Box 401, Planetarium Station, New York, N.Y., 10024, v + 336 pp.

Dickinson, F.G. 1940. An Aftercost of the World War to the United States. *The American Economic Review* 30, No. 1, Supplement:326–339.

Director, A. 1940. Does Inflation Change the Economic Effects of War? *The American Economic Review* 30(1), Supplement:351–361.

Dolan, C. 1983. WPPSS Bond Fiasco is Shattering Episode to Ex-director, too. *Wall Street Journal*, July 21: 1–20.

Dyer, G. 1985. *War*. Crown Publishers, New York. xii + 272 pp.

Eckstein, O., and A. Sinai. 1986. The Mechanisms of the Business Cycle in the Postwar Era. *In* R.J. Gordon, ed.(q.v.). *The American Business Cycle. Continuity and Change*, pp. 39–122.

Economist (of London). 1985. Eternal Triangles. *Aircraft Industry Survey*, June 1: 5–24.

Ehrlich, P.R., and J.P. Holdren (eds.). 1988. *The Cassandra Conference. Resources and the Human Predicament*. Texas A & M University Press, College Station, Texas. xi + 330 pp.

Elgerd, O.I. 1967. *Control Systems Theory*. McGraw-Hill Book Co., New York. 562 pp.

Elton, C, and M. Nicholson. 1942. The Ten-year Cycle in Numbers of the Lynx in Canada. *Journal of Animal Ecology* 11:215–244.

Essex, C. 1986. Trace Gases and the Problem of False Invariants in Climate Models. *Climatological Bulletin* 20 (1):19–25.

Ezzell, C. 1989. Uncertain Start in Montreal. *Nature* 339:410.

Fay, S.B. 1928. *The Origins of the World War II. After Sarajevo: Immediate Causes of the War*. The Macmillan Company, New York. xi + 577 pp.

Ferro, M. 1987. *The Great War 1914–1918*. ARK Paperbacks. Routledge & Kegan Paul Ltd. London. xi + 239 pp.

Finerty, J.P.. 1976. *The Population Ecology of Cycles in Small Mammals. Mathematical Theory and Biological Fact*. Yale University Press. New Haven, Conn. xiv + 234 pp.

Fletcher, R. 1987. *Practical Methods of Optimization*. John Wiley and Sons, Chichester. xiv + 436 pp.

Food And Agriculture Organization. 1977. *Yearbook of the Food and Agriculture Organization of the United Nations*. Rome.

Francis, J. 1968. *A History of the English Railway, Its Social Relations and Revelations 1820–1845* (Volumes 1 and 2 of 1851 edition combined). Augustus M. Kelley, New York. xii +308 pp.; viii + 282 pp.

Gaines, T.C. 1962. *Techniques of Treasury Debt Management.* The Free Press of Glencoe, The Macmillan Company, New York, xii + 317 pp.

Galbraith, J.K. 1961. *The Great Crash 1929.* Houghton Mifflin, Boston. xiii + 212 pp.

Gammon, R.H., W.D. Komhyr, and J.T. Peterson. 1986. The Global Atmospheric CO2 Distribution 1968–1983: Interpretation of the Results of the NOAA/ GMCC Measurement Program. *In* J.R. Trabalka and D.E. Reichle, eds., (q.v.) *The Changing Carbon Cycle. A Global Analysis,* pp 1–15.

Gandara, A. 1977. *Electric Utility Decisionmaking and the Nuclear Option.* The RAND Corporation, Santa Monica, California. R-2148-NSF. xv + 109 pp.

Gardner, M.R. and W.R. Ashby. 1970. Connectance of Large Dynamical (Cybernetic) Systems: Critical Values for Stability. *Nature* 228:784.

Garrison, J. 1989. AIDS Cases Up, Possibly Due to Under-Reporting. *San Francisco Examiner*, May 3, pp. A1 and A20.

Gauvreau, E. 1945. *The Wild Blue Yonder. Sons of the Prophet Carry On.* E.P. Dutton, New York. 386 pp.

Gever, J., R. Kaufman, D. Skole, and C. Vorosmarty. 1986. *Beyon Oil. The Threat to Food and Fuel in the Coming Decades.* Ballinger, Cambridge, Mass. 304 pp.

Godet, M. 1979. *The Crisis in Forecasting and the Emergence of the "Prospective" Approach with Case Studies in Energy and Air Transport.* Pergamon Press, New York. xi + 134 pp.

Goldstein, J.S. 1985. Kondratieff Waves as War Cycles. *International Studies Quarterly* 29(4):411–444.

Goldstein, J.S. 1988. *Long Cycles. Prosperity and War in the Modern Age.* Yale University Press, New Haven. xiii + 433 pp.

Goleman, D. 1988. For Presidential Candidates, Optimism Appears a Winner. *The New York Times*, May 8, 1–11.

Goodridge, J. 1988. Air Temperature Trends in California 1916 to 1987. ms.

Gordon, R.J. (ed.) 1986. *The American Business Cycle. Continuity and Change.* University of Chicago Press, Chicago. xiv + 868 pp.

Gore, R. 1985. No Way To Run a Desert. The Rising Great Salt Lake. *National Geographic* 167(6):694–719.

Griffiths,J.F., and K.C. Vining. 1984. Problems with Environmental Data: A Case Study in Climatology. *International Journal of Environmental Studies* 22:103–108.

Gulland, J.A. (ed.) 1977. *Fish Population Dynamics.* Wiley-Interscience, New York. xi + 372 pp.

Haberler, G. 1941. *Prosperity and Depression*. 3rd. ed. League of Nations, Geneva. xxiv + 532 pp.

Hall, C.A.S., C.J. Cleveland, and R.K. Kaufmann. 1986. *Energy and Resource Quality. The Ecology of the Economic Process*. John Wiley and Sons, New York. xxi + 577 pp.

Hall, P. 1982. *Great Planning Disasters*. University of California Press, Berkeley. xxviii + 308 pp.

Hanson, K., G.A. Maul, and T.R. Kark. 1989. Are Atmospheric "Greenhouse" Effects Apparent in the Climatic Record of the Contiguous U.S. (1895–1987)? *Geophysical Research Letters* 16(1):49–52.

Hayes, R.H. 1986. Why Strategic Planning goes Awry. *The New York Times*, April 20, Section 3:2F.

Hiltzik, M.A. 1985. Big Forecasters Failed to Predict Own Misfortune. *Los Angeles Times Business Section*, March 3:1–8.

Himmelblau, D.M. 1972. *Applied Nonlinear Programming*. McGraw-Hill, New York. xi + 498 pp.

Hirsch, R.L. 1987. Impending United States Energy Crisis. *Science* 235:1467–1473.

Holland, M. 1987. Don't Blame The Japanese. *Los Angeles Times Magazine*, July 12:16–23.

Holland, M. 1989. *When the Machine Stopped. A cautionary tale from industrial America*. Harvard Business School Press. Boston, Mass. xiii + 335 pp.

Holling, C.S. 1986. The Resilience of Terrestrial Ecosystems: Local Surprise and Global Change. *In* W.C. Clark, and R.E. Munn, eds. (q.v.). *Sustainable Development of the Biosphere*, pp. 292–317.

Hubbert, M.K. 1962. *Energy Resources*. Publication 1000-D. U.S. National Academy of Sciences–National Research Council, Washington, D.C. 141 pp.

Hughes, B. 1980. *World Modeling. The Mesarovic–Pestel World Model in the Context of its Contemporaries*. Lexington Books, Lexington, Mass. 227 pp.

Hughes, B.B. 1985. *World Futures. A Critical Analysis of Alternatives*. The Johns Hopkins University Press, Baltimore. xii + 243 pp.

Humphreys, W.J. 1913. Volcanic dust and other factors in the production of climatic change, and their possible relation to ice ages. *Journal of the Franklin Institute*, 176:131-172.

Hurley, A.F. 1975. *Billy Mitchell. Crusader for Air Power*. Indiana University Press, Bloomington, Indiana. ix + 190 pp.

Idso, S.B. 1989. *Carbon Dioxide and Global Change: Earth in Transition*. IBR Press, Tempe, Arizona. 292 pp.

Jacobsen,T. and R.M. Adams. 1958. Salt and Silt in Ancient Mesopotamian Agriculture. *Science* 128:1251–1258.

Johnston, W.B. and K.R. Hopkins. 1990. *The Catastrophe Ahead: AIDS and the Case for a New Public Policy*. Praeger, New York.

Karnopp, D., and R. Rosenberg 1975. *Systems Dynamics: A Unified Approach*. John Wiley and Sons. New York. x + 422 pp.

Keepin, B. 1986. Review of Global Energy and Carbon Dioxide Projections. *Annual Review of Energy* 11:357—392.

Keith, L.B. 1963. *Wildlife's Ten-year Cycle*. University of Wisconsin Press, Madison, Wisconsin. 201 pp.

Keith, L.B. and L.A. Windberg. 1978. A Demographic Analysis of the Snowshoe Hare Cycle. *Wildlife Monographs* No. 58. 70 pp.

Keith, L.B., J.R. Cary, O.J. Rongstad, and M.C. Brittingham. 1984. Demography and Ecology of a declining Snowshoe Hare Population. Wildlife Monographs... No. 90. 43 pp.

Kennedy, J.F. 1961. *Why England Slept*. Wilfred Funk, Inc., New York. xxviii + 252 pp.

Kermack, W.O., and A.G. McKendrick. 1927. A Contribution to the Mathematical Theory of Epidemics. *Proceedings of the Royal Society*, London, Series A, 115:700–721.

Key, W.B. 1974. *Subliminal Seduction: Ad Media's Manipulation of a Not So Innocent America*. New American Library, New York. xviii + 220 pp.

Key, W.B. 1976. *Media Sexploitation*. Prentice-Hall, Englewood Cliffs, New Jersey. xv + 234 pp.

Kimball, B.A. 1983. Carbon Dioxide and Agricultural Yield: An Assemblage and Analysis of 430 Prior Observations. *Agronomy Journal* 75:779–788.

Klein, L.R., and E. Burmeister (eds.) 1976. *Econometric Model Performance. Comparative Simulation Studies of the U.S. Economy*. University of Pennsylvania Press, Philadelphia, 407 pp.

Knight, B. 1940. Postwar Costs of a New War. *The American Economic Review*, Part 2, 30(1), Supplement:340–350.

Kondtratieff, N. 1925. (repub. 1984). *The Long Wave Cycle*. International Moneyline, St. Moritz, Switzerland. ii + 138 pp.

Koon, B. 1986. San Francisco's Skyline Abounds with Office Space. *San Francisco Examiner*, Real Estate Section, April 20:1–4.

Lamb, H.H. 1972. *Climate: Present, Past and Future. Volume 1. Fundamentals and Climate Now*. Methuen & Co. Ltd., London. xxxi + 613 pp.

Lamb, H.H. 1977. *Climate: Present, Past and Future. Volume 2. Climate History and the Future*. Methuen & Company Ltd., London. xxx + 835 pp.

Lamb, H.H. 1982. *Climate, History and the Modern World*. Methuen, London. xix + 387 pp.

Lamb, H.H. 1988. *Weather, Climate & Human Affairs*. Routledge, London. xiv + 364 pp.

Land, K.C., and S.H. Schneider (eds.) 1987. *Forecasting in the Social and Natural Sciences*. Reidel, Dordrecht, The Netherlands.

Landsberg, H.E. 1979. Atmospheric Changes in a Growing Community (The Columbia Maryland Experience). *Urban Ecology* 4:53–81.

Langer, W.C. 1972. *The Mind of Adolf Hitler*. Basic Books, New York. ix + 269 pp.

Laumann, E.O., J.H. Gagnon, S. Michaels, R.T. Michael, and J.S. Coleman. Monitoring the AIDS Epidemic in the United States: A Network Approach. *Science* 244:1186–1189.

Lee, T.H., B.C. Ball, Jr., and R.D. Tabors. 1990. *Energy Aftermath. How we can learn from the blunders of the past to create a hopeful energy future*. Harvard Business School Press. Boston, Mass. xiii + 274 pp.

Leigland, J., and R. Lamb. 1986. *WPP$$. Who is to Blame for the WPPSS Disaster*. Ballinger. Cambridge, Mass. xii + 253 pp.

Levine, I.D. 1958. *Mitchell. Pioneer of Air Power*. Duell, Sloan and Pearce, New York. 429 pp.

Lincoln, W.B. 1983. *In War's Dark Shadow. The Russians Before the Great War*. Dial Press. xvi + 557 pp.

Linstone, H.A., and W.H.C. Simmonds (eds.) 1977. *Futures Research—New Directions*. Addison-Wesley, Reading, Mass. xvi + 270 pp.

Lootsma, F.A. (ed.) 1972. *Numerical Methods for Non-Linear Optimization*. Academic Press, London. xi + 440 pp.

Lovins, A.B. 1977. *Soft Energy Paths: Toward a Durable Peace*. Ballinger, Cambridge, Mass.xx + 231 pp.

Lovins, A.B., L.H. Lovins, F. Krause and W. Bach. 1981. *Least Cost Energy. Solving the CO2 Problem*. Brick House Publishing Company, Andover, Mass. xi + 184 pp.

Lovins, A.B., and J.H. Price. 1975. *Non-nuclear Futures: The Case for an Ethical Energy Strategy*. Ballinger Publishing Co., Cambridge, Mass. xxxii + 223 pp.

Makridakis, S., A. Andersen, R. Carbone, R. Fildes, M. Hiborn, R. Lewandowski, J. Newton, E. Parzen, and R. Winkler. 1984. *The Forecasting Accuracy of Major Time Series Methods*. John Wiley and Sons, Chichester. viii + 301 pp.

Manabe, S., and R.T. Wetherald. 1980. On the Distribution of Climate Change Resulting from an Increase in CO2 Content of the Atmosphere. *Journal of the Atmospheric Sciences* 37:99–118.

Marshall, A. 1961. *Principles of Economics*. Ninth (Variorum) ed. Macmillan, New York. xxxiv + 858 pp.

Martinez-Alier, J. 1987. *Ecological Economics: Energy, Environment and Society*. Basil Blackwell, New York. 304 pp.

May, R.M. (ed.) 1981. *Theoretical Ecology. Principles and Applications*. Second Ed. Sinauer Associates, Sunderland, Mass. ix + 489 pp.

May, R.M. 1981. Models for Single Populations. *In* R.M. May, ed. (q.v.). *Theoretical Ecology*. Second Ed. pp. 5–29.

McClean, M. 1977. Getting the Problem Right—A Role for Structural Modeling. *In* H.A. Linstone and W.H.C. Simmonds, eds. (q.v.). *Futures Research—New Directions*, pp. 144–157.

McConnell, C.R. 1966. *Economics*. Third Ed. McGraw-Hill, New York. xxv + 792 pp.

Meadows, D., J. Richardson, and G. Bruckmann 1982. *Groping in the Dark. The First Decade of Global Modelling*. John Wiley and Sons, Chichester. xxvii + 311 pp.

Mesarovic, M.D., and E.C. Pestel. 1974. *Mankind at the Turning Point*. E.P. Dutton, New York. xiii + 210 pp.

Miller, J.G. 1978. *Living Systems*. McGraw-Hill. New York. xii + 1102 pp.

Miller, K.A., and M.H. Glantz. 1988. Climate and Economic Competitiveness: Florida Freezes and the Global Citrus Processing Industry. *Climatic Change* 12:135–164.

Mishkin, M. and T. Appenziler 1987. The Anatomy of Memory. *Scientific American* 256 (6):80–89.

Mitchell, B.R. 1975. *European Historical Statistics 1750–1970*. Columbia University Press, New York. xx + 827 pp.

Mitchell, B.R. 1981. *European Historical Statistics 1750–1975*. Second Revised Ed. Facts on File, New York. 868 pp.

Mitchell, J.M., Jr. 1953. On the Causes of Instrumentally Observed Secular Temperature Trends. *Journal of Meteorology* 10:244–261.

Mitchell, W. 1925. *Winged Defence. The Development and Possibilities of Modern Air Power—Economic and Military*. G.P. Putnam's Sons, New York. xxiv + 261 pp.

Mooz, W.E. 1978. *Cost Analysis of Light Water Reactor Power Plants*. R-2304-DOE. The RAND Corporation, Santa Monica, California.

Murdoch, W.W. (ed.) 1971. *Environment. Resources, Pollution & Society*. Sinauer Associates, Stamford, Conn., vii + 440 pp.

Murphy, G.J. 1977. Clupeoids. *In* J.A. Gulland, ed., (q.v.). *Fish Population Dynamics*, pp. 283–308.

Myhra, D. 1984. *Whoops!/WPPSS. Washington Public Power Supply System Nuclear Plants*. McFarland & Co., Jefferson, North Carolina. x + 206 pp.

National Research Council. 1989. *Everybody Counts: A Report to the Nation on the Future of Mathematics Education*. Board on Mathematical Sciences and Mathematical Sciences Education Board, National Research Council. National Academy Press, Washington, D.C. xi + 114 pp.

Namenwirth, J.Z. 1973. Wheels of Time and the Interdependence of Value Change in America. *Journal of Interdisciplinary History* 3(4):649–683.

Nebel, B.J. 1981. *Environmental Science*. Second ed. Prentice-Hall, Inc., Englewood Cliffs, New Jersey. xv + 671 pp.

Nef, J.U. 1932. *The Rise of the British Coal Industry*. Vol. 1–2. George Routledge, London. xiv + 448 pp.; vii + 490 pp.

Nelder, J.A., and R. Mead. 1965. A Simplex Method for Function Minimization. *Computer Journal* 7:308–313.

Neto, R.B. 1989. Amazon Forests. Dispute Enters New Round. *Nature* 339:245.

Odum, H.T.1983. *Systems Ecology: An Introduction*. John Wiley & Sons, New York. xv + 644 pp.

Odum, H.T. 1988. Self-organization, Transformity, and Information. *Science* 242:1132–1139.

Oke, T.R.1973. City Size and the Urban Heat Island. *Atmospheric Environment* 7:769–779.

O' Neill, R.V., D.L. DeAngelis, J.B. Waide, and T.F.H. Allen. 1986. *A Hierarchical Concept of Ecosystems*. Princeton University Press, Princeton, New Jersey. vii + 253 pp.

Passonneau, J.R., and R.S. Wurman. 1966. *Urban Atlas: 20 American Cities*. M.I.T. Press, Cambridge, Mass. no pagination.

Paulik, G. 1971. Anchovies, Birds and Fishermen in the Peru Current. *In* W.W. Murdoch, ed. (q.v.). *Environment. Resources, Pollution & Society*, pp. 156–185.

Pease, J.L., R.H. Vowles and L.B. Keith. 1979. Interaction of Snowshoe Hares and Woody Vegetation. *Journal of Wildlife Management* 43(1):43–60.

Perry, A.M. 1982. Carbon Dioxide Production Scenarios. *In*W.C. Clark, ed. (q.v.). *Carbon Dioxide Review: 1982*, Oxford University Press, New York, pp.

Programme for AIDS Prevention. 1988. *AIDS Prevention and Control: Invited Presentations and Papers from the World Summit of Ministers of Health on Programmes for AIDS Prevention*. World Health Organization, Geneva. xxii + 169 pp.

Ramanathan, V., R.D. Cess, E.F. Harrison, P. Minnis, B.R. Barkstrom, E. Ahmad, and D. Hartmann. 1989. Cloud-Radiative Forcing and Climate: Results from the Earth Radiation Budget Experiment. *Science* 243:57–63.

Roeckner, E. 1988. Cloud-radiation Feedbacks in a Climate Model. *Atmospheric Research* 21:293–303.

Rostow, W.W. 1978. *The World Economy. History and Prospect*. University of Texas Press. Austin, Texas. xvix + 833 pp.

Rotty, R. M. and G. Marland. 1986. Fossil Fuel Combustion: Recent Amounts, Patterns, and Trends of CO_2. *In* J.R. Trabalka and D. E. Reichle, eds. (q.v.). *The Changing Carbon Cycle. A Global Analysis*, pp. 474–490.

Rudolph, R., and S. Ridley. 1986. *Power Struggle. The Hundred-year War Over Electricity*. Harper and Row, New York. xiii + 305 pp.

Sabloff, J. (ed.) 1981. *Simulations in Archaelogy*. University of New Mexico Press, Albuquerque. xiv + 340 pp.

Schrack, G., and N. Borowski. 1972. An Experimental Comparison of Three Random Searches. *In* F.A. Lootsma, ed. (q.v.). *Numerical Methods for Non-Linear Optimization*, pp. 137–147.

Schwefel, H.P. 1981. *Numerical Optimization of Computer Models*. John Wiley and Sons, Chichester. vii + 389 pp.

Schweingruber, F.H. , O.U. Braker, and E. Schar. 1979. Dendroclimatic Studies on Conifers from Central Europe and Great Britain. *Boreas* 8:427–452.

Seaver, W., and J. Lee. unpublished ms. on cloud cover.

Shirk, G. 1985. The Producer Price Index, 1720–1984. *Cycles* Jan./Feb., pp. 16–20.

Slesser, M. 1978. *Energy in the Economy*. St. Martin's Press, New York. 164 pp.

Smiles,S. 1865. *Lives of Boulton and Watt*. John Murray, London. xv + 521 pp.

Specter, M. 1989. Estimates on AIDS Called too low. *Sacramento Bee*, June 25, p. A23.

Spengler, O. 1928. *The Decline of the West. Vol. II.* Perspectives of World History. Alfred A. Knopf, New York. 507 + xxxii pp.

Sperling, D. 1988. *New Transportation Fuels. A Strategic Approach to Technological Change*. University of California Press, Berkeley. xiv + 532 pp.

Steele, J.D. 1987. The Buck Ought to be Stopping in Board Room. *Los Angeles Times*, Business Section, August 9:3.

Sugai, W. H. 1987. *Nuclear Power and Ratepayer Protest. The Washington Public Power Supply System Crisis*. Westview Press, Boulder, Colorado. xi + 475 pp.

Tann, J. 1981. *The Selected Papers of Boulton and Watt*. Vol. 1. The Engine Partnership 1775–1825. The MIT Press, Cambridge, Mass. xv + 425 pp.

Taylor, E. 1948. *The Fall of the Dynasties. The Collapse of the Old Order*. Doubleday & Co., Garden City, New York, x + 421 pp.

Temin, P. 1976. *Did Monetary Forces Cause the Great Depression?* W.W. Norton and Company, New York. xiii + 201 pp.

Thatcher, R.W. and E.R. John. 1977. *Foundations of Cognitive Processes*. Halstead Press, New York. xviii + 382 pp.

Thomson, J. M. 1977. *Great Cities and their Traffic*. Victor Gollancz, London. 344 pp.

Thorp, W.L. 1941. Postwar Depressions. *The American Economic Review* 30 (5), Papers and Proceedings of 53rd. Annual Meeting:352–361.

Tolstoy, L. 1968. *War and Peace*. The New American Library, New York. 1455 pp. (Ann Dunnigan translation of 1869 ed.)

Trabalka, J.R., and D.E. Reichle (eds.). 1986. *The Changing Carbon Cycle. A Global Analysis*. Springer-Verlag, New York. xxvi + 592 pp.

Tuchman, B. W. 1984. *The March to Folly. From Troy to Vietnam*. Alfred A. Knopf, New York. 447 pp.

Vaughan, M.R., and L.B. Keith. 1981. Demographic Response of Experimental Snowshoe Hare Populations to Overwinter Food Shortage. *Journal of Wildlife Management* 45(2):354–380.

von Mises, L. 1944. *Bureaucracy*. Yale University Press, New Haven, Conn. v + 128 pp.

Wachs, M. 1987. Forecasts in Urban Transportation Planning: Uses, Methods, and Dilemmas. *Climatic Change* 11:61–80.

Watt, K.E.F. 1964. The Use of Mathematics and Computers to Determine Optimal Strategy and Tactics for a Given Insect Pest Control Problem. *The Canadian Entomologist* 96:202–220.

Watt, K.E.F. 1974. *The Titanic Effect: Planning for the Unthinkable*. E.P. Dutton, New York. xiv + 268 pp.

Watt, K.E.F. 1978. The Structure of Post-Industrial Economies. *The Journal of Social and Biological Structures* 1:53–70.

Watt, K.E.F. 1982. *Understanding the Environment*. Allyn and Bacon. Boston. xv + 431 pp.

Watt, K. E. F. 1984. Future Shock in Coastal and ocean Affairs: What will the Impacts be? *Shore and Beach* 52(2):15–17.

Watt, K.E.F. 1989. Evidence for the Role of Energy Resources in Producing Long Waves in the United States Economy. *Ecological Economics* 1 (2):181–195.

Watt, K.E.F., L.F. Molloy , C.K. Varshney, D. Weeks, and S. Wirosardjono. 1977. *The Unsteady State. Environmental Problems, Growth, and Culture*. The University Press of Hawaii, Honolulu. xi + 287 pp.

Watt, K.E.F., and P.P. Craig. 1986. System Stability Principles. *Systems Research* 3(4):191–201.

Watt, K.E.F., J.W. Young, J.L. Mitchiner, and J.L. Brewer. 1975. A Simulation of the Use of Energy and Land at the National Level. *Simulation* 24(5):129–153.

Watt, K.E.F., P. Craig and J.S. Auburn. 1988. World Economic Modeling. *In* P. Ehrlich and J. Holdren, eds. (q.v.). *The Cassandra Conference. Resources and the Human Predicament*. Texas A & M University Press, College Station, Texas, pp 233–255. [Title was left out. Is this correct work?]

Weber, R.P. 1981. Society and Economy in the Western World System. *Social Forces* 59 (4):1130–1148.

Weber, R.P. 1983. Cyclical Theories of Crisis in the World System. *In* A. Bergesen, ed. (q.v.). *Crises in the World System*, pp 37–55.

Wigley, T.M.L. 1989. Possible Climate Change Due to SO-Derived 2 Cloud Condensation Nuclei. *Nature* 339:365.

Wildavsky, A., and E. Tennenbaum. 1981. *The Politics of Mistrust. Estimating American Oil and Gas Resources*. Sage Publications, Beverly Hills, California. 363 pp.

Winkless, N. and I. Browning. *Climate and the affairs of Men*.

Wood, F. 1988. Comment: On the Need for Validation of the Jones et al Temperature Trends with Respect to Urban Warming. *Climatic Change* 12(3):297–312.

Wood, F. 1988. Global Alpine Glacier Trends, 1960's to 1980's. *Arctic and Alpine Research* 20(4):404–413.

Wood, F. 1988. The Need for Systems Research on Global Climate Change. *Systems Research* 5(3):225–240.

Yago, G. 1984. *The Decline of Transit*. Cambridge University Press, Cambridge. ix + 293 pp.

Index

— A —

— B —

— C —

— E —

— F —

— G —

— H —

— I —

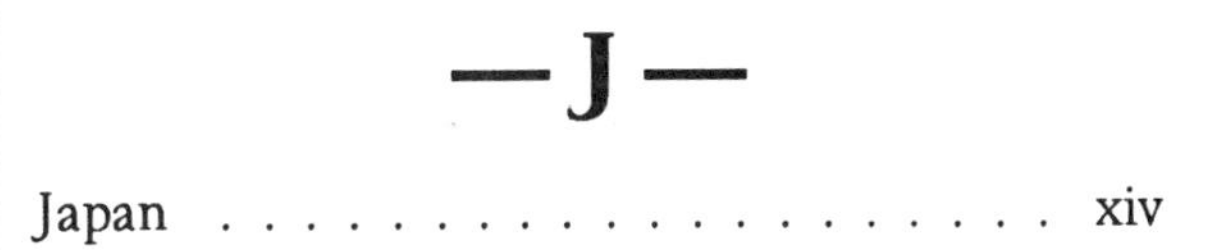

— J —

— K —

— L —

— M —

— N —

— O —

— P —

— R —

— S —

— T —

— U —

— V —

— W —

— Y —

Further Reading

This volume has been designed as a short, simple, easy-to-read introduction to a new way of looking at society, and the problem of forecasting. If you wish to pursue this subject further, The Contextured Web Press is developing three more volumes, which will be available in 1993.

☒ Volume 2 is for people who wish to develop expertise in this new means of forecasting. It presents extensive discussion of the techniques for building computer forecasting models. It is much more technical than the present volume, dealing the underlying mathematics, statistics, and computer methodology. It also explains how to develop models for metropolitan areas where activities and patterns of land use are being related to positions on maps. This book is necessary for anyone who wants to become expert in forecasting. For investors and corporate executives, we **think that it is mandatory for you to get expert and objective assistance in this area if you don't have the tine to learn it yourself**. The book is targeted at people who have already had some geometry, algebra, and calculus, and some experience in computer programming.

☒ Volume 3 is an explanation of our proprietary software, developed by, and the property of Dr. Jill Shore Auburn. The results presented in Volume 1 could not have been achieved without this software. It presents completely new computer routines for curve-fitting nonlinear equations, and has many useful features for dealing with historical data series affected by time lags and cumulative effects. Only people with a high level of aptitude for applied mathematics, statistics, and computer operations should order this volume.

☒ Volume 4 is targeted at scholars and policy makers who want a deep understanding of how modern global socio-political-economic-environmental systems operate. It considers how different kinds of forces interact, such as AIDS and energy prices. It also tracks causal pathways through the international trade and monetary systems.